GCSE
Core Science
Foundation

Complete Revision
and Practice

For the Year 10 exams

Contents

Contents

The Periodic Table

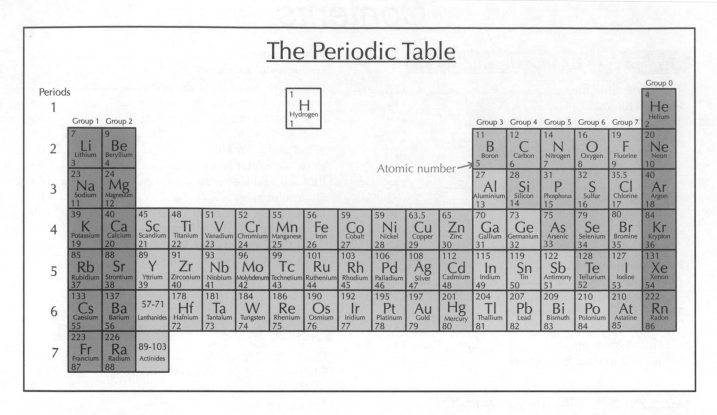

Published by CGP

From original material by Richard Parsons.

Editors:
Joe Brazier, Emma Elder, Ben Fletcher, Felicity Inkpen, Sharon Keeley-Holden,
Edmund Robinson, Helen Ronan, Hayley Thompson, Jane Towle, Sarah Williams, Dawn Wright.

Contributors:
Mike Bossart, Max Fishel, Paddy Gannon, John Myers, Adrian Schmit.

ISBN: 978 1 84762 664 6

With thanks to Katherine Craig, Ian Francis, Julie Jackson and Karen Wells for the proofreading.
With thanks to Jan Greenway, Laura Jakubowski and Laura Stoney for the copyright research.

Graph to show trend in atmospheric CO_2 concentration and global temperature on pages 149
and 221 based on data by EPICA Community Members 2004 and Siegenthaler et al 2005.

With thanks to Tom D Thacher, MD., for permission to reproduce the photograph on page 31.

Groovy website: www.cgpbooks.co.uk

Printed by Elanders Ltd, Newcastle upon Tyne.
Jolly bits of clipart from CorelDRAW®

Photocopying – it's dull, grey and sometimes a bit naughty. Luckily, it's dead cheap, easy and quick to order
more copies of this book from CGP – just call us on 0870 750 1242. Phew!

The Scientific Process

Before you get into the fun stuff, it's a good idea to understand exactly <u>how</u> the <u>world of science works</u>.

Science is All About **Testing** a **Hypothesis**

1. Scientists make an **observation**

1) Scientists <u>observe</u> (look at) something they don't understand
   — e.g. an illness that a person has.

2) Then they come up with a possible <u>explanation</u> for what they've observed.

3) This explanation is called a <u>hypothesis</u>.

About 100 years ago, we thought atoms looked like this.

2. They **test** their hypothesis

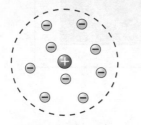

Then we thought they looked like this.

1) Next, they <u>test</u> whether the hypothesis might be <u>right or not</u>.

2) They begin by making a <u>prediction</u> — a statement based on the hypothesis that can be <u>tested</u> by carrying out <u>experiments</u>.

3) Then they <u>collect evidence</u> (<u>data</u> from <u>experiments</u>) to test their prediction.

4) If their prediction is <u>right</u>, this shows that their <u>hypothesis might be right too</u>.

5) This <u>doesn't</u> mean the hypothesis is <u>true</u> though — other predictions might turn out to be <u>wrong</u>.

3. **Other scientists** test the hypothesis too

1) Once a scientist has come up with and tested a hypothesis, they'll show their work to <u>other scientists</u> to be <u>checked</u>. This is called the <u>peer review</u> process.

2) They then show their work to everyone by printing it in <u>journals</u> (science magazines) and talking about it at <u>conferences</u> (meetings).

3) Other scientists then try to <u>repeat</u> the results of the original experiment. They also carry out their own experiments to <u>collect more evidence</u>.

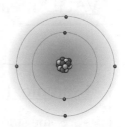

And then we thought they looked like this.

4. The hypothesis is **accepted** or **changed**

1) If all the <u>evidence</u> that's been found <u>supports</u> the hypothesis, scientists start to have a lot of <u>trust</u> in it. (A hypothesis that is accepted by pretty much every scientist is called a <u>theory</u>.)

2) But, if someone does an experiment and the results <u>don't</u> fit with the hypothesis then scientists must:

> a) <u>change</u> the hypothesis, OR
> b) come up with a completely <u>new</u> hypothesis.

Quality of Data

Scientists won't just accept any old results... They've got to be <u>reliable</u> and <u>valid</u>.

*Evidence Needs to be **Reliable***

<u>RELIABLE</u> means that the data can be <u>repeated</u>, and <u>reproduced</u> by others.

<u>Reliable evidence</u> comes from <u>experiments</u> that give the <u>same data</u>:

- each time the experiment is <u>repeated</u>
- each time the experiment is <u>reproduced</u> (copied) by <u>other scientists</u>.

Example: Cold fusion

- In 1989, two scientists claimed that they'd produced '<u>cold fusion</u>' (the energy source of the Sun).

- Other scientists <u>couldn't</u> get the <u>same results</u> though — they <u>weren't reliable</u>.

---

*Evidence Also Needs to Be **Valid***

<u>VALID</u> means that the data is <u>reliable</u> AND <u>answers the original question</u>.

Example: Do power lines cause cancer?

- Some studies have found that in areas where there were <u>power lines</u>, <u>more children</u> had <u>cancer</u>.

- This evidence is <u>NOT enough</u> to say that the power lines <u>CAUSE</u> cancer. Other explanations might be possible, e.g. power lines are often near <u>busy roads</u>, so the areas tested could contain <u>different levels</u> of <u>pollution</u> from traffic.

- So these studies <u>don't</u> show a <u>definite link</u> and so <u>don't answer the original question</u>.

RRRR — Remember, Reliable means Repeatable and Reproducible

Scientists <u>won't accept</u> someone's data if it can't be <u>repeated</u> by anyone else. It may sound like a really great new theory, but if there's no other support for it, it just isn't <u>reliable</u>.

Quality of Data

The way evidence is <u>gathered</u> can have a big effect on how much you should <u>trust</u> it...

The **Bigger** the **Sample Size** the **Better**

1) Sample size is <u>how many things you test</u> in an experiment or study.

> <u>Examples</u>: 500 people or 20 types of metal.

2) The <u>bigger</u> the sample size the <u>better</u> — to <u>reduce</u> the chance of any <u>weird results</u>.

3) But scientists have to be <u>realistic</u> when choosing how big their sample should be.

> <u>Example</u>: if you were studying how lifestyle affects weight it'd be great to study everyone in the UK (a huge sample), but it'd <u>take ages</u> and <u>cost loads</u>.

Don't Always **Believe** What You're Being Told **Straight Away**

1) People who want to make a point might <u>present data</u> in a <u>biased way</u> — i.e. in a way that's <u>meant to affect how other people think</u>.

2) There are all sorts of reasons <u>why</u> people might <u>want</u> to do this — for example, <u>companies</u> might want to make their products sound better.

3) If an investigation is done by a team of <u>well-respected scientists</u> it's often taken <u>more seriously</u> than evidence from <u>less well-known scientists</u>.

4) But having experience, power or a fancy qualification <u>doesn't</u> always mean the evidence is <u>good</u>. The only way to tell is to look at the evidence scientifically (e.g. is it reliable, valid, etc.).

Things are not always what they seem

No matter <u>what</u> you're reading or <u>who</u> it's written by, you've always got to be really careful about what you <u>believe</u>. Ask yourself whether the <u>sample</u> is a decent <u>size</u> and check whether the author has anything to gain from what's written. For example, an article on the magical fat-busting power of spinach written by the country's leading spinach grower may not be all it seems. <u>Don't be fooled</u>.

Limits of Science

It isn't all fun and games in the world of science — there are <u>some problems</u>...

Some Questions are **Unanswered** by Science...

1) At the moment scientists <u>don't agree</u> on some things.

<u>Example</u>: what the Universe is made of.

2) This is because there <u>isn't</u> enough reliable and valid <u>evidence</u>.

3) But <u>eventually</u>, we probably <u>will</u> be able to answer these questions once and for all.

4) All we need is <u>more evidence</u>.

... Others are **Unanswerable**

1) The question of whether something is <u>ethically</u> right or wrong <u>can't ever be answered</u> by experiments. There is no "right" or "wrong" answer.

2) Take <u>embryo screening</u> (which allows you to choose an embryo with particular characteristics):

Some people say it's <u>good</u>...
- Couples whose child needs a <u>bone marrow transplant</u> will be able to have <u>another</u> child to donate <u>matching</u> bone marrow.
- This would <u>save</u> the life of their first child — and if they <u>want</u> another child anyway... where's the harm?

Other people say it's <u>bad</u>...
- They say it could have serious effects on the new <u>child</u>.
- In the example above, the new child might feel <u>unwanted</u>.

3) The best we can do is make a decision that <u>most people</u> are more or less happy to live by.

To answer or not to answer, that is the question

Right — just to clear this one up — science <u>can't</u> tell you whether you <u>should</u> or <u>shouldn't</u> do something. That kind of thing is up to you and society to decide. But there are tons of questions that science <u>might be able to answer</u> in the future — we just need to do <u>more experiments</u>.

Issues in Science

Scientific developments can be pretty useful, but they often come along with some issues too.

Scientific Developments are Great, but they can Raise Issues

Scientific knowledge increases by doing experiments.
This knowledge leads to scientific developments, e.g. new technology or new advice.
These developments can create issues though. For example:

Economic (money) issues:

Governments can't always afford to do things scientists recommend.
E.g. spend money on green energy sources.

Social (people) issues:

Decisions based on scientific evidence affect people.
E.g. should alcohol be banned (to prevent health problems)?

Environmental issues:

Nuclear power helps us produce more energy — but some people think it causes too many environmental problems.

Ethical (moral) issues:

There are a lot of things science has made possible, but should we do them?
E.g. clone humans, develop better nuclear weapons.

It's not all test tubes and explosions

Life can be hard as a scientist. You think you've got it all figured out and then someone comes along with some issues. But it's for the best really — the world would be pretty messed up if no-one ever thought about the issues created by scientific developments (just watch Jurassic Park...).

Planning Investigations

The next few pages show how <u>investigations</u> should be carried out — by both <u>scientists</u> and <u>you</u>.

In a **Fair Test** You Have to **Control the Variables**

Investigations that you plan should always be a <u>fair test</u>.

1) In a lab experiment you usually <u>change one thing</u> (a variable) and <u>measure</u> how it affects <u>another thing</u> (another variable).

> <u>EXAMPLE</u>: you might change only the temperature of a reaction and measure how it affects the rate of reaction.

2) <u>Everything else</u> that could affect the results needs to <u>stay the same</u>. Then you know that the thing you're <u>changing</u> is the <u>only</u> thing that's affecting the results.

> <u>EXAMPLE continued</u>: you need to keep the pH the same. If you don't, you won't know if any change in the rate of reaction is caused by the change in temperature, or the change in pH.

3) The variable that you <u>change</u> is called the <u>INDEPENDENT</u> variable.

4) The variable that's <u>measured</u> is called the <u>DEPENDENT</u> variable.

5) The variables that you <u>keep the same</u> are called <u>CONTROL</u> variables.

> <u>EXAMPLE continued</u>:
> Independent = temperature
> Dependent = rate of reaction
> Control = pH

6) You can't always control all the variables. So you often need to use a <u>control experiment</u>.

7) A control experiment is kept under the <u>same conditions</u> as the rest of the investigation, but <u>nothing is done to it</u>. It lets you see <u>what happens</u> when you don't change anything at all.

Experiments Must be **Safe**

1) A <u>hazard</u> is something that <u>could cause harm</u>.

2) There are lots of <u>hazards</u> you could be faced with during an investigation, e.g. <u>radiation</u>, <u>electricity</u>, <u>gas</u>, <u>chemicals</u> and <u>fire</u>.

3) Scientists need to <u>manage the risk</u> of hazards by doing things to reduce them. For example:

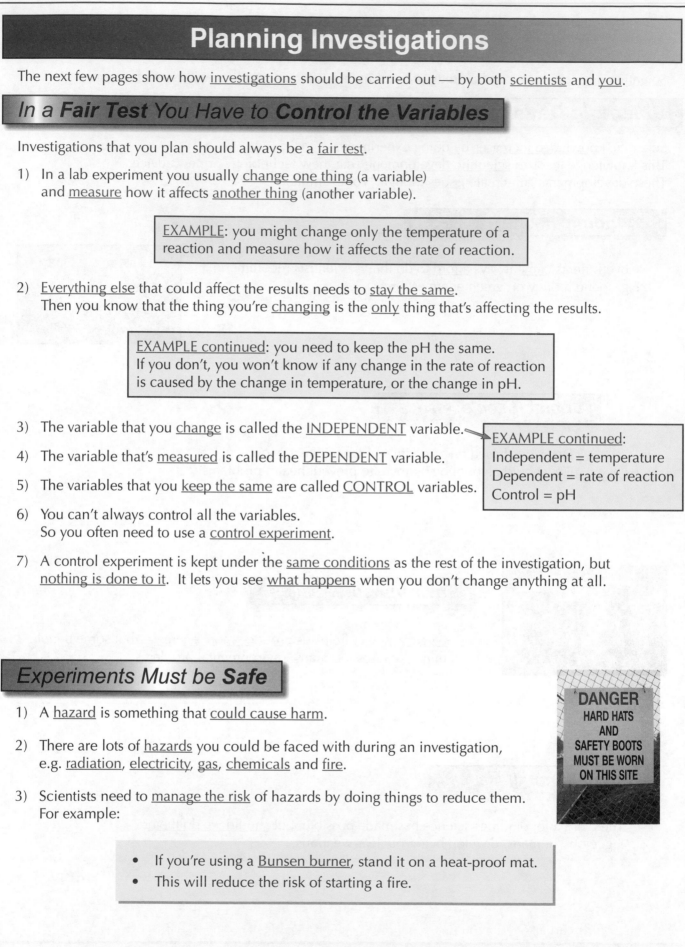

> • If you're using a <u>Bunsen burner</u>, stand it on a heat-proof mat.
> • This will reduce the risk of starting a fire.

Hazard: revision boredom. Reduce by: using CGP books

Labs are dangerous places — you need to know the <u>hazards</u> of what you're doing <u>before you start</u>.

Collecting Data

There are a few things that can be done to make sure that you get the <u>best results</u> you possibly can.

The *Equipment* Used has to be *Right for the Job*

1) You need to make sure you choose the <u>right equipment</u>.

> For example, the measuring equipment you use has to be able to <u>accurately</u> measure the chemicals you're using. If you need to measure out 11 ml of a liquid, use a measuring cylinder that can measure to 1 ml, not 5 or 10 ml.

2) The <u>smallest change</u> a measuring instrument can <u>measure</u> is called its <u>RESOLUTION</u>. E.g. some mass balances have a resolution of 1 g and some have a resolution of 0.1 g.

3) Equipment needs to be <u>CALIBRATED</u> (set up properly) so that your data is <u>more accurate</u>. E.g. mass balances need to be set to zero before you start weighing things.

Trial Runs give you the *Range* and *Interval* of *Variable Values*

1) A <u>trial run</u> is a <u>quick version</u> of your experiment.

2) Trial runs help you work out whether your plan is <u>right or not</u> — you might decide to make some <u>changes</u> after trying out your method.

3) They're used to figure out the <u>range</u> of independent variable values used (the highest and lowest value).

> <u>Rate of reaction example from previous page continued</u>:
> You might do trial runs at 10, 20, 30, 40 and 50 °C. If there was no reaction at 10 or 50 °C, you might narrow the range to 20-40 °C.

4) And they're used to figure out the <u>interval</u> (gaps) between the values too.

> <u>Rate of reaction example continued</u>:
> If using 10 °C intervals gives you a big change in rate of reaction you might decide to use 5 °C intervals, e.g. 20, 25, 30, 35 °C...

5) Trial runs can also help you figure out <u>how many times</u> the experiment has to be <u>repeated</u> to get reliable results. E.g. if you repeat it two times and the <u>results</u> are all <u>similar</u>, then two repeats is enough.

Collecting Data

Data Should be as **Reliable**, **Accurate** and **Precise** as Possible

Reliable

1) Reliable results are results that always come out <u>the same every time</u> you do the same experiment (see page 2).

2) You can make your results <u>more reliable</u> by <u>repeating</u> the readings at least twice (so that you have at least <u>three</u> readings). Then you can calculate the <u>mean</u> (average, see next page).

3) Checking your results match with <u>secondary sources</u>, e.g. studies that other people have done, also makes your data more reliable.

Accurate

1) You should always make sure that your results are <u>ACCURATE</u>.

2) Really accurate results are those that are <u>really close</u> to the <u>true answer</u>.

Precise

1) You should also always make sure your results are <u>PRECISE</u>.

2) Precise results are ones that are <u>really similar</u> to the <u>mean</u>.

Errors can Pop Up if You're Not Careful

1) The results of your experiment will always <u>vary a bit</u>.

2) Sometimes, errors will be made. If the <u>same error</u> is made every time, it's called a <u>SYSTEMATIC ERROR</u>.

3) If a systematic error is caused by using <u>equipment</u> that <u>isn't calibrated properly</u> it's called a <u>ZERO ERROR</u>.

Errors can **Affect** Your **Results**

1) Sometimes you get a result that <u>doesn't seem to fit in</u> with the rest at all.

2) These results are called <u>ANOMALOUS RESULTS</u>.

3) You should investigate them and try to <u>work out what happened</u>.

4) If you can work out what happened (e.g. you measured something wrong) you can <u>ignore</u> them when processing your results.

Park	Number of pigeons	Number of litter bins
A	28	4
B	42	2
C	1127	0

Anomalous result

Results need to be reliable, accurate and precise

All this stuff is really important — your data will be <u>meaningless</u> if it's not reliable and accurate. Read through this page a couple of times and your data will be the envy of scientists everywhere.

Organising and Processing Data

The fun doesn't stop once the data's been collected — it then needs to be <u>organised</u> and **processed**...

Data Needs to be Organised

1) Data that's been collected needs to be <u>organised</u> so it can be processed later on.

2) <u>Tables</u> are dead useful for <u>organising data</u>.

3) You should always make sure that <u>each column</u> has a <u>heading</u> and that you've included the <u>units</u>.

Test tube	Result (ml)	Repeat 1 (ml)	Repeat 2 (ml)
A	28	37	32
B	47	51	60
C	68	72	70

You Might Have to Process Your Data

When you've done repeats of an experiment you can calculate the <u>MEAN</u> (average) and the <u>RANGE</u> (how spread out the data is).

Ignore anomalous results when calculating these.

Mean: the average

- To calculate the mean <u>ADD TOGETHER</u> all the data values.

- Then <u>DIVIDE</u> by the total number of data values.

Test tube	Result (ml)	Repeat 1 (ml)	Repeat 2 (ml)	Mean (ml)	Range (ml)
A	28	37	32	$(28 + 37 + 32) \div 3 = 32.3$	$37 - 28 = 9$
B	47	51	60	$(47 + 51 + 60) \div 3 = 52.7$	$60 - 47 = 13$
C	68	72	70	$(68 + 72 + 70) \div 3 = 70.0$	$72 - 68 = 4$

Range: how spread out the data is

- To find the range take the <u>LARGEST</u> number...

- ... and <u>SUBTRACT</u> the <u>SMALLEST</u> number from it.

Processing data requires a teeny bit of maths — don't panic

This data stuff is pretty straightforward — but it's <u>really important</u>. Different measurements scattered on random bits of paper at the bottom of your bag just ain't gonna cut it. Get your ruler out, draw a lovely table, pop your data in, calculate the mean and the range and <u>breathe</u>... Much better.

Presenting Data

Data has to be presented, and graphs are just about the best way of doing it...

If Your Data Comes in Categories, Present it in a Bar Chart

1) If the independent variable comes in clear categories (e.g. blood types, metals) you should use a bar chart to display the data.

2) There are some golden rules you need to follow for drawing bar charts:

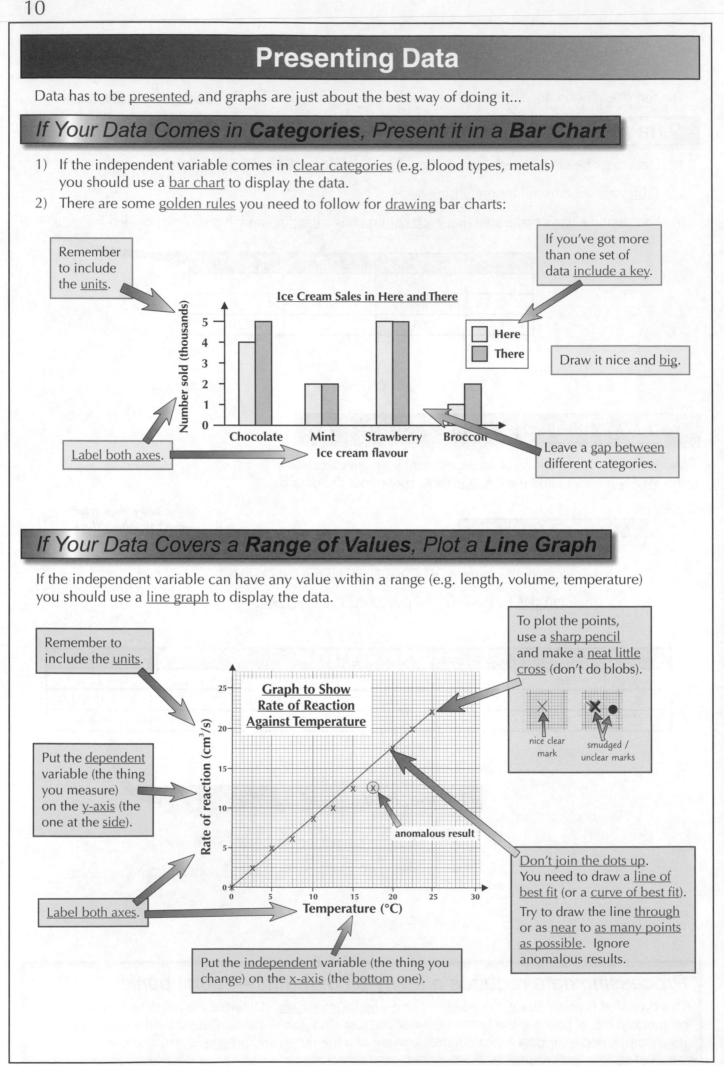

If Your Data Covers a Range of Values, Plot a Line Graph

If the independent variable can have any value within a range (e.g. length, volume, temperature) you should use a line graph to display the data.

Interpreting Data

Once you've drawn your graph (using all the tips on the previous page) you need to be able to <u>understand</u> what it's <u>telling you</u>. That's where this page comes in handy.

Line Graphs Can Show Patterns in Data

1) Line graphs are used to <u>show the relationship</u> between two variables (just like other graphs).

2) The relationship between two variables is called a <u>CORRELATION</u>:

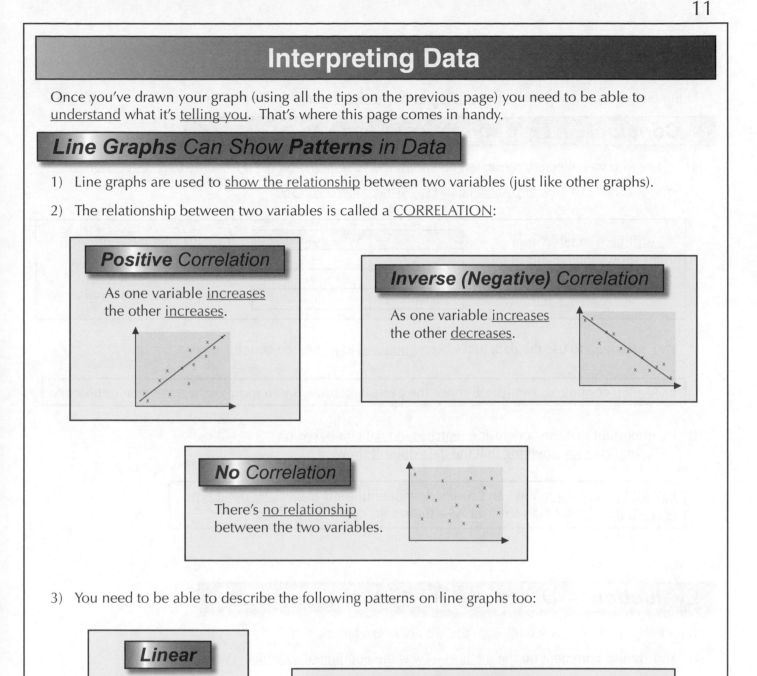

Positive Correlation
As one variable <u>increases</u> the other <u>increases</u>.

Inverse (Negative) Correlation
As one variable <u>increases</u> the other <u>decreases</u>.

No Correlation
There's <u>no relationship</u> between the two variables.

3) You need to be able to describe the following patterns on line graphs too:

Linear
The graph is a <u>straight line</u>.

Directly Proportional
The graph is a <u>straight line</u> where both variables increase (or decrease) in the <u>same ratio</u>.

4) If there's a <u>pattern</u> between two variables, it doesn't always mean that one is <u>causing</u> the other to change.

5) There are <u>three possible reasons</u> for a correlation. It could be down to <u>chance</u>, it could be that there's a <u>third variable</u> linking the two things, or it might actually be that one variable is <u>causing</u> the other to change.

A correlation is a relationship between sets of data

Wow. What a snazzy page. But don't get distracted by all those crazy lines and crosses — <u>interpreting</u> data's dead important, so make sure you know how to do it properly.

Concluding and Evaluating

At the end of an investigation, the conclusion and evaluation are waiting. Don't worry, they won't bite.

A Conclusion is a Summary of What You've Learnt

1) Once you've collected, presented and analysed your data, you need to come to a conclusion.

2) You just have to look at your data and say what pattern you see.

EXAMPLE: The table on the right shows the heights of pea plant seedlings grown for three weeks with different fertilisers.

Fertiliser	Mean growth (mm)
A	13.5
B	19.5
No fertiliser	5.5

CONCLUSION: Fertiliser B makes pea plant seedlings grow taller over a three week period than fertiliser A.

3) You also need to use the data that's been collected to justify the conclusion (back it up).

EXAMPLE continued: Fertiliser B made the pea plants grow 6 mm more on average than fertiliser A.

4) It's important that the conclusion matches the data it's based on — it shouldn't say anything that the data doesn't show.

EXAMPLE continued: You can't conclude that fertiliser B makes any other type of plant grow taller than fertiliser A — the results could be totally different.

Evaluation — Describe How it Could be Improved

In an evaluation you look back over the whole investigation.

1) You should comment on the method — was the equipment suitable? Was it a fair test?

2) Comment on the quality of the results — were they reliable and accurate?

3) Were there any anomalous results — if there were none then say so.

4) If there were any anomalous results, try to explain them — were they caused by errors in measurement? Were there any other variables that could have affected the results?

5) When you look back at your investigation like this, you'll be able to say how sure you are that your conclusion is right.

6) Then you can suggest any changes that would improve the quality of the results. For example, you might suggest changing the way you controlled a variable, or changing the interval of values you measured.

7) This would mean you could be more sure about your conclusion.

8) When you suggest an improvement to the investigation, always say why you think this would make the results better.

An experiment must have a conclusion and an evaluation

I know it doesn't seem very nice, but writing about where you went wrong is an important skill — it shows you've got a really good understanding of what the investigation was about.

The Nervous System

The <u>nervous system</u> allows you to <u>react</u> to what goes on around you — you'd find life tough without it.

Sense Organs Detect Stimuli

A <u>stimulus</u> is a <u>change in your environment</u> which you may need to react to (e.g. a lion charging at you).

1) You have five different <u>sense organs</u> — <u>eyes</u>, <u>ears</u>, <u>nose</u>, <u>tongue</u> and <u>skin</u>.

2) They all contain different <u>receptors</u>.

3) Receptors are groups of cells that <u>detect stimuli</u>.

4) Receptors change <u>stimuli</u> into <u>electrical impulses</u>.

<u>Sense organs</u> and <u>Receptors</u>
Don't get them mixed up:
The <u>eye</u> is a <u>sense organ</u> — it contains <u>light receptors</u>.

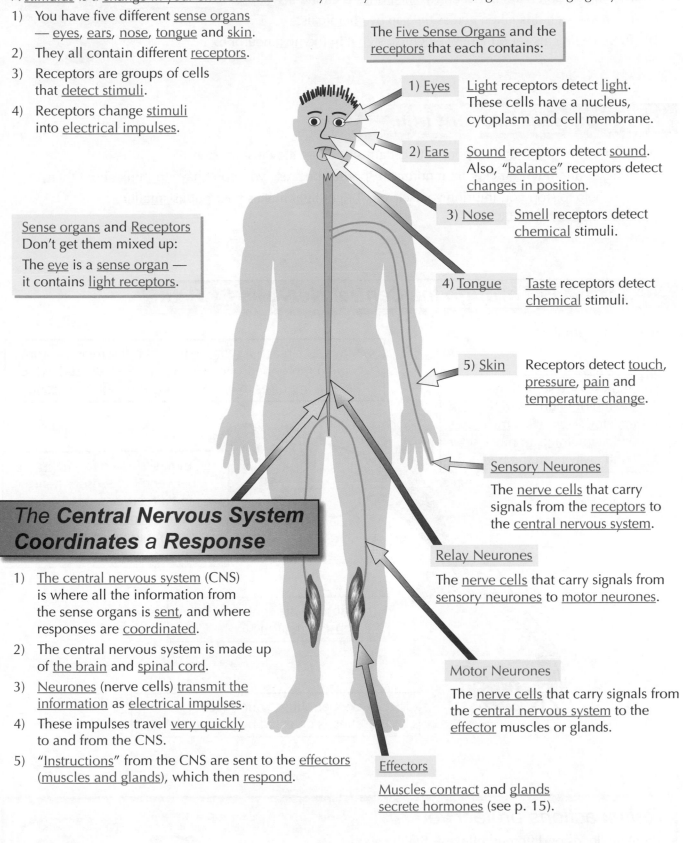

The <u>Five Sense Organs</u> and the <u>receptors</u> that each contains:

1) <u>Eyes</u>   <u>Light</u> receptors detect <u>light</u>. These cells have a nucleus, cytoplasm and cell membrane.

2) <u>Ears</u>   <u>Sound</u> receptors detect <u>sound</u>. Also, "<u>balance</u>" receptors detect <u>changes in position</u>.

3) <u>Nose</u>   <u>Smell</u> receptors detect <u>chemical</u> stimuli.

4) <u>Tongue</u>   <u>Taste</u> receptors detect <u>chemical</u> stimuli.

5) <u>Skin</u>   Receptors detect <u>touch</u>, <u>pressure</u>, <u>pain</u> and <u>temperature change</u>.

Sensory Neurones

The <u>nerve cells</u> that carry signals from the <u>receptors</u> to the <u>central nervous system</u>.

Relay Neurones

The <u>nerve cells</u> that carry signals from <u>sensory neurones</u> to <u>motor neurones</u>.

Motor Neurones

The <u>nerve cells</u> that carry signals from the <u>central nervous system</u> to the <u>effector</u> muscles or glands.

Effectors

<u>Muscles contract</u> and <u>glands secrete hormones</u> (see p. 15).

The Central Nervous System Coordinates a Response

1) <u>The central nervous system</u> (CNS) is where all the information from the sense organs is <u>sent</u>, and where responses are <u>coordinated</u>.

2) The central nervous system is made up of <u>the brain</u> and <u>spinal cord</u>.

3) <u>Neurones</u> (nerve cells) <u>transmit the information</u> as <u>electrical impulses</u>.

4) These impulses travel <u>very quickly</u> to and from the CNS.

5) "<u>Instructions</u>" from the CNS are sent to the <u>effectors</u> (<u>muscles and glands</u>), which then <u>respond</u>.

Synapses and Reflexes

Your brain <u>quickly decides</u> how to respond to a stimulus. But <u>reflexes</u> are even quicker...

Synapses Connect Neurones

1) The <u>connection</u> (gap) between <u>two neurones</u> is called a <u>synapse</u>.

2) The nerve signal is taken across the gap by <u>chemicals</u>.

3) These chemicals set off a <u>new electrical signal</u> in the <u>next</u> neurone.

chemicals released

end of neurone

next neurone

nerve impulse

synapse

Reflexes Help Prevent Injury

1) <u>Reflexes</u> are <u>automatic responses</u> to certain stimuli — they just happen.

2) Reflexes are much <u>quicker</u> than normal responses because you <u>don't have to think</u> about them.

3) They help to stop you <u>injuring</u> yourself, e.g. <u>bright light</u> makes your <u>pupils smaller</u> to <u>prevent eye damage</u>.

Reflexes Go Through the Central Nervous System

Here's an example:

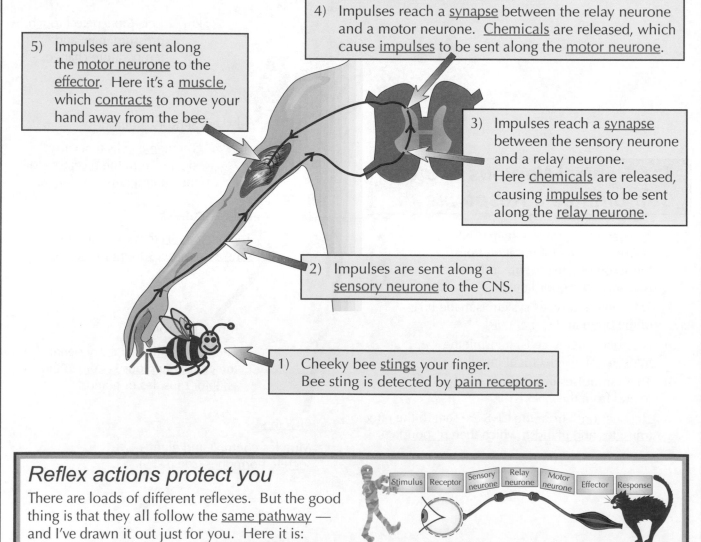

4) Impulses reach a <u>synapse</u> between the relay neurone and a motor neurone. <u>Chemicals</u> are released, which cause <u>impulses</u> to be sent along the <u>motor neurone</u>.

5) Impulses are sent along the <u>motor neurone</u> to the <u>effector</u>. Here it's a <u>muscle</u>, which <u>contracts</u> to move your hand away from the bee.

3) Impulses reach a <u>synapse</u> between the sensory neurone and a relay neurone. Here <u>chemicals</u> are released, causing <u>impulses</u> to be sent along the <u>relay neurone</u>.

2) Impulses are sent along a <u>sensory neurone</u> to the CNS.

1) Cheeky bee <u>stings</u> your finger. Bee sting is detected by <u>pain receptors</u>.

Reflex actions protect you

There are loads of different reflexes. But the good thing is that they all follow the <u>same pathway</u> — and I've drawn it out just for you. Here it is:

Stimulus | Receptor | Sensory neurone | Relay neurone | Motor neurone | Effector | Response

Hormones

The other way to send information around the body (apart from along nerves) is by using <u>hormones</u>.

Hormones Are Chemical Messengers Sent in the Blood

1) <u>Hormones</u> are <u>chemicals</u> released directly into the <u>blood</u>.
2) They're <u>carried</u> in the <u>blood</u> to other parts of the body.
3) Hormones only affect <u>particular cells</u> in particular places (called <u>target cells</u>).
4) Hormones are produced in (and secreted by) various <u>glands</u>, as shown on the diagram.

<u>HORMONES</u>...
are <u>chemical messengers</u> which <u>travel in the blood</u> to <u>activate target cells</u>.

<u>THE PITUITARY GLAND</u>

This produces many important hormones including <u>FSH</u> and <u>LH</u>. They're involved in the <u>menstrual cycle</u> (see page 16).

<u>OVARIES</u> — females only

Produce <u>oestrogen</u>, which is involved in the <u>menstrual cycle</u> (see page 16).

These are just examples — there are loads more, each doing its own thing.

Hormones and Nerves Do Similar Jobs, but with Differences

<u>NERVES</u>:

1) Very <u>FAST</u> action.
2) Act for a very <u>SHORT TIME</u>.
3) Act on a very <u>PRECISE AREA</u>.

<u>HORMONES</u>:

1) <u>SLOWER</u> action.
2) Act for a <u>LONG TIME</u>.
3) Act in a more <u>GENERAL</u> way.

Hormones are really useful

Hormones control various <u>organs</u> and <u>cells</u> in the body. For example, hormones take care of all things to do with the menstrual cycle, fertility, blood sugar level, ion content, water content... and so on.

The Menstrual Cycle

The <u>menstrual cycle</u> is the <u>monthly</u> release of an <u>egg</u> from a woman's <u>ovaries</u>.
It's also the build-up and breakdown of the protective lining in the <u>uterus</u> (womb).

The Menstrual Cycle Has Four Stages

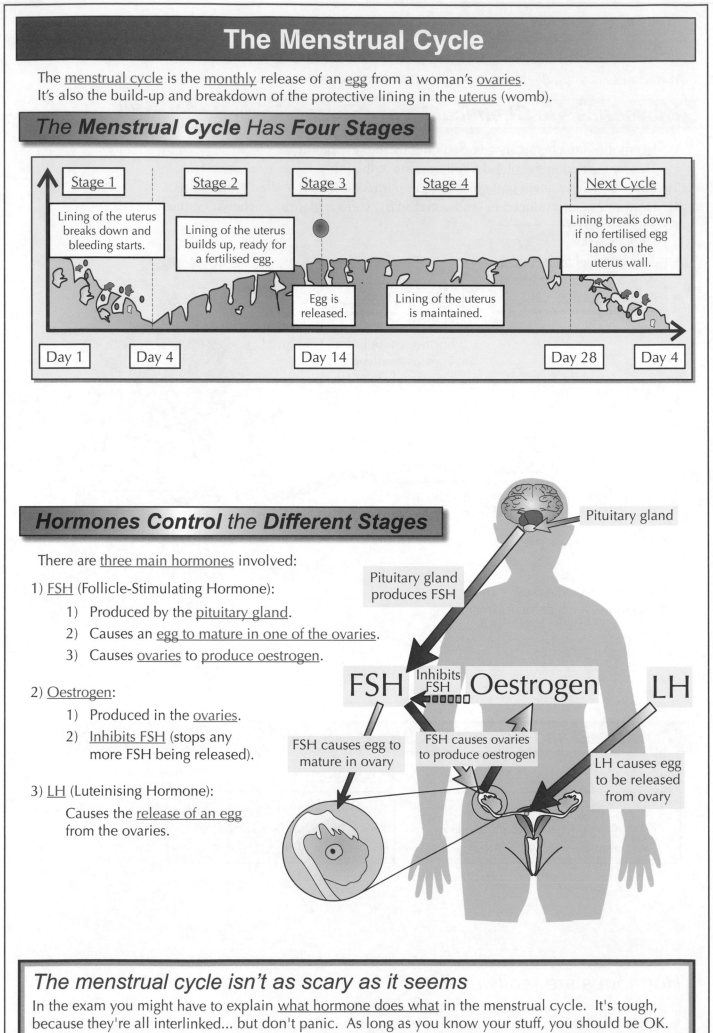

| Stage 1 | Stage 2 | Stage 3 | Stage 4 | Next Cycle |

Lining of the uterus breaks down and bleeding starts.

Lining of the uterus builds up, ready for a fertilised egg.

Egg is released.

Lining of the uterus is maintained.

Lining breaks down if no fertilised egg lands on the uterus wall.

| Day 1 | Day 4 | Day 14 | Day 28 | Day 4 |

Hormones Control the Different Stages

There are <u>three main hormones</u> involved:

1) <u>FSH</u> (Follicle-Stimulating Hormone):

   1) Produced by the <u>pituitary gland</u>.

   2) Causes an <u>egg to mature in one of the ovaries</u>.

   3) Causes <u>ovaries</u> to <u>produce oestrogen</u>.

2) <u>Oestrogen</u>:

   1) Produced in the <u>ovaries</u>.

   2) <u>Inhibits FSH</u> (stops any more FSH being released).

3) <u>LH</u> (Luteinising Hormone):

   Causes the <u>release of an egg</u> from the ovaries.

Pituitary gland

Pituitary gland produces FSH

FSH   Inhibits FSH   Oestrogen   LH

FSH causes egg to mature in ovary

FSH causes ovaries to produce oestrogen

LH causes egg to be released from ovary

The menstrual cycle isn't as scary as it seems

In the exam you might have to explain <u>what hormone does what</u> in the menstrual cycle. It's tough, because they're all interlinked... but don't panic. As long as you know your stuff, you should be OK.

Controlling Fertility

Hormones can be used to <u>change</u> how <u>fertile</u> a woman is (how able she is to have children).

Hormones Can Be Used to **Reduce Fertility...**

1) <u>Oestrogen</u> reduces fertility because it <u>inhibits FSH</u> (see page 16), so <u>no eggs mature</u>.
2) <u>The pill</u> is an <u>oral contraceptive</u> (a birth-control pill that you swallow).
3) The first version of the pill contained <u>high levels</u> of <u>oestrogen</u> and <u>progesterone</u>.
4) But there were concerns about a <u>link</u> between oestrogen in the pill and <u>side effects</u> like <u>blood clots</u>.
5) The pill now contains <u>lower doses</u> of oestrogen so has <u>fewer side effects</u>.

Progesterone is another hormone that reduces fertility.

PROS
1) The pill's <u>very effective</u> at preventing pregnancy.
2) It <u>reduces</u> the <u>risk</u> of getting some types of <u>cancer</u>.

CONS
1) There's still a <u>very slight chance</u> of getting pregnant.
2) It can cause <u>side effects</u> like headaches.
3) It <u>doesn't protect</u> against <u>STDs</u> (sexually transmitted diseases).

6) There's also a <u>progesterone-only pill</u> — it has <u>fewer side effects</u> than the pill.

...or **Increase It**

1) Some women have levels of <u>FSH</u> that are <u>too low</u> to cause their <u>eggs to mature</u>.
2) This means that <u>no eggs</u> are <u>released</u> and the women <u>can't get pregnant</u>.
3) The hormones <u>FSH</u> and <u>LH</u> can be injected by these women to stimulate <u>egg release</u> in their <u>ovaries</u>.

PRO
It helps a lot of women to <u>get pregnant</u>.

CONS
1) It <u>doesn't always work</u>.
2) It can cause <u>multiple pregnancies</u> (twins etc.).

IVF Can Also Help Couples to **Have Children**

1) <u>IVF</u> stands for "<u>in vitro fertilisation</u>".
2) It involves giving <u>FSH</u> and <u>LH</u> to a woman to <u>stimulate egg production</u>.
3) Then the <u>eggs</u> are collected from the woman's ovaries and fertilised in a <u>lab</u> using the man's <u>sperm</u>.
4) The fertilised eggs are then grown into <u>embryos</u>.
5) Once the embryos are <u>tiny balls of cells</u>, one or two of them are <u>transferred</u> to the woman's uterus (womb).

PRO
It can give an infertile couple a <u>child</u>.

CONS
1) Some women have a strong <u>reaction</u> to the hormones — e.g. <u>vomiting</u>.
2) <u>Multiple births</u> can happen — these are <u>risky</u> for the mother and babies.

Warm-Up and Exam Questions

Welcome to the Warm-Up and Exam Questions — the most powerful weapons in the fight against exams.

Warm-Up Questions

1) What are the five sense organs in the human body?
2) What name is given to the connection between two nerve cells?
3) What are hormones secreted by?
4) Give one difference in the way nerves and hormones do their job.
5) Describe what happens at Day 1 in the menstrual cycle.

Exam Questions

1   Gordon accidentally touches a hot object, causing his hand to immediately move away from it.
    The diagram below shows some of the parts involved in this response.

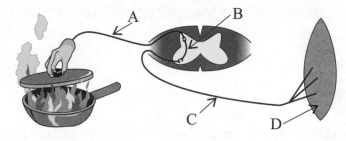

   (a) What is the name of this type of automatic response?

(1 mark)

   (b) On the diagram:

   (i)   Which letter points to a relay neurone?

(1 mark)

   (ii) Which letter points to an effector?

(1 mark)

   (c) Explain how an electrical impulse in one neurone is able to pass to the next neurone.

(2 marks)

2   The menstrual cycle is controlled by several different hormones.

   (a) What effect does oestrogen have on the release of FSH?

(1 mark)

   (b) Which hormone causes an egg to mature in an ovary?

(1 mark)

   (c) On what day of the menstrual cycle is the egg released?

(1 mark)

3   *In this question you will be assessed on the quality of your English, the organisation
    of your ideas and your use of appropriate specialist vocabulary.*

   *Don't panic — this isn't as scary as it looks. All it means is that you need to write in full sentences and
   use proper spelling and punctuation. You'll also need to use scientific words that relate to the question.*

   Many women use the pill as a form of birth control, but it has risks.
   Discuss the advantages and disadvantages of using the pill.

(6 marks)

Plant Hormones

Just like animals, plants <u>respond</u> to changes in their <u>environment</u>.
A plant <u>growth response</u> is called a <u>tropism</u>.

Auxins are Plant **Growth Hormones**

1) <u>Plant growth</u> is controlled by <u>hormones</u> called plant growth hormones.

2) They control the growth of <u>shoots</u> and <u>roots</u>, <u>flowering</u> and the <u>ripening of fruit</u>.

3) The plant hormones that control the <u>growth</u> of <u>shoots</u> and <u>roots</u> are called <u>auxins</u>.
   They move through the plant in <u>solution</u> (dissolved in water).

4) Auxins are made in the <u>tips</u> of the <u>shoots</u> and <u>roots</u>.

5) Auxins are involved in the growth responses of plants to <u>light</u> (phototropism)
   and <u>gravity</u> (geotropism).

Auxins Change the **Direction of Shoot Growth...**

SHOOTS ARE POSITIVELY
PHOTOTROPIC
(grow towards light)

SHOOTS ARE NEGATIVELY
GEOTROPIC
(grow away from gravity)

gravity   gravity

...Giving the Plant a **Better Chance** *of* **Survival**

1) Plants <u>need light</u> to make their own <u>food</u> through <u>photosynthesis</u>.

2) If plants don't get enough light, they <u>die</u>.

3) So plant shoots grow towards the light to <u>increase</u> the <u>plant's chances</u> of <u>survival</u>.

Plant Hormones

This **Experiment** Shows That **Shoots** Grow **Towards Light**

1) Place a plant inside a <u>cardboard box</u>, with a <u>hole</u> in <u>one</u> side, as shown.

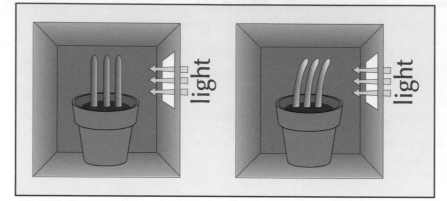

2) If you leave the plant for a <u>few days</u> you'll notice that the shoots will start to bend and <u>grow towards the light</u>.

3) You also need a <u>control experiment</u>. This is used to show that there are <u>no other factors</u> making the plant bend.

4) The control experiment should be a plant <u>surrounded by light</u> on all sides. This plant <u>shouldn't bend</u> at all.

Auxins **Change** the **Direction** of **Root Growth** Too

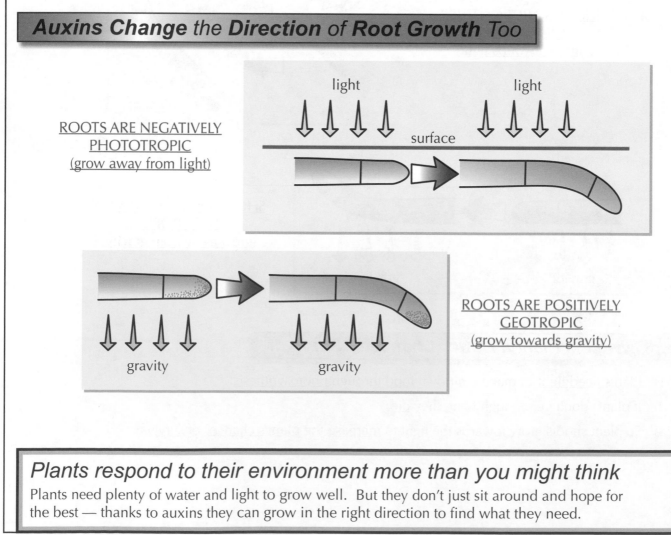

<u>ROOTS ARE NEGATIVELY PHOTOTROPIC</u>
<u>(grow away from light)</u>

<u>ROOTS ARE POSITIVELY GEOTROPIC</u>
<u>(grow towards gravity)</u>

Plants respond to their environment more than you might think

Plants need plenty of water and light to grow well. But they don't just sit around and hope for the best — thanks to auxins they can grow in the right direction to find what they need.

Commercial Uses of Plant Hormones

Plant hormones can be used to <u>speed up</u> or <u>slow down</u> plant growth.
This means they can be used for all sorts of useful things...

1) As *Selective Weedkillers*

1) <u>Selective weedkillers</u> are <u>plant growth hormones</u> that only affect <u>weeds</u>.

2) The weedkillers change the weeds' normal growth patterns, which soon <u>kills</u> them.

3) Grass and crops <u>aren't affected</u> by these weedkillers.

dying weeds, grass unharmed

2) Growing from *Cuttings* with *Rooting Powder*

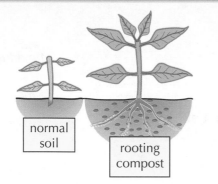

normal soil

rooting compost

1) A <u>cutting</u> is part of a plant that has been <u>cut off it</u>, like the end of a branch with a few leaves on it.

2) Normally, if you stick cuttings in the soil they <u>won't grow</u>.

3) But if you add <u>rooting powder</u>, which contains a plant <u>growth hormone</u>, they will <u>produce roots</u> rapidly and start growing as <u>new plants</u>.

4) This lets growers produce lots of <u>clones</u> (exact copies) of a really good plant <u>very quickly</u>.

3) Controlling the *Ripening of Fruit*

1) Plant hormones can be used to <u>delay the ripening</u> of fruits.

2) This allows the fruit to be picked while it's still <u>unripe</u>. (This means it's firmer and <u>less easily damaged</u>.)

3) <u>Ripening hormone</u> is then added and the fruit will ripen on the way to the supermarket — so it's <u>perfect</u> just as it reaches the shelves.

4) Controlling *Dormancy*

1) Lots of seeds <u>won't germinate</u> (start growing) until they've been through <u>certain conditions</u>, e.g. a period of cold. This is called <u>dormancy</u>.

2) Plant hormones can break this dormancy and cause seeds to <u>germinate</u>.

3) These hormones can be used to make seeds germinate at <u>times of year</u> when they <u>wouldn't</u> normally.

Warm-Up and Exam Questions

You could skim through this page in a few minutes, but there's no point unless you check over any bits you don't know and make sure you understand everything. It's not quick but it's the only way.

Warm-Up Questions

1) What is phototropism?
2) Name the plant hormones that control phototropism.
3) What parts of a plant are positively phototrophic?
4) Describe how plant hormones can be used to produce clones.

Exam Questions

1   Complete the following sentences on selective weedkillers.

(a) Selective weedkillers contain plant ....

(1 mark)

(b) They work by changing the normal growth patterns of ....

(1 mark)

(c) Farmers often use selective weedkillers because they don't affect

grass or ....

(1 mark)

2   Ben is investigating the effect of light on plant growth hormones.
He sets up three plants as shown in the diagrams below.

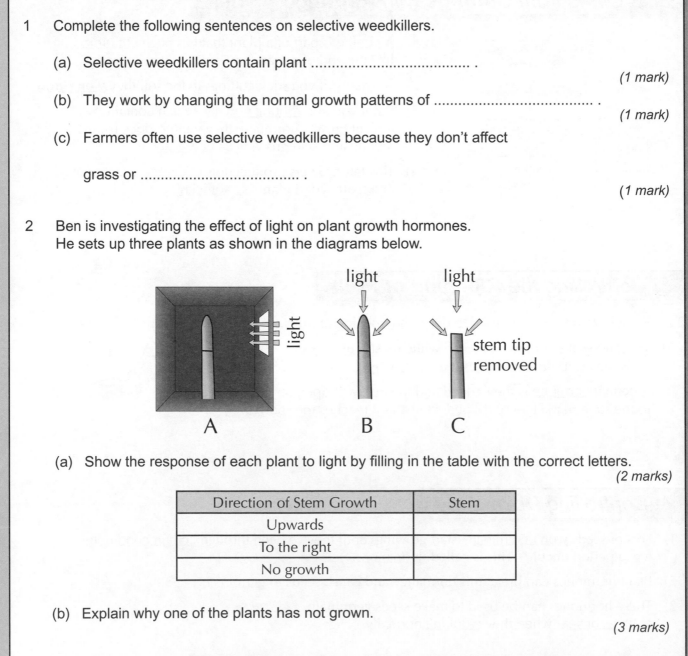

(a) Show the response of each plant to light by filling in the table with the correct letters.

(2 marks)

Direction of Stem Growth	Stem
Upwards	
To the right	
No growth	

(b) Explain why one of the plants has not grown.

(3 marks)

Homeostasis

Homeostasis — a word that strikes fear into the heart of many a GCSE student.
But it's really not that bad.

Homeostasis — Maintaining a Constant Internal Environment

1) Homeostasis is all about balancing the stuff going into your body
   with the stuff leaving to keep the conditions inside your body steady.

2) The technical way of saying this is that homeostasis is about
   maintaining a constant internal environment.

3) The conditions inside your body need to be kept steady
   so that your cells can function (work) properly.

4) You have loads of automatic control systems in your body that are used to keep different factors
   at steady levels. These include both nervous and hormonal communication systems.

5) The control systems are made up of three main parts:

> 1) Receptors — detect (notice) changes in the environment.

> 2) Processing centres — receive information about these
>   changes and automatically organise the response.

> 3) Effectors — produce the response to the change.

Your Body Needs to Keep Ion and Water Levels Constant

Ions

1) Ions (e.g. sodium ions) are taken into the body in food.

2) Some ions are lost in sweat.

3) If your body has more ions than it needs, they're removed
   by the kidneys and got rid of in urine (wee).

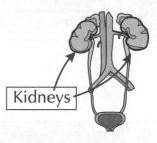

Kidneys

Water

1) Water is taken into the body in food and drink.

2) It's lost from the body in these ways:

> • through the skin as sweat...

> • via the lungs in breath...

> • via the kidneys as urine.

*There's more on
controlling water content
on the next page.*

Controlling Water Content

Your body controls water content using <u>homeostasis</u>.

Your **Urine** isn't Always the **Same**

1) The kidneys balance water levels by producing <u>dilute</u> or <u>concentrated urine</u>.

2) Dilute urine contains <u>more water</u>, concentrated urine contains <u>less</u>.

3) The concentration of the urine depends on the <u>concentration of the blood plasma</u>.

4) This changes with the <u>external temperature</u>, <u>exercise level</u>, and the <u>intake of fluids and salt</u>.

External temperature

1) Temperature affects the amount you <u>sweat</u>.
   Sweat contains water so sweating causes <u>water loss</u>.

2) This means when it's <u>HOT</u> the kidneys will <u>reabsorb</u> more water back into the blood —
   so only a <u>small amount</u> of quite <u>concentrated</u> urine will be produced.

3) On a <u>COLD</u> day you <u>don't sweat much</u>, so you'll
   produce a <u>larger amount</u> of more <u>dilute</u> urine.

Exercise

1) Exercise makes you <u>hotter</u>, so you <u>sweat</u> to cool down.

2) This produces the same effect as heat — a <u>concentrated</u>, <u>small volume</u> of urine.

Intake of fluids and salts

1) Not drinking <u>enough water</u> or eating <u>too
   much salt</u> will produce <u>concentrated</u> urine.

2) Drinking lots of water will produce <u>lots</u> of <u>dilute</u> urine.

Who knew wee could be so interesting

This wasn't the most <u>thrilling</u> page in the world, but it could be worse. You could be doing <u>maths</u>.

Controlling Body Temperature

If you get too hot or too cold it can be pretty unpleasant — at worst it can even kill you.
So it's a good job that your body has got ways of controlling its temperature.

Core Body Temperature *is 37 °C*

1) All enzymes have an optimum temperature — this is the temperature they work best at.
    For enzymes in the human body it's about 37 °C.

2) Your body is kept at the right temperature by homeostasis. For example:

When You're **TOO HOT**:

1) Lots of sweat is produced — when sweat evaporates it uses heat from the skin.
    This transfers heat from your skin to the environment, which cools you down.

2) More blood flows near the surface of the skin
    so more heat can be lost to the surroundings.

If you get too hot you can get:
- dehydrated
- heat stroke

These conditions can kill you.

When You're **TOO COLD:**

1) Very little sweat is produced.

2) Less blood flows near the surface of the skin so that less heat is lost to the surroundings.

3) Shivering produces heat through respiration.

4) Exercising warms you up in the same way.

5) Adding extra clothes helps keep your body warm.

- Your body temperature can drop dangerously if you stay out in the cold for a long time.
- This is called hypothermia.
- If you don't get help quickly you can die.

Heat stroke is no laughing matter

If you're in really high temperatures for a long time you can get heat stroke — and if you don't cool
down it can kill you. Fortunately, British drizzle means that heat stroke needn't worry most of us.

Controlling Blood Sugar

<u>Homeostasis</u> keeps the <u>level</u> of <u>sugar</u> in your <u>blood steady</u>. Here's <u>how</u>:

Insulin Controls Blood Sugar Level

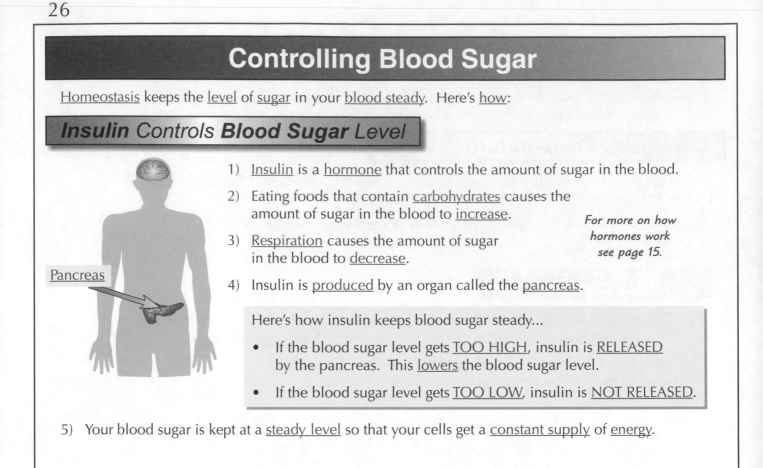

Pancreas

1) <u>Insulin</u> is a <u>hormone</u> that controls the amount of sugar in the blood.

2) Eating foods that contain <u>carbohydrates</u> causes the amount of sugar in the blood to <u>increase</u>.

3) <u>Respiration</u> causes the amount of sugar in the blood to <u>decrease</u>.

For more on how hormones work see page 15.

4) Insulin is <u>produced</u> by an organ called the <u>pancreas</u>.

Here's how insulin keeps blood sugar steady...

- If the blood sugar level gets <u>TOO HIGH</u>, insulin is <u>RELEASED</u> by the pancreas. This <u>lowers</u> the blood sugar level.

- If the blood sugar level gets <u>TOO LOW</u>, insulin is <u>NOT RELEASED</u>.

5) Your blood sugar is kept at a <u>steady level</u> so that your cells get a <u>constant supply</u> of <u>energy</u>.

Diabetics Can't Control Their Blood Sugar Level

<u>Diabetes</u> is a condition that affects your ability to <u>control</u> your blood sugar level. There are <u>two types</u>:

Type 1 Diabetes

1) Type 1 diabetes is where the <u>pancreas can't produce insulin</u>.

2) The result is that a person's blood sugar can rise to a level that can <u>kill them</u>.

3) People with type 1 diabetes can partly control the condition by having a carefully controlled diet (see below). But they also need to <u>inject insulin</u> into the blood at mealtimes.

Type 2 Diabetes

1) Type 2 diabetes is where a person <u>can't respond to insulin</u> properly. This can also cause blood sugar level to rise to a dangerous level.

2) Type 2 diabetes is usually just controlled by <u>avoiding sugary foods</u>, which cause the blood sugar level to rise rapidly.

My blood sugar feels low after all that — pass the biscuits...

The level of <u>sugar</u> in your <u>blood</u> needs to be <u>controlled</u>. <u>Diabetes</u> is a condition where the body can't do this. But there are <u>two types</u> of diabetes and they're treated in different ways. Don't confuse them.

Warm-Up and Exam Questions

By now you should be a homeostasis genius. But even geniuses have to check that they know their stuff, so grab a cup of tea, roll up your sleeves and dive into these questions. It'll be fun. No, really.

Warm-Up Questions

1) Explain why the conditions in your body need to be kept steady.
2) Name two of the body's automatic control systems.
3) What are the roles of receptors and effectors in automatic control systems?
4) Why is it important that human body temperature is kept at about 37 °C?
5) Explain why more blood flows near the surface of your skin when you're too hot.
6) What is the difference between type 1 and type 2 diabetes?

Exam Questions

1   The level of sugar in your blood needs to be kept steady.

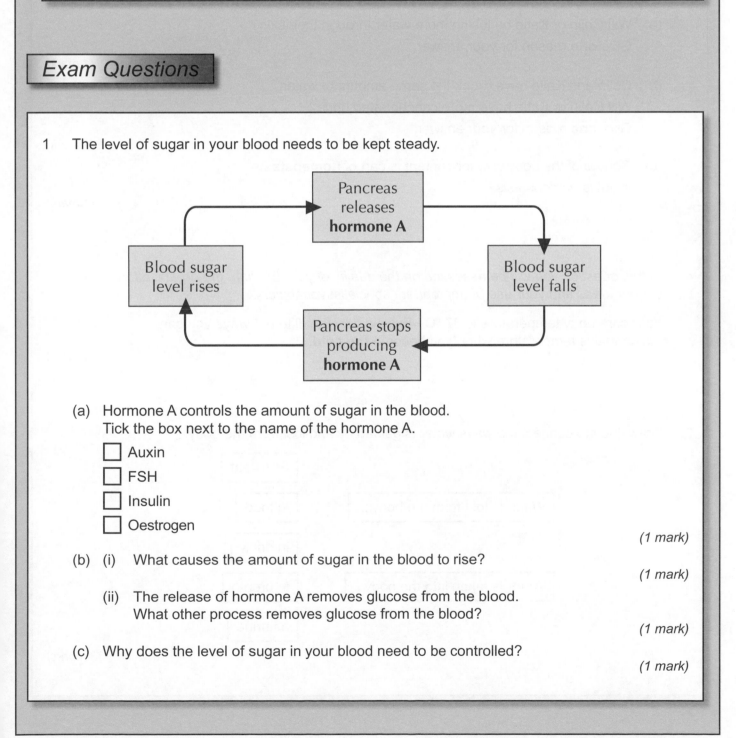

(a)   Hormone A controls the amount of sugar in the blood.
       Tick the box next to the name of the hormone A.

    ☐ Auxin

    ☐ FSH

    ☐ Insulin

    ☐ Oestrogen

(1 mark)

(b) (i)   What causes the amount of sugar in the blood to rise?

(1 mark)

     (ii)   The release of hormone A removes glucose from the blood.
            What other process removes glucose from the blood?

(1 mark)

(c)   Why does the level of sugar in your blood need to be controlled?

(1 mark)

Exam Questions

2   Brian eats chips covered in salt for lunch. Salt contains ions.

     (a)   Describe how the level of ions in Brian's blood will change following his lunch.

(1 mark)

     (b)   Give **two** ways that ions are lost from the body.

(2 marks)

     (c)   Which organ is responsible for regulating the ion content of the blood?

(1 mark)

3   On a hot summer day Katie is running in the park, while Colin is sitting still at home reading a book.

     (a)   Will Colin or Katie be losing more water through their skin?
         Give **one** reason for your answer.

(1 mark)

     (b)   Colin and Katie have drunk the same amount of water.
         Will Colin or Katie have more concentrated urine?
         Give **one** reason for your answer.

(1 mark)

     (c)   Control of the body's water content is part of **homeostasis**.
         What is homeostasis?

(1 mark)

4   *In this question you will be assessed on the quality of your English, the organisation of your ideas and your use of appropriate specialist vocabulary.*

     Your core body temperature is 37 °C. Explain fully the different ways you can maintain this temperature when you become **too cold**.

(6 marks)

5   Draw lines to connect the ways water is gained by and lost from the body.

	as sweat
Water is lost from the body....	in food
	in drink
Water is taken into the body...	in breath
	as urine

(3 marks)

Revision Summary for Section 1

Congratulations, you've made it to the end of the first section. I reckon that section wasn't too bad. There's some pretty interesting stuff there — nerves, reflexes, hormones, wee... what more could you want? Actually, I know what more you could want, some questions to make sure you know it all.

1) Where would you find the following receptors in a dog: a) smell
                                                            b) taste
                                                            c) light?

2) What is a synapse?

3) Why do we have reflexes?

4) Define "hormone".

5)* Here's a table of data about response times.

    a) Which response (A or B) is carried by nerves?

    b) Which is carried by hormones?

Response	Reaction time (s)	Length of response (s)
A	0.005	0.05
B	2	10

6) Describe two effects of FSH on the body.

7) State one advantage and one disadvantage of using the contraceptive pill.

8) Briefly describe how IVF is carried out.

9) What are auxins?

10) What is geotropism?

11) Give three ways that plant growth hormones are used commercially.

12) Name the three main components of the body's automatic control systems.

13) Name two things the body needs to keep constant.

14) Describe how the external temperature can affect the concentration of urine produced by the kidneys.

15) What effect does exercise have on urine production?

16) Describe how body temperature is reduced when you're too hot.

17) Explain how insulin controls blood sugar level.

18) What is the difference between how type 1 and type 2 diabetes are usually controlled?

Answers on page 237.

Diet and Metabolic Rate

The first thing on the Section 2 menu is... well... food. It's where you get your energy from, to do all sorts of things like talking, partying and maybe a bit of revision.

A Balanced Diet Keeps You Healthy

For good health, your diet must give you the energy you need (but not more).
You need to have the right balance of different foods as well.
So you need:

...enough carbohydrates to release energy,

...enough fats to keep warm and release energy,

...enough protein to build and repair cells,

...some fibre to prevent constipation (difficulty pooing),

...enough water to prevent dehydration (where the body doesn't have enough water),

...and tiny amounts of various vitamins and mineral ions to keep
   your skin, bones, blood and everything else generally healthy.

A Balanced Diet is Different for Different People

A balanced diet isn't a set thing — it's different for everyone.
The balance of different nutrients a person needs depends on things like:

AGE ⟹ Children and teenagers need more protein for growth.

GENDER ⟹ Females need more iron to replace the iron lost in blood during their period.

Different People have Different Energy Needs

You need energy to fuel the chemical reactions in the body that keep you alive.
These reactions are called your metabolism.
The speed these reactions happen at is your metabolic rate.
Your metabolic rate varies depending on:

1) How much Muscle you have

If you have more muscle than fat, you'll need more energy, so you'll have a high metabolic rate.

2) How Active you are

If you have an active job or exercise lots, you'll need more energy,
so you'll have a high metabolic rate.

3) Inherited Factors

Inherited factors (i.e. your genes) can affect your metabolic rate (see page 32).

Factors Affecting Health

What you eat, and how much you eat, is dead important — because it affects your health.

Your **Health** is Affected by Having an **Unbalanced Diet**...

1) People whose diet is badly out of balance are said to be <u>malnourished</u>.
2) An <u>unbalanced diet</u> can be where people <u>eat too much</u> or <u>don't eat enough</u>:

Some People **Eat Too Much**

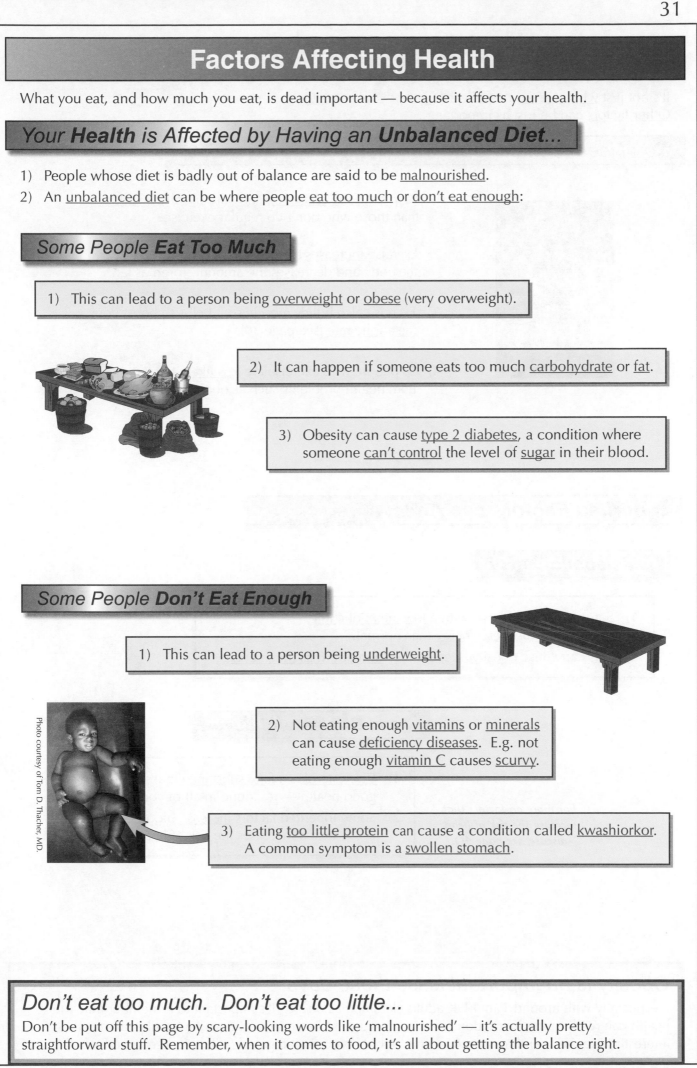

1) This can lead to a person being <u>overweight</u> or <u>obese</u> (very overweight).

2) It can happen if someone eats too much <u>carbohydrate</u> or <u>fat</u>.

3) Obesity can cause <u>type 2 diabetes</u>, a condition where someone <u>can't control</u> the level of <u>sugar</u> in their blood.

Some People **Don't Eat Enough**

1) This can lead to a person being <u>underweight</u>.

2) Not eating enough <u>vitamins</u> or <u>minerals</u> can cause <u>deficiency diseases</u>. E.g. not eating enough <u>vitamin C</u> causes <u>scurvy</u>.

3) Eating <u>too little protein</u> can cause a condition called <u>kwashiorkor</u>. A common symptom is a <u>swollen stomach</u>.

Photo courtesy of Tom D. Thacher, MD.

Don't eat too much. Don't eat too little...

Don't be put off this page by scary-looking words like 'malnourished' — it's actually pretty straightforward stuff. Remember, when it comes to food, it's all about getting the balance right.

Factors Affecting Health

It's not just <u>what you eat</u> that affects whether you're <u>healthy</u>.
<u>Other factors</u> can be just as important...

You Need to Make Sure You Get Enough *Exercise*

1) People who <u>exercise regularly</u> are usually <u>healthier</u> than those who don't do regular exercise.

2) Exercise <u>increases</u> the amount of <u>energy</u> used by the body and <u>decreases</u> the amount <u>stored</u> as <u>fat</u>.

3) Exercise also <u>builds muscle</u> so it helps to boost your <u>metabolic rate</u> (see page 30).

4) So people who exercise are <u>less likely</u> to suffer from health problems such as <u>obesity</u>.

Inherited Factors can Affect a Person's...

...Metabolic Rate...

1) Some people are born with a <u>low metabolic rate</u>, so their cells use <u>less energy</u> than normal.
2) This can cause <u>obesity</u> because they <u>don't burn as much energy</u>.

...and Cholesterol Level

For more on factors that increase the risk of heart disease, see page 40.

1) <u>Cholesterol</u> is a <u>fatty substance</u> that's needed for good health — it's found in all of your cells.
2) Some inherited factors <u>increase</u> blood cholesterol level, which increases the risk of <u>heart disease</u>.

Obesity is an important issue these days...

...especially with around 1 in 4 UK adults classified as obese. It's important to remember that your health can really <u>suffer</u> if you don't look after yourself. Exercise might not sound like the most interesting way of spending your free time — but if you do it regularly it'll help keep you fit.

Food and All its Labels

So, you know the importance of eating a balanced diet and doing regular exercise. But how you can tell if a food product is <u>healthy</u>? Well read on to find out...

You Might Have to **Evaluate Information** on **Food...**

1) In the exam, you may get asked to <u>evaluate</u> (weigh up) <u>information</u> about <u>how food affects health</u>.

2) Don't panic — you just need to use <u>what you know</u> from pages 30-31 to answer the question.

3) Have a look at the <u>examples</u> in the box below:

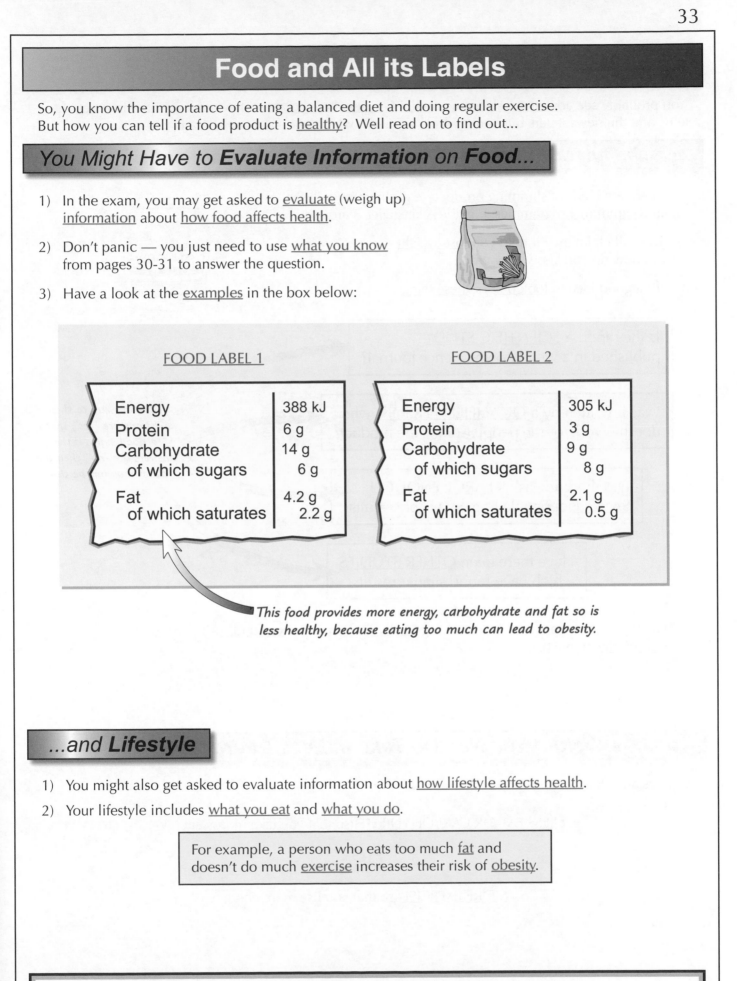

FOOD LABEL 1

Energy	388 kJ
Protein	6 g
Carbohydrate	14 g
of which sugars	6 g
Fat	4.2 g
of which saturates	2.2 g

FOOD LABEL 2

Energy	305 kJ
Protein	3 g
Carbohydrate	9 g
of which sugars	8 g
Fat	2.1 g
of which saturates	0.5 g

This food provides more energy, carbohydrate and fat so is less healthy, because eating too much can lead to obesity.

...and **Lifestyle**

1) You might also get asked to evaluate information about <u>how lifestyle affects health</u>.

2) Your lifestyle includes <u>what you eat</u> and <u>what you do</u>.

For example, a person who eats too much <u>fat</u> and doesn't do much <u>exercise</u> increases their risk of <u>obesity</u>.

Read the side of your crisp packet next time you're peckish...

...all those <u>words and numbers</u> should make a bit more sense after you've read this page. If you're really ~~dull~~ interested, grab a few of your <u>favourite snacks</u> and compare their food labels. You can work out which ones are <u>worst</u> for you and which ones aren't actually <u>as bad as you thought</u>. Fun times.

Evaluating Slimming Claims

You probably see <u>adverts for slimming products everywhere you go</u>. They're all over the internet, the telly, and the newspapers but here's where you learn which ones you can actually trust.

*Watch Out for **Slimming Claims** that Aren't **Scientifically Proven***

1) There are loads of <u>slimming products</u> (e.g. slimming milkshakes) and <u>slimming programmes</u> (e.g. the Atkins Diet™) around.

2) They all claim they'll help you <u>lose weight</u> — but how do you know they work...

3) It's a good idea to <u>look out</u> for <u>these things</u>:

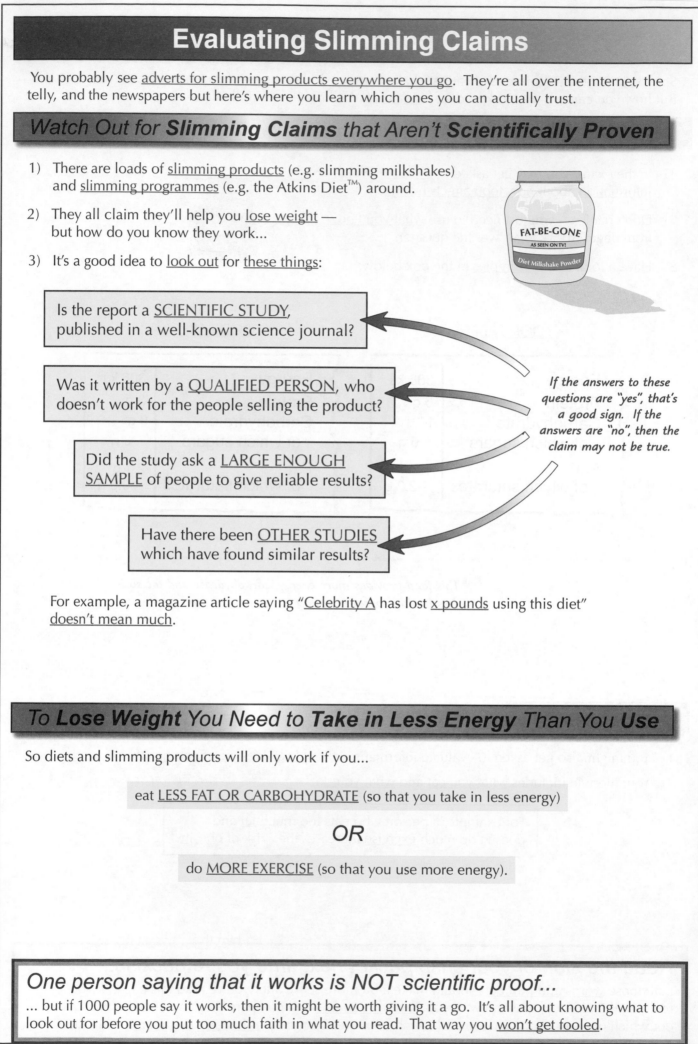

Is the report a <u>SCIENTIFIC STUDY</u>, published in a well-known science journal?

Was it written by a <u>QUALIFIED PERSON</u>, who doesn't work for the people selling the product?

Did the study ask a <u>LARGE ENOUGH SAMPLE</u> of people to give reliable results?

Have there been <u>OTHER STUDIES</u> which have found similar results?

If the answers to these questions are "yes", that's a good sign. If the answers are "no", then the claim may not be true.

For example, a magazine article saying "<u>Celebrity A</u> has lost <u>x pounds</u> using this diet" <u>doesn't mean much</u>.

*To **Lose Weight** You Need to **Take in Less Energy** Than You **Use***

So diets and slimming products will only work if you...

eat <u>LESS FAT OR CARBOHYDRATE</u> (so that you take in less energy)

OR

do <u>MORE EXERCISE</u> (so that you use more energy).

One person saying that it works is NOT scientific proof...

... but if 1000 people say it works, then it might be worth giving it a go. It's all about knowing what to look out for before you put too much faith in what you read. That way you <u>won't get fooled</u>.

Warm-Up and Exam Questions

Well, you've ploughed your way through another chunk of biology goodness, so what better way to celebrate than with some warm-up and exam questions. I'm just so good to you...

Warm-Up Questions

1) Why is it important to eat carbohydrates as part of a balanced diet?
2) Does exercising regularly increase or decrease your metabolic rate?
3) Give two possible effects of eating too little.
4) Why is having a high blood cholesterol level a health risk?
5) Name one thing to look out for when evaluating a claim about a slimming product.

Exam Questions

1   Eating too much of some foods, and too little of others, can affect your health.
    Draw lines to link the eating habits below to the conditions they can cause.

    Not eating enough vitamin C...   ...can cause obesity.

    Not eating enough protein...   ...can cause scurvy.

    Eating too much carbohydrate or fat...   ...can cause Kwashiorkor.

    (3 marks)

2   The labels below show some basic nutritional information from two food packets.

    (a) Calculate how much energy a
        40 g serving of **Food A** contains.
        Show your working.
        (2 marks)

    (b) Which of the two foods,
        A or B, is healthier?
        Explain your answer.
        (3 marks)

FOOD A

NUTRITIONAL INFORMATION	
	per 100 g
Energy	512 kcal
Protein	6.9 g
Carbohydrate	49 g
Fat	5.2 g

FOOD B

NUTRITIONAL INFORMATION	
	per 100 g
Energy	307 kcal
Protein	7.4 g
Carbohydrate	25 g
Fat	4.7 g

3   To stay healthy you need to keep active.

    (a) John and Dave are twins. John is a receptionist and Dave is a builder.
        Copy and complete the following sentence about John and Dave:

        .... has the most active job, so he will need the most .... per day.
        (2 marks)

    (b) Explain why taking regular exercise decreases your risk of becoming obese.
        (3 marks)

    (c) Dave takes regular exercise and is fit, but his doctor tells him that he is at high
        risk of becoming obese.
        Give **one** reason why Dave might be at risk of becoming obese despite being fit.
        (1 mark)

The Circulatory System

Blood is <u>vital</u> stuff. But it needs a way to get around the body. This is where the <u>circulatory system</u> steps in...

The **Heart** and **Blood Vessels** Supply Blood to the Body

1) <u>Blood</u> is circulated around the body in tubes called <u>blood vessels</u>.

There's more on blood vessels on the next page.

2) The <u>heart</u> is a pumping organ that keeps the blood flowing through the vessels.

3) It's actually a <u>double pump</u>:
   - The <u>right side</u> pumps blood to the <u>lungs</u>.
   - The <u>left side</u> pumps blood around the rest of the <u>body</u>.

4) The heart's made up of <u>muscle cells</u> that keep it beating <u>all the time</u>.

5) These cells need their own <u>blood supply</u> to bring the <u>nutrients</u> and <u>oxygen</u> needed to keep the heart beating <u>all the time</u>.

The diagram shows the right and left side of the person in the diagram, not your right and left as you look at them.

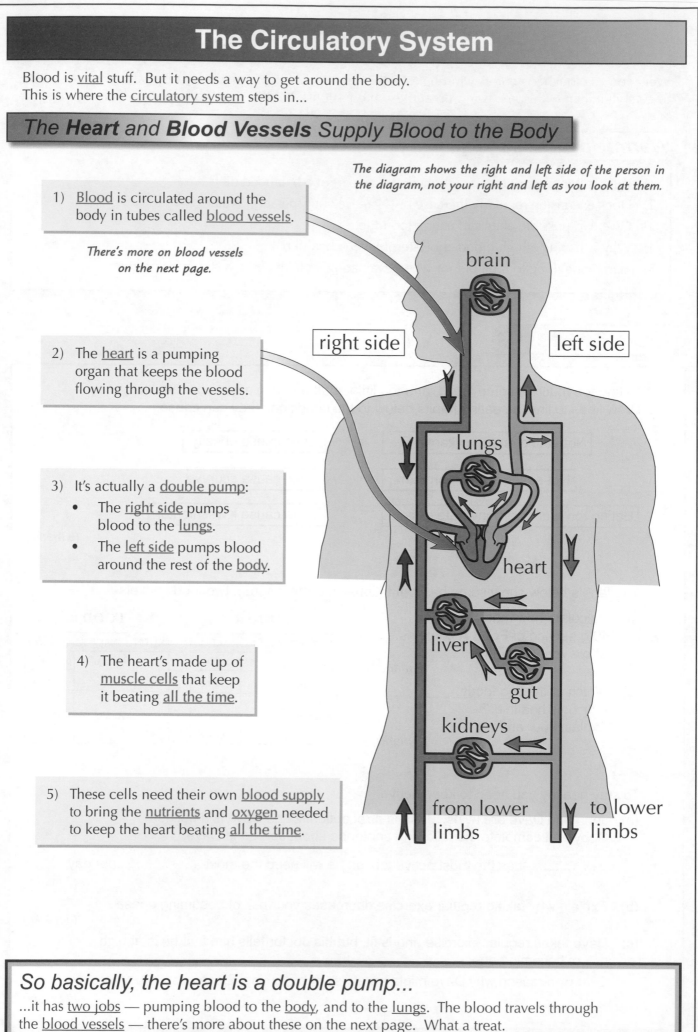

right side   left side

brain

lungs

heart

liver

gut

kidneys

from lower limbs   to lower limbs

So basically, the heart is a double pump...

...it has <u>two jobs</u> — pumping blood to the <u>body</u>, and to the <u>lungs</u>. The blood travels through the <u>blood vessels</u> — there's more about these on the next page. What a treat.

The Circulatory System

The <u>heart's</u> an <u>important</u> part of the circulatory system, but you'd be snookered without <u>blood vessels</u>.

There are **Three** Major Types of **Blood Vessel**

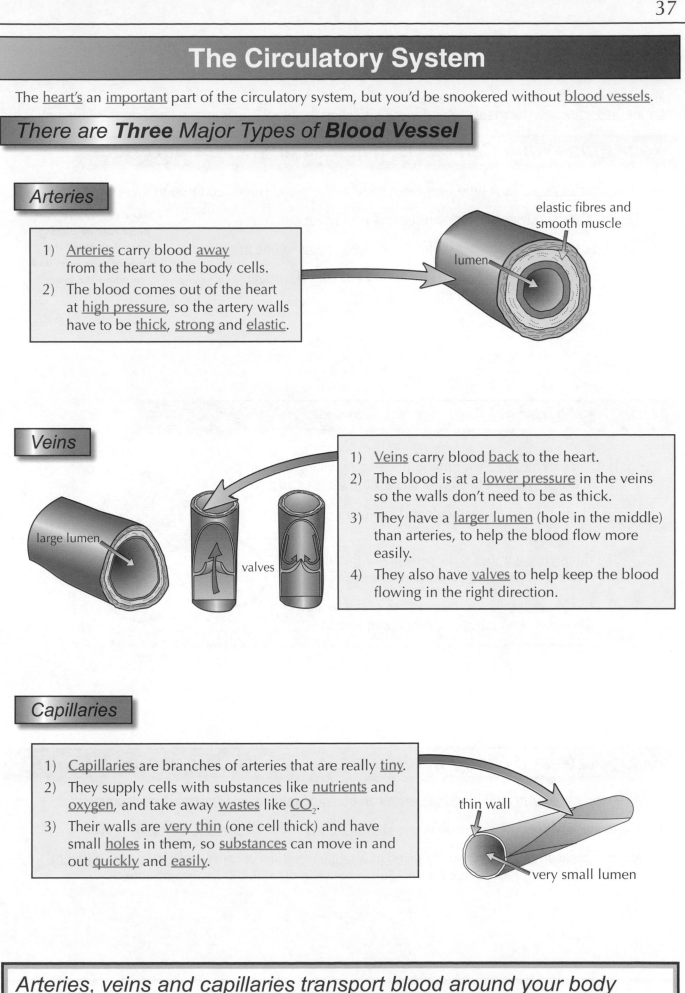

Arteries

1) <u>Arteries</u> carry blood <u>away</u> from the heart to the body cells.

2) The blood comes out of the heart at <u>high pressure</u>, so the artery walls have to be <u>thick</u>, <u>strong</u> and <u>elastic</u>.

elastic fibres and smooth muscle

lumen

Veins

1) <u>Veins</u> carry blood <u>back</u> to the heart.

2) The blood is at a <u>lower pressure</u> in the veins so the walls don't need to be as thick.

3) They have a <u>larger lumen</u> (hole in the middle) than arteries, to help the blood flow more easily.

4) They also have <u>valves</u> to help keep the blood flowing in the right direction.

large lumen

valves

Capillaries

1) <u>Capillaries</u> are branches of arteries that are really <u>tiny</u>.

2) They supply cells with substances like <u>nutrients</u> and <u>oxygen</u>, and take away <u>wastes</u> like CO_2.

3) Their walls are <u>very thin</u> (one cell thick) and have small <u>holes</u> in them, so <u>substances</u> can move in and out <u>quickly</u> and <u>easily</u>.

thin wall

very small lumen

Arteries, veins and capillaries transport blood around your body

The heart wouldn't be much use without blood vessels to carry the blood to where it actually needs to go. That's why blood vessels are so great. The differences between them aren't too hard to remember — especially when you've got those beautiful diagrams to help you out. Gosh, I am good to you.

Heart Rate and Blood Pressure

Your blood has got to travel a <u>long way</u> around your body. The only way it can do this is if it's <u>under pressure</u>. Your heart <u>beats</u> continuously to keep the blood moving and keep up this pressure.

Your **Pulse Rate** Can be Used to **Measure** Your **Heart Rate**

1) Your <u>arteries pulse</u> each time your heart <u>beats</u> as the blood is pushed through them.

2) The <u>number of pulses</u> felt in <u>one minute</u> is your <u>pulse rate</u>.

3) Your <u>heart rate</u> is the number of times your <u>heart beats</u> in <u>one minute</u>.

4) So, you can measure your pulse rate to find out your <u>heart rate</u>. They're the <u>same</u>.

You can measure your pulse rate by placing two fingers on the inside of your wrist and counting the beats.

Blood is **Pumped** Around Your Body Under **Pressure**

1) You can <u>measure</u> your blood pressure by taking a reading of the <u>pressure</u> of the blood <u>against the walls</u> of an <u>artery</u>.

2) Blood pressure measurements have <u>two numbers</u>, e.g. 135 over 85.

3) The <u>higher number</u> is the pressure of the blood when the heart <u>contracts</u> (systolic pressure).

4) The <u>lower number</u> is the pressure of the blood when the heart <u>relaxes</u> (diastolic pressure).

Heart Rate and **Blood Pressure** Can Show if **Something's Wrong**

1) A person's <u>heart rate</u> and <u>blood pressure</u> can be <u>compared</u> against <u>"normal" measurements</u>.

2) These are what people's measurements <u>should be</u> when there's <u>nothing wrong</u> with them.

3) Normal measurements are usually given as a <u>range</u> of values because <u>individuals are different</u>, e.g. a normal resting heart rate for an adult is between 60 and 100 beats a minute.

Don't let exam stress send your blood pressure through the roof...

Measuring your <u>pulse rate</u> is something you can do at home, and having your <u>blood pressure</u> taken is always fun. The stuff on the next few pages is a bit more gloomy though — you've been warned...

Factors Affecting Heart Disease

I'm afraid this isn't a very <u>cheery page</u> — heart disease is about as funny as <u>soggy Brussel sprouts</u>. Sorry. But chin up, because there's some <u>exciting stuff</u> just around the corner, like <u>drugs</u>. Hurrah.

High Blood Pressure *Increases* the *Risk* of *Heart Disease*

1) <u>High blood pressure</u> can <u>damage</u> the <u>inside</u> of an artery.

2) <u>Fatty deposits</u> can sometimes <u>build up</u> in damaged areas of arteries.

3) These deposits <u>restrict</u> blood flow and cause the <u>blood pressure</u> in arteries to <u>increase</u> even more.

Heart disease is just any disease that affects the heart — including heart attacks.

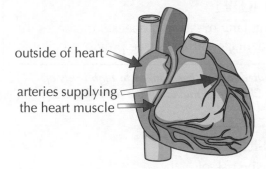

outside of heart

arteries supplying the heart muscle

4) Damage caused by fatty deposits can <u>eventually</u> cause an artery to be <u>blocked completely</u>.

5) If an artery that's supplying the heart becomes <u>completely blocked</u> an area of the heart muscle will be totally <u>cut off</u> from its blood supply.

6) This causes a <u>heart attack</u>.

Epidemiological Studies Can Identify Possible *Risk Factors*

1) Epidemiology is the study of <u>patterns</u> of diseases and the <u>factors</u> that affect them.

2) Epidemiological studies can be used to <u>identify</u> (find out) the factors that <u>increase the risk</u> of <u>heart disease</u>.

There's more on the factors that increase the risk of heart disease on the next page.

Lifestyle factors

For example, you could study a group of people who all <u>died</u> from heart disease. You'd look for <u>similarities</u> in their lifestyle that may be <u>linked</u> to heart disease, e.g. they were all smokers.

Genetic factors

For example, you could look at the <u>genes</u> of a large group of people, then see if the people affected by heart disease all had <u>similar genes</u>.

I told you it wasn't going to be a cheery page...

It doesn't get much more serious than <u>heart disease</u> — and there's even more to learn about it over the page. At least now you should understand why having <u>high blood pressure</u> is <u>not</u> a good thing.

Factors Affecting Heart Disease

Your risk of getting heart disease depends on what you do...

Lifestyle Factors Can Increase the Risk of Heart Disease

1) Heart disease is often linked to lifestyle factors, e.g. what someone eats.

2) Some people might be more at risk because of their genes too.

3) The lifestyle factors that increase the risk of heart disease include:

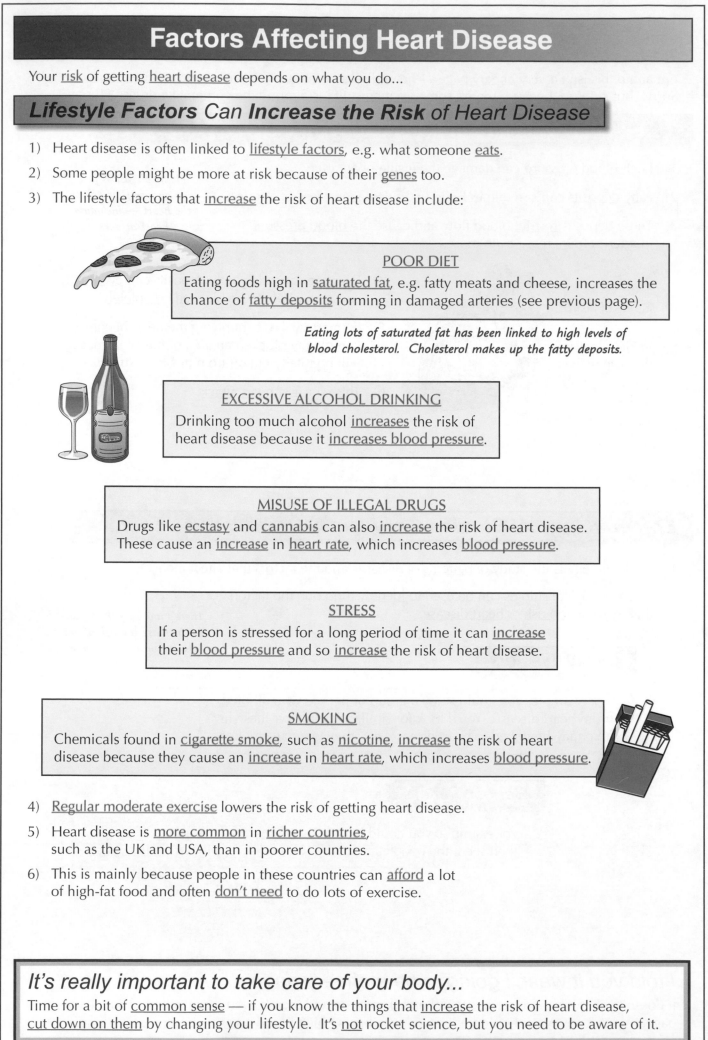

POOR DIET
Eating foods high in saturated fat, e.g. fatty meats and cheese, increases the chance of fatty deposits forming in damaged arteries (see previous page).

Eating lots of saturated fat has been linked to high levels of blood cholesterol. Cholesterol makes up the fatty deposits.

EXCESSIVE ALCOHOL DRINKING
Drinking too much alcohol increases the risk of heart disease because it increases blood pressure.

MISUSE OF ILLEGAL DRUGS
Drugs like ecstasy and cannabis can also increase the risk of heart disease. These cause an increase in heart rate, which increases blood pressure.

STRESS
If a person is stressed for a long period of time it can increase their blood pressure and so increase the risk of heart disease.

SMOKING
Chemicals found in cigarette smoke, such as nicotine, increase the risk of heart disease because they cause an increase in heart rate, which increases blood pressure.

4) Regular moderate exercise lowers the risk of getting heart disease.

5) Heart disease is more common in richer countries, such as the UK and USA, than in poorer countries.

6) This is mainly because people in these countries can afford a lot of high-fat food and often don't need to do lots of exercise.

It's really important to take care of your body...

Time for a bit of common sense — if you know the things that increase the risk of heart disease, cut down on them by changing your lifestyle. It's not rocket science, but you need to be aware of it.

Warm-Up and Exam Questions

Exam questions are the best way to practise what you've learnt. After all, they're exactly what you'll have to do on the big day — so work through these (and the warm-up questions) very carefully.

Warm-Up Questions

1) Explain why the heart's muscle cells need their own blood supply.
2) What is the purpose of the valves in veins?
3) How many cells thick is the wall of a capillary?
4) Why are normal heart rate measurements given as a range of values?
5) Why might you undertake a genetic study when investigating the causes of heart disease?

Exam Questions

1 The table below describes the functions of different parts of the circulatory system.
Match the words **A**, **B**, **C** and **D** with the numbers **1 - 4** in the table.

A Capillaries

B Heart

C Arteries

D Veins

Structure	Function
1	Pumps blood around the body
2	Return blood to the heart
3	Take blood away from the heart
4	Supply cells with substances and remove wastes

(4 marks)

2 This question is about heart disease.

(a) Name **one** chemical found in cigarette smoke that can increase the risk of heart disease.

(1 mark)

(b) Explain how drinking excessive amounts of alcohol can affect the risk of developing heart disease.

(2 marks)

(c) Heart disease is more common in richer countries than in poorer countries. Explain why this is the case.

(2 marks)

3 *In this question you will be assessed on the quality of your English, the organisation of your ideas and your use of appropriate specialist vocabulary.*

The risk of having a heart attack is increased by high blood pressure.
Describe and explain how high blood pressure can lead to a heart attack.

(6 marks)

Drugs

Drugs alter the <u>chemical reactions</u> in your body — sometimes for the better, sometimes not.

Drugs Change Your **Body Chemistry**

1) The chemical changes caused by a drug can make people become <u>addicted</u> to it (want it really badly). E.g. <u>heroin</u> and <u>cocaine</u> are very addictive.

2) If the drug <u>isn't</u> taken, an addict can suffer <u>withdrawal symptoms</u> — these are often pretty <u>unpleasant</u>.

3) Some drugs are medicines that may be <u>prescribed</u> by a doctor, or got <u>over the counter</u> (<u>non-prescribed</u>).

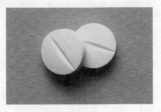

Performance-Enhancing Drugs have **Health** and **Ethical Impacts**

1) Some athletes take <u>performance-enhancing</u> drugs to make them better at sport. For example, <u>steroids</u> increase muscle size and <u>stimulants</u> increase heart rate.

2) But these drugs can have <u>negative health effects</u>, e.g. steroids can cause <u>high blood pressure</u>.

3) Some of these drugs are <u>banned</u> by <u>law</u>, some are <u>prescription-only</u>, but all are <u>banned</u> by <u>sporting bodies</u>.

4) There are also <u>ethical problems</u> with taking them:

AGAINST DRUGS...	1) It's <u>unfair</u> if people gain an <u>advantage</u> by taking drugs. 2) Athletes may <u>not know</u> the <u>health risks</u>.

FOR DRUGS...	1) Drug-free sport <u>isn't really fair</u> anyway, e.g. athletes may have <u>different coaches</u>. 2) Athletes have the right to make their <u>own decision</u> about whether taking drugs is worth the risk or not.

Claims About **Drugs** need to be **Carefully Looked At**

E.g. **Statins** are a Type of **Prescribed Drug**

1) They're used to lower the risk of <u>heart</u> and <u>circulatory disease</u>.

2) There's evidence that statins <u>lower blood cholesterol</u> and lower the risk of <u>heart disease</u> in diabetics.

3) The original research for this was good because:
   - It was done by <u>government</u> scientists with <u>no connection</u> to the manufacturers.
   - The <u>sample</u> was <u>big</u> — 6000 patients.
   - The study compared patients who <u>had</u> taken statins with those who <u>hadn't</u>.

4) Other studies have <u>backed up</u> these findings.

Heart and circulatory disease means diseases of your heart and blood vessels.

E.g. **Cannabis** is an **Illegal Drug**

1) Scientists have looked at whether the <u>chemicals</u> in cannabis smoke cause <u>mental health problems</u>.

2) The results <u>vary</u>, so they're still <u>not sure</u>.

Testing Medicinal Drugs

<u>New drugs</u> are always being <u>developed</u>. But before they can be given to the general public, they have to go through lots of <u>thorough testing</u>. This is what usually happens...

There are **Three Main Stages** in Drug Testing

1 Drugs are tested on <u>human cells and tissues</u> in the lab.

2
1) The next step is to test the drug on <u>live animals</u>.
2) This is to see whether the drug <u>works</u> and to find out about its <u>toxicity</u> (how harmful it is).
3) It's also to find the best <u>dosage</u> — the dose at which it's most effective (works best).

3
1) If the drug <u>passes</u> the tests on animals then it's tested on <u>human volunteers</u> in a <u>clinical trial</u>.
2) First, the drug is tested on <u>healthy</u> volunteers.
3) At the start of the trial, a <u>very low dose</u> of the drug is given and this is <u>slowly increased</u>.
4) If the results of the tests on healthy volunteers are <u>good</u>, the drug can be tested on <u>patients</u>.
5) The <u>optimum dose</u> is found. This is the dose of drug that's <u>most effective</u> and has <u>few side effects</u>.
6) To test how well the drug works, patients are put into <u>two groups</u>...

Group 1 is given the <u>new drug</u>.

Group 2 is given a <u>placebo</u> (a substance that's like the real drug but doesn't do anything).

7) The doctor <u>compares</u> the two groups of patients to see the <u>actual difference</u> the drug makes.
8) Clinical trials are <u>blind</u> — the patient <u>doesn't know</u> whether they're getting the <u>drug</u> or the <u>placebo</u>.
9) In fact, they're often <u>double-blind</u> — neither the patient nor the <u>doctor</u> knows who's taken the drug and who's taken the placebo until <u>all the results</u> have been gathered.

Things Have **Gone Wrong** in the Past

1) <u>Thalidomide</u> is a drug that was developed as a <u>sleeping pill</u>.
2) Later it was also found to be good at relieving <u>morning sickness</u> in pregnant women.
3) But thalidomide <u>hadn't been tested</u> as a drug for morning sickness.
4) So it wasn't known that thalidomide could affect the <u>unborn baby</u> and cause <u>arm and leg problems</u>. E.g. some babies were born with very short arms and legs.
5) Thalidomide was <u>banned</u>, and stricter testing procedures were introduced.
6) More recently, thalidomide has been used in the treatment of <u>leprosy</u> and <u>other diseases</u>.

You've got to be sure that a drug is safe before you give it to people

Thalidomide is an example of a drug that was developed to try to <u>improve</u> people's lives... but it ended up causing some <u>tragic</u> effects. Hopefully we'll be able to avoid similar mistakes in the future — but there's no such thing as perfect knowledge and you can never get rid of risk completely.

Recreational Drugs

Not all drugs are used by people with illnesses — some are just used for <u>fun</u>. But fun comes with <u>risk</u>.

*Recreational Drugs Can Be **Illegal** or **Legal***

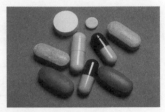

1) <u>Illegal</u> drugs are often divided into two main classes — <u>soft</u> and <u>hard</u>.
2) Hard drugs are generally more <u>harmful</u>, but soft drugs can be harmful too.
    E.g. <u>heroin</u> and <u>ecstasy</u> (hard drugs), and <u>cannabis</u> (a soft drug)
    can all cause <u>heart</u> and <u>circulatory system</u> problems.

*There Are **Various Reasons** Why People Use Recreational Drugs*

1) So if all these recreational drugs are so dangerous, why do so many people use them...
2) When asked why they use cannabis, most users say they <u>enjoy</u> it, it <u>relaxes</u> them or it gets rid of <u>stress</u>.
3) But there may be other reasons too, e.g. <u>problems</u> in someone's <u>personal life</u>.

Some** Studies Link **Cannabis** and **Hard Drug** Use — Others **Don't

1) Almost all users of <u>hard drugs</u> have tried <u>cannabis</u> first.
2) The <u>link</u> between cannabis and hard drugs isn't clear, but <u>three</u> opinions are common...

<u>Cannabis is a "stepping stone"</u>: The effects of cannabis create a desire to try harder drugs.	<u>Cannabis is a "gateway drug"</u>: Cannabis use brings people into contact with drug dealers.	<u>It's all down to genetics</u>: Certain people are more likely to take drugs generally, so cannabis users will also try other drugs.

*Some **Legal Drugs** have **More** of an **Impact** than **Illegal Drugs***

1) <u>Tobacco</u> and <u>alcohol</u> are both <u>legal</u> recreational drugs.
2) They have a much <u>bigger impact</u> in the UK than illegal drugs, as <u>so many</u> people take them.

SMOKING CAUSES:	ALCOHOL CAUSES:
• <u>lung disease</u> • <u>cancer</u> • <u>addiction</u> (to <u>nicotine</u>)	• <u>slower reactions</u> and <u>poor coordination</u> • <u>liver disease</u> • <u>addiction</u>

3) It <u>costs the NHS loads</u> to <u>treat</u> the effects of tobacco and alcohol.
4) The <u>cost</u> of people being <u>too ill to work</u> also has a big impact on the <u>economy</u>.
5) The <u>crimes</u> committed due to alcohol (e.g. fights, damaging property) take up <u>police time</u> and <u>cost a lot</u>.

SECTION 2 — DIET AND HEALTH

Warm-Up and Exam Questions

There's no point in whizzing through the section and glancing over the questions. Do the warm-up questions and go back over any bits you don't know. Then practise and practise the exam questions.

Warm-Up Questions

1) Why might a patient be prescribed statins?
2) What is a placebo? Why are placebos often used in drug trials?
3) Name two illegal recreational drugs.
4) Name one legal drug to which people may become addicted.

Exam Questions

1   Some athletes take drugs to make them better at sport.

(a) Which of the following are performance enhancing drugs taken by athletes?
Circle the correct answer.

   stimulants   **statins**   **steroids**   **tobacco**   **cannabis**

(2 marks)

(b) Explain why an athlete may choose to take performance enhancing drugs.

(2 marks)

2   In the UK it is illegal to drive if your blood alcohol concentration exceeds
80 mg of alcohol per 100 ml of blood.

(a) Alcohol affects the nervous system, slowing down the body's reactions.
Suggest why drinking alcohol increases the risk of having a car accident.

(1 mark)

(b) Alcohol is addictive. What does this mean?

(1 mark)

(c) Other than drink-related driving accidents, give **two** ways in which
excessive alcohol consumption has a negative effect on society.

(2 marks)

3   Thalidomide was used to treat morning sickness in pregnant women,
but it hadn't been tested for this use.

(a) Describe the effect that thalidomide had on fetuses.

(1 mark)

(b) Name **one** disease that thalidomide is currently used in the treatment of.

(1 mark)

4   Drugs are often tested on live animals. Tick the boxes next to the reasons why.

☐ To see if the animals enjoy them.

☐ To check the drug works.

☐ To find out the drug's toxicity.

☐ To treat sick animals.

☐ To find the best dosage of the drug.

(3 marks)

Fighting Disease

<u>Microorganisms</u> that enter the body and <u>cause disease</u> are called <u>pathogens</u>. Pathogens cause <u>infectious diseases</u> — diseases that can easily spread.

There Are **Two Main Types** of **Pathogen**: **Bacteria** and **Viruses**

1) *Bacteria* Are Very Small **Living Cells**

Diseases can also be caused by fungi and protozoa (single-celled organisms).

1) Bacteria <u>reproduce rapidly</u> inside your body.

2) They make you <u>feel ill</u> by:

   <u>damaging your cells</u>   *AND*   <u>producing toxins</u> (<u>poisons</u>).

2) *Viruses* Are **Not** Cells — *They're Much Smaller*

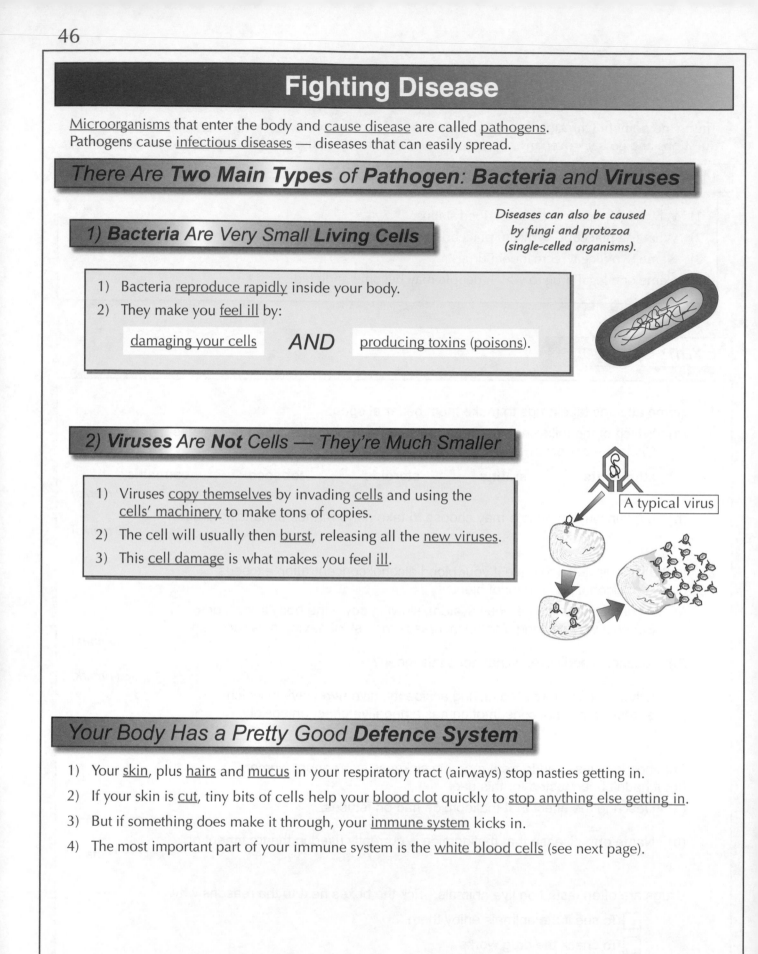

A typical virus

1) Viruses <u>copy themselves</u> by invading <u>cells</u> and using the <u>cells' machinery</u> to make tons of copies.

2) The cell will usually then <u>burst</u>, releasing all the <u>new viruses</u>.

3) This <u>cell damage</u> is what makes you feel <u>ill</u>.

Your Body Has a Pretty Good **Defence System**

1) Your <u>skin</u>, plus <u>hairs</u> and <u>mucus</u> in your respiratory tract (airways) stop nasties getting in.

2) If your skin is <u>cut</u>, tiny bits of cells help your <u>blood clot</u> quickly to <u>stop anything else getting in</u>.

3) But if something does make it through, your <u>immune system</u> kicks in.

4) The most important part of your immune system is the <u>white blood cells</u> (see next page).

Don't get confused between bacteria and viruses...

...bacteria are cells, viruses aren't. Your body is pretty good at <u>defending itself</u> against nasty pathogens — and it's got lots of different ways to do it. The role of <u>white blood cells</u> is important, but don't forget about the <u>skin</u>, <u>hairs</u>, <u>mucus</u> and <u>blood clots</u> — they're your body's first line of defence.

Fighting Disease — White Blood Cells

<u>White blood cells</u> help to <u>protect you</u> from disease by patrolling your body and fighting off any <u>pathogens</u> that they stumble across.

White blood cells have **three lines of attack** against pathogens:

1) *Consuming* Them

White blood cells can <u>engulf</u> (surround) the pathogens and <u>digest</u> them.

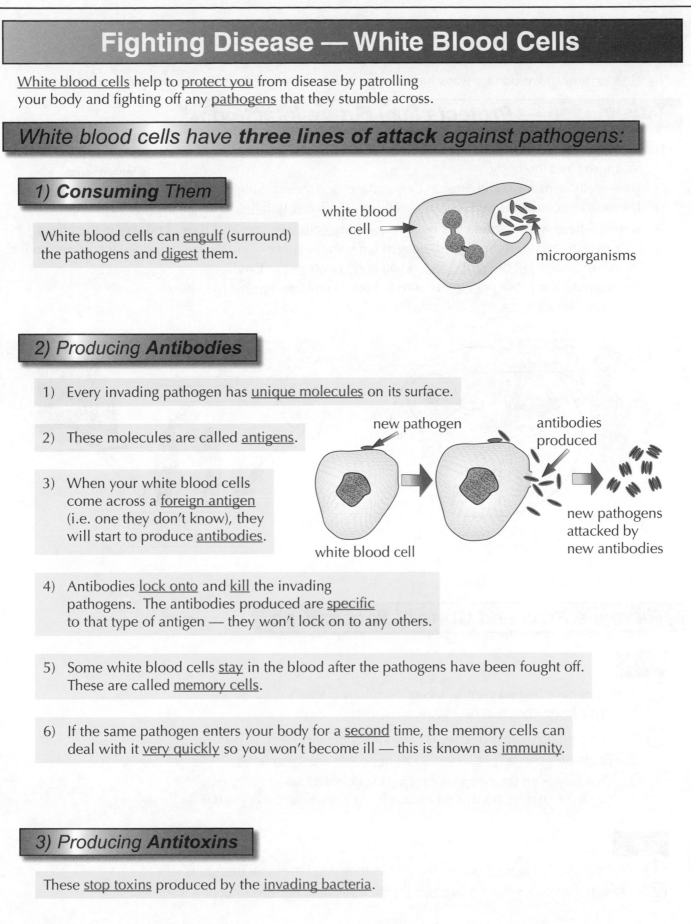

white blood cell

microorganisms

2) *Producing* **Antibodies**

1) Every invading pathogen has <u>unique molecules</u> on its surface.

2) These molecules are called <u>antigens</u>.

3) When your white blood cells come across a <u>foreign antigen</u> (i.e. one they don't know), they will start to produce <u>antibodies</u>.

new pathogen

antibodies produced

white blood cell

new pathogens attacked by new antibodies

4) Antibodies <u>lock onto</u> and <u>kill</u> the invading pathogens. The antibodies produced are <u>specific</u> to that type of antigen — they won't lock on to any others.

5) Some white blood cells <u>stay</u> in the blood after the pathogens have been fought off. These are called <u>memory cells</u>.

6) If the same pathogen enters your body for a <u>second</u> time, the memory cells can deal with it <u>very quickly</u> so you won't become ill — this is known as <u>immunity</u>.

3) *Producing* **Antitoxins**

These <u>stop toxins</u> produced by the <u>invading bacteria</u>.

White blood cells are life-savers...

White blood cells are pretty bloomin' <u>important</u> and you'd be in <u>a lot of trouble</u> without them. <u>Cover</u> the page, <u>scribble</u> down what you can remember and <u>check</u> what you missed.

Fighting Disease — Vaccination

Vaccinations mean we don't always have to treat a disease — we can stop the disease in the first place.

Vaccination — Protects from Future Infections

Another word for 'vaccination' is 'immunisation'.

1) Vaccinations involve injecting small amounts of dead or inactive pathogens into the body.
2) These pathogens have antigens on their surface (see previous page).
3) The antigens cause your white blood cells to produce antibodies to attack the pathogens.
4) Some of these white blood cells become memory cells (see previous page) and stay in the blood.
5) If you're infected with the same pathogen later, your memory cells quickly produce lots of antibodies.
6) These antibodies kill the pathogen so you don't become ill. Cool.
7) For example, the MMR vaccine is used to protect children against the viruses that cause measles, mumps and rubella.

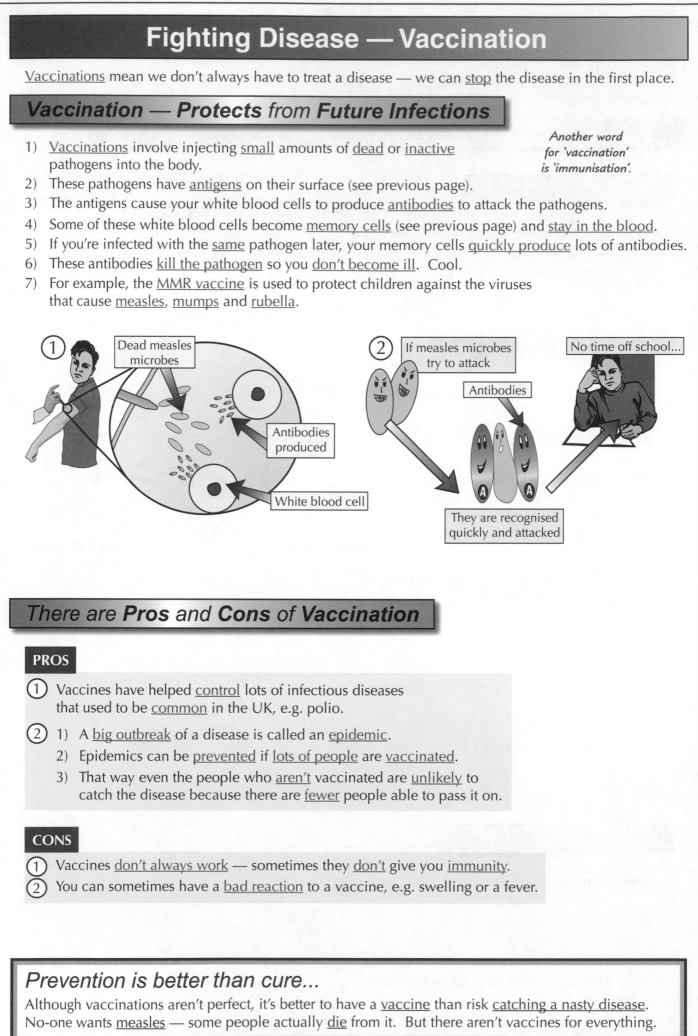

1

Dead measles microbes

Antibodies produced

White blood cell

2

If measles microbes try to attack

Antibodies

They are recognised quickly and attacked

No time off school...

There are Pros and Cons of Vaccination

PROS

① Vaccines have helped control lots of infectious diseases that used to be common in the UK, e.g. polio.

② 1) A big outbreak of a disease is called an epidemic.
   2) Epidemics can be prevented if lots of people are vaccinated.
   3) That way even the people who aren't vaccinated are unlikely to catch the disease because there are fewer people able to pass it on.

CONS

① Vaccines don't always work — sometimes they don't give you immunity.
② You can sometimes have a bad reaction to a vaccine, e.g. swelling or a fever.

Prevention is better than cure...

Although vaccinations aren't perfect, it's better to have a vaccine than risk catching a nasty disease. No-one wants measles — some people actually die from it. But there aren't vaccines for everything.

Fighting Disease — Drugs

Well knock me down with a feather — it looks like there are even more ways of fighting disease...

Some Drugs Get Rid of Symptoms — Others Cure the Problem

1) Some drugs help to get rid of the symptoms of a disease, e.g. painkillers reduce pain.

2) But these drugs don't kill the pathogens that cause the disease.

3) Antibiotics (e.g. penicillin) kill bacteria.

4) Different antibiotics kill different types of bacteria, so it's important to be treated with the right one.

Antibiotics are a type of antimicrobial — chemicals that kill microorganisms.

5) But antibiotics don't destroy viruses (e.g. flu viruses).

6) Viruses reproduce using your own body cells (see page 46).

7) This makes it very difficult to develop drugs that destroy the virus without killing the body's cells.

Bacteria Can Become Resistant to Antibiotics

1) Bacteria can mutate (have changes in their DNA).

2) Some of these mutations cause the bacteria to become resistant to (not killed by) an antibiotic.

3) Resistant strains (types) of bacteria, e.g. MRSA, have increased as a result of natural selection (see p. 70).

You can Investigate Antibiotics by Growing Microorganisms

You can test the action of antibiotics or disinfectants by growing microorganisms in the lab:

1) Microorganisms are grown in a 'culture medium' (nutrient jelly) in round plastic dishes called Petri dishes.

2) Inoculating loops (wire loops) are used to transfer microorganisms to the jelly.

microorganisms

culture medium (nutrient jelly)

3) The microorganisms then multiply.

4) Paper discs are soaked in different types of antibiotics and placed on the jelly.

5) Strains of bacteria that are resistant to the antibiotics will keep growing around the discs.

6) Non-resistant strains of bacteria will die.

7) The Petri dishes, culture medium and inoculating loops must be sterilised (cleaned) before use to kill unwanted microorganisms. For example, the inoculating loops are passed through a flame.

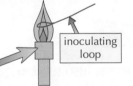

inoculating loop

8) The Petri dish must also have a lid taped on to stop any microorganisms in the air getting in.

9) In the lab at school, microorganisms are kept at 25 °C so that harmful pathogens won't grow.

10) In industrial conditions they're kept at higher temperatures, so that microorganisms can grow a lot faster.

Fighting Disease — Past and Future

The treatment of disease has changed over the last 200 years or so.

Semmelweis Cut Deaths by Using Antiseptics

1) A guy called <u>Ignaz Semmelweis</u> worked in a hospital in the 1840s.

2) He saw that lots of women were <u>dying</u> from a disease <u>after giving birth</u>.

3) He believed that <u>doctors</u> were <u>spreading</u> the disease on their <u>unwashed hands</u>.

4) Semmelweis told doctors to <u>wash</u> their hands in an <u>antiseptic solution</u> before seeing patients — and this <u>cut the death rate</u>.

5) The antiseptic solution <u>killed bacteria</u> on doctors' hands (though Semmelweis didn't know this at the time).

6) Now we know that <u>basic hygiene</u> (keeping things <u>clean</u>) is really important to control the spread of disease.

Antibiotic Resistance is Becoming More Common

Remember, antibiotics kill bacteria (see page 49).

1) The number of <u>deaths</u> from bacterial diseases has <u>fallen</u> because of <u>antibiotics</u>.

2) But now there are strains of bacteria that are <u>resistant to antibiotics</u>.

3) We need to <u>slow down</u> the speed at which resistant types develop by <u>not over-using antibiotics</u>.

4) And drug companies are trying to develop <u>new antibiotics</u> that will <u>kill resistant strains</u> of bacteria.

We Face New and Scary Dangers All the Time

Bacteria

1) Bacteria can <u>mutate</u>, producing <u>new strains</u> (see previous page).

2) A new strain could be <u>antibiotic-resistant</u>, so antibiotics <u>won't work</u>.

3) Or a new strain could be one that we've <u>not come across before</u>, so <u>no-one</u> would be <u>immune</u> to it.

4) This means a new strain of bacteria could <u>spread rapidly</u> in a population of people.

5) It could even cause an <u>epidemic</u> — a big outbreak of disease.

Viruses

1) Viruses also tend to <u>mutate often</u>.

2) A mutation can lead to a virus having <u>different antigens</u> (see page 47).

3) If you've been vaccinated your antibodies <u>won't recognise</u> the new antigens, so the <u>vaccine won't work</u>.

4) It's possible that a new virus could <u>spread all over the world</u> — this is called a <u>pandemic</u>.

Warm-Up and Exam Questions

It's easy to think you've learnt everything in the section until you try the warm-up questions.
Don't panic if there's a bit you've forgotten, just go back over that bit until it's firmly fixed in your brain.

Warm-Up Questions

1) What is a pathogen?
2) Explain how viruses make you feel ill.
3) What are antigens?
4) What are antibiotics designed to do?
5) Why are cultures of microorganisms grown at temperatures no higher than 25 °C in school laboratories?
6) What is an epidemic?

Exam Questions

1   Describe **three** ways that white blood cells fight pathogens.

(3 marks)

2   Read the following passage.

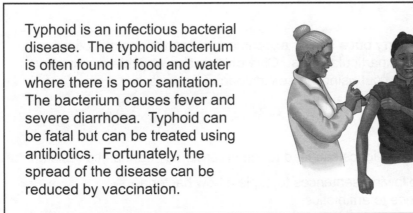

Typhoid is an infectious bacterial disease. The typhoid bacterium is often found in food and water where there is poor sanitation. The bacterium causes fever and severe diarrhoea. Typhoid can be fatal but can be treated using antibiotics. Fortunately, the spread of the disease can be reduced by vaccination.

When a person is vaccinated against typhoid they are injected with inactive typhoid bacteria.

(a)   Explain how being vaccinated against typhoid can prevent a person catching the disease.

(4 marks)

(b)   Typhoid epidemics can be prevented by large-scale vaccination programmes, even if a small percentage of the population remains unvaccinated. Explain why this is the case.

(1 mark)

(c)   Describe **two** potential disadvantages of vaccination.

(2 marks)

Exam Questions

3   Rageh carried out an experiment to see which of three antibiotics were most effective at killing a particular strain of bacteria. He grew a layer of bacteria on an agar plate. He then added paper discs that had been previously soaked in one of the three antibiotics to the agar plate. He left the agar plate for 24 hours. The diagram below shows his results.

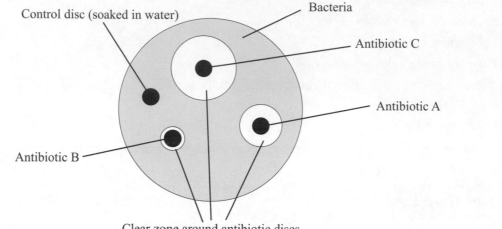

(a)   Using Rageh's results, explain which antibiotic, A, B, or C, is the most effective at killing the bacteria.

(2 marks)

(b)   What could Rageh do to make sure that his results were reliable?

(1 mark)

(c)   Rageh sterilised his equipment before he began the experiment.
Why was this necessary?

(1 mark)

(d)   Rageh wants to carry out a similar experiment to see which antibiotic is most effective at killing a particular virus. Give **one** reason why this experiment could not be carried out using viruses instead of bacteria.

(1 mark)

4   Inappropriate use of antibiotics can lead to the emergence of antibiotic-resistant bacteria.

(a)   Complete the following sentences to explain how bacteria develop resistance to antibiotics.

(i)   .... (changes in DNA) can lead to bacteria becoming resistant to antibiotics.

(1 mark)

(ii)   Resistant strains of bacteria can become more common by

.... selection.

(1 mark)

(iii)   .... is an example of a resistant strain of bacteria.

(1 mark)

(b)   Suggest how we can slow down the rate of development of resistant strains of bacteria.

(1 mark)

Revision Summary for Section 2

Well, that's another chunk of biology under your belt. But before you do the most satisfying stretch in the world, I've got a little gift for you... a whole bunch of questions to test just how much of this section you've got to grips with. Don't be sad if you get any wrong — just go back and have another read of the topic and be glad that you're finding out what you do and don't know before the exam. Once you've got them all right, feel free to bend your limbs into weird shapes and let out yelps of joy.

1) Name two food groups needed for providing energy.

2)* Who do you think would have a higher metabolic rate: a secretary or a professional runner?

3) Name one health problem that is linked to not eating enough protein.

4) In terms of energy, what does a person have to do to lose weight?

5) Suggest a way of boosting your metabolic rate.

6) The heart is a double pump. Explain what this means.

7) How does the structure of an artery help with its function?

8) How does the structure of a vein help with its function?

9) You can measure your heart rate by measuring your pulse rate. True or false?

10) When a blood pressure measurement is taken, what is actually being measured?

11) Describe one way that high blood pressure can cause heart disease.

12)*Have a look at the table below:

Name	Occupation	Cigarettes per day	Exercise per week	Favourite meal
Tricia	Florist	0	5 hours	Houmous and pitta bread
Dave	Stock broker	40	20 minutes	Cheeseburger and chips

    a)   Who is more at risk from heart disease, Tricia or Dave? Give two reasons for your answer.

    b)   Give two ways of reducing the risk of heart disease.

12) Give two arguments against athletes taking drugs in sporting competitions.

13) What is a double-blind drug trial?

14) Name a drug that was not tested thoroughly enough.

15) Describe one opinion about the link between cannabis and hard drug use.

16) Which has the bigger impact on society in the UK, legal or illegal drugs?

17) Give one way that your immune system defends the body against disease.

18) What are vaccinations?

19) What practice did Semmelweis introduce in the 1840s?

20) Why have resistant strains of bacteria increased?

* Answers on page 239.

Genes, Chromosomes and DNA

Ah, genetics — the love of my life. First on the menu is the basics. And trust me — it's all good stuff.

1) Most cells in your body have a <u>nucleus</u>.
2) The nucleus contains <u>chromosomes</u>.

nucleus

3) The human cell nucleus contains <u>23 pairs of chromosomes</u>.
4) There are two number 19 chromosomes, two number 12s, two number 3s, etc.

A single <u>chromosome</u>.

A <u>pair</u> of <u>chromosomes</u>. (They're always in pairs, one from each <u>parent</u>.)

5) Chromosomes carry <u>genes</u>.
6) Different genes <u>control</u> the development of different <u>characteristics</u>, e.g. eye colour.

7) A <u>gene</u> is a <u>short length</u> of the chromosome.
8) There can be <u>different versions</u> of the <u>same gene</u>, called <u>alleles</u>.
9) These alleles give different versions of a characteristic, like blue or brown eyes.
10) Since there are <u>two copies</u> of each chromosome, there are <u>two copies</u> of each gene.
11) So you might have two alleles the <u>same</u> or two <u>different</u> alleles (see the next page).

It's hard being a DNA molecule, there's so much to remember...
If you can get your head around the stuff here it should help everything else <u>make sense later on</u>.

Genetic Diagrams

Genetic diagrams are handy for working out how characteristics move from <u>parents</u> to their <u>children</u>.

The **Combination of Alleles** Determines the **Characteristics**

1) <u>Different versions</u> of the <u>same gene</u> are called <u>alleles</u> (see page 54).
2) Alleles can be <u>dominant</u> or <u>recessive</u>.
3) If you have <u>two dominant alleles</u> the <u>dominant characteristic</u> will be shown.
4) If you have <u>one dominant</u> and <u>one recessive</u> allele only the <u>dominant characteristic</u> will be shown.
5) To show a <u>recessive characteristic</u>, <u>both alleles</u> for a gene have to be <u>recessive</u>.

Genetic Diagrams Show How **Alleles** are **Inherited**

1) Imagine you're cross-breeding <u>hamsters</u>, and that some behave normally while others do crazy acrobatics.
2) Let's say that the allele which causes the crazy behaviour is <u>recessive</u> — so use a '<u>b</u>'.
3) And normal behaviour is due to a <u>dominant allele</u> — call it '<u>B</u>'.
4) So a <u>crazy</u> hamster <u>must</u> have the alleles <u>bb</u>.
5) But, a <u>normal hamster</u> could be BB <u>or</u> Bb, because the dominant allele (B) <u>overrides</u> the recessive one (b).

In genetic diagrams, capital letters represent dominant alleles and small letters represent recessive alleles.

6) The <u>genetic diagram</u> below shows what could happen when <u>two normal hamsters</u> (Bb) are crossed:

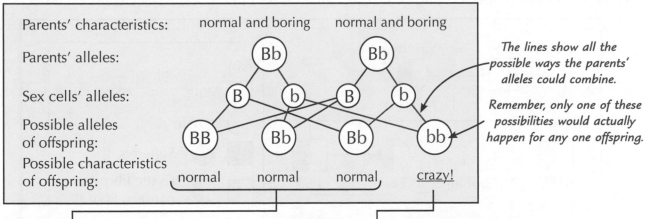

The lines show all the possible ways the parents' alleles could combine.

Remember, only one of these possibilities would actually happen for any one offspring.

There's a <u>75%</u> chance of having a <u>normal</u> hamster, and a <u>25%</u> chance of a <u>crazy</u> one.

7) This is a genetic diagram too — it shows exactly the same thing as the one above. Diagrams like these are called <u>Punnett squares</u>.

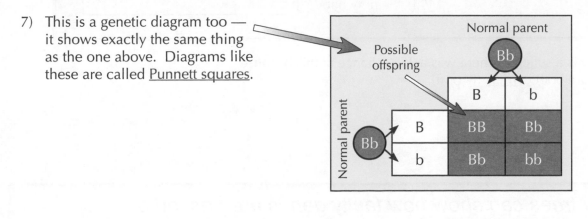

Genetic Disorders and Genetic Diagrams

Usually we don't notice our genes — they quietly bumble away.
But a <u>faulty allele</u> can cause a <u>genetic disorder</u>.

Cystic Fibrosis is Caused by a Recessive Allele

1) <u>Cystic fibrosis</u> is a <u>genetic disorder</u>.

2) It <u>results</u> in the body producing a lot of thick sticky <u>mucus</u> in the <u>air passages</u>, <u>gut</u> and <u>pancreas</u>.

3) Symptoms include:

> <u>breathing problems</u>   <u>lung infections</u>   <u>fertility problems</u>

4) The allele which causes cystic fibrosis is a <u>recessive allele</u>, 'f'.

5) People with only <u>one copy</u> of the allele (e.g. Ff)
   <u>won't</u> have the disorder — they're <u>carriers</u>.

6) For a <u>child</u> to have a chance of <u>inheriting</u> the disorder,
   <u>both parents</u> must be either <u>carriers</u> or <u>sufferers</u> (ff).

Genetic disorders can also be caused by a dominant allele, e.g. Huntington's disease.

Family Trees are Another Type of Genetic Diagram

The diagram below is a <u>family tree</u> (or <u>pedigree</u>) to show how <u>cystic fibrosis</u> can be passed on:

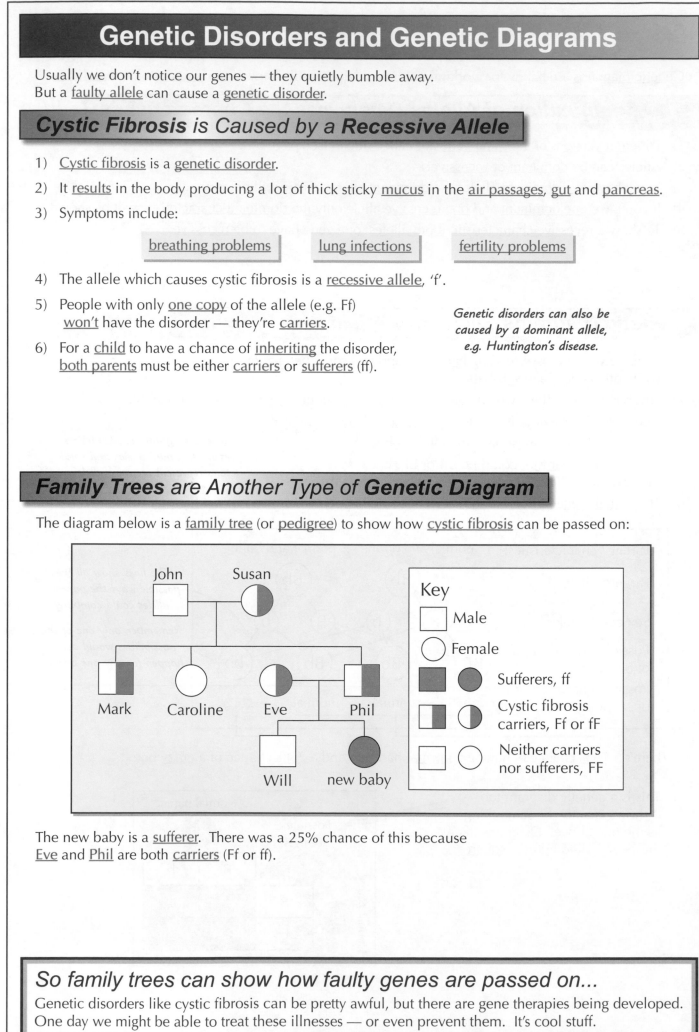

The new baby is a <u>sufferer</u>. There was a 25% chance of this because
<u>Eve</u> and <u>Phil</u> are both <u>carriers</u> (Ff or ff).

So family trees can show how faulty genes are passed on...

Genetic disorders like cystic fibrosis can be pretty awful, but there are gene therapies being developed.
One day we might be able to treat these illnesses — or even prevent them. It's cool stuff.

Sex Chromosomes

Ever wondered why you're male or female? Nope, me neither. But the answer is pretty interesting...

Your **Chromosomes** Control Whether You're **Male** or **Female**

1) There are <u>23 pairs</u> of <u>chromosomes</u> in every human body cell. The <u>23rd pair</u> are labelled <u>XY</u>.

2) These are <u>sex chromosomes</u> — they decide whether you turn out <u>male</u> or <u>female</u>.

> <u>All men</u> have an <u>X</u> and a <u>Y</u> chromosome: XY
> The <u>Y chromosome</u> causes <u>male characteristics</u>.

> <u>All women</u> have <u>two X chromosomes</u>: XX
> The <u>lack of a Y chromosome</u> causes <u>female characteristics</u>.

You Can Work Out the **Probability** of Having a **Boy** or a **Girl**

1) The <u>genetic diagram</u> to show how sex chromosomes are passed on to offspring
    is fairly similar to a genetic diagram for alleles.

2) It just shows the <u>sex chromosomes</u> rather than different alleles.

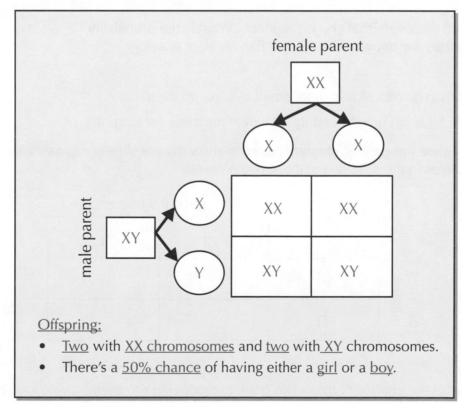

Offspring:
- <u>Two</u> with <u>XX chromosomes</u> and <u>two</u> with <u>XY</u> chromosomes.
- There's a <u>50% chance</u> of having either a <u>girl</u> or a <u>boy</u>.

The X and Y chromosomes are the sex chromosomes

Don't get confused — you can use a <u>genetic diagram</u> to show the inheritance of <u>chromosomes</u> as well as alleles. It still works in exactly the same way. And remember, the 'results' are only <u>probabilities</u>. It doesn't mean they'll actually happen...

Warm-Up and Exam Questions

Take a deep breath and go through these warm-up questions one by one.
If you don't know these basic facts there's no way you'll cope with the exam questions.

Warm-Up Questions

1) Where are chromosomes found in body cells?
2) What is a gene?
3) What are alleles?
4) What are the symptoms of cystic fibrosis?
5) Which chromosome causes the development of male characteristics?

Exam Questions

1   Karen and Frank have two children: a daughter called Anne and a son called Jake.

   (a) Anne and Jake inherited different sex chromosomes from their parents.
        State the sex chromosomes of:

        (i)   Anne

        (1 mark)

        (ii) Jake

        (1 mark)

   (b) Karen discovers that she is pregnant. What is the probability
        that the new baby will be a boy? Explain your answer.

        (2 marks)

2   Hair length in guinea pigs is determined by a particular gene.

   The allele for short hair, H, is dominant over the allele for long hair, h.

   (a) Complete the genetic diagram below to show the possible combinations
        of alleles in the offspring of these two parents.

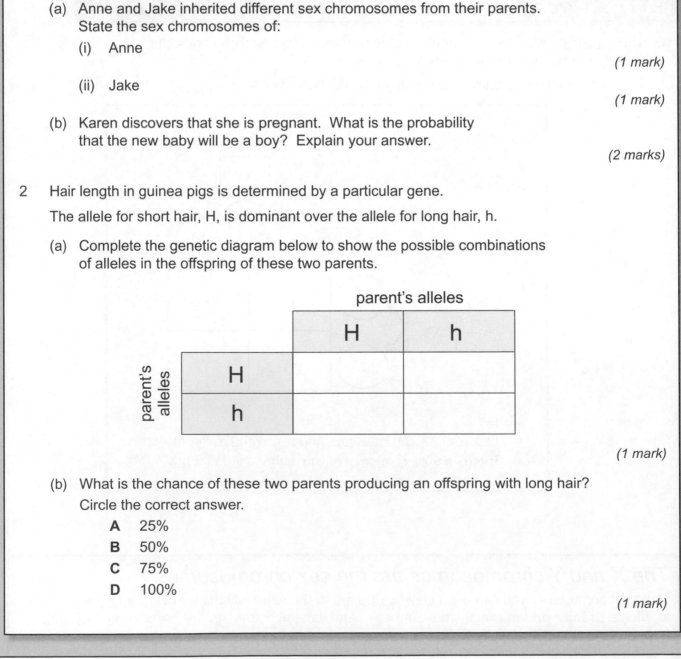

parent's alleles

		H	h
parent's alleles	H		
	h		

        (1 mark)

   (b) What is the chance of these two parents producing an offspring with long hair?
        Circle the correct answer.
        A   25%
        B   50%
        C   75%
        D   100%

        (1 mark)

Exam Questions

3 The ability to roll your tongue is controlled by a gene.
The allele for tongue rolling, R, is dominant over the non-tongue rolling allele, r.
The diagram below shows how the tongue rolling ability has been passed through a family.

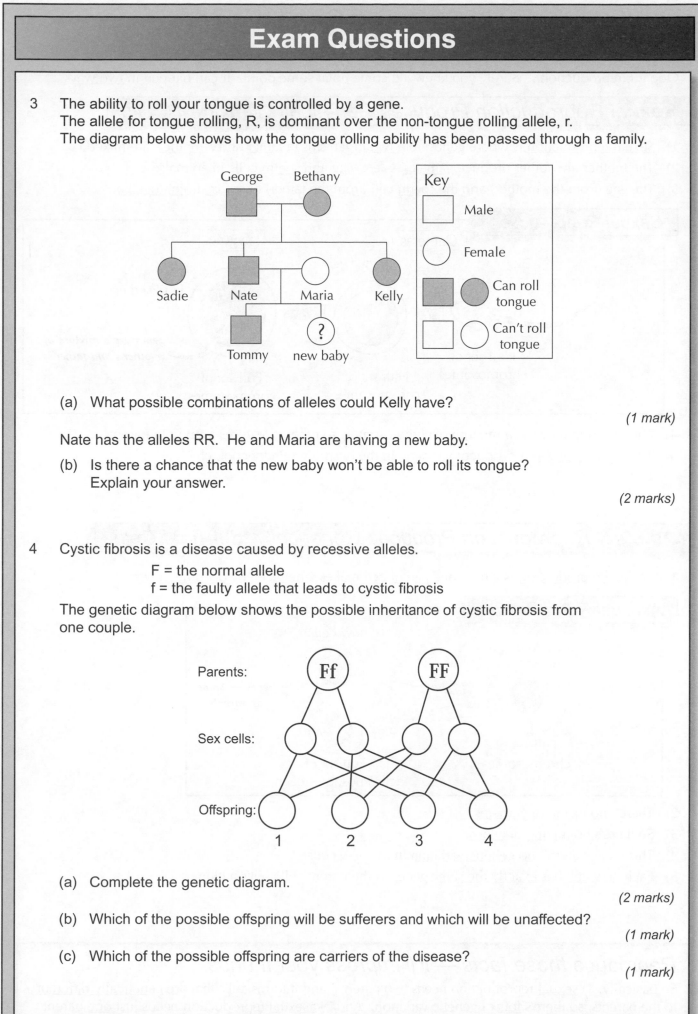

(a) What possible combinations of alleles could Kelly have?

(1 mark)

Nate has the alleles RR. He and Maria are having a new baby.

(b) Is there a chance that the new baby won't be able to roll its tongue?
Explain your answer.

(2 marks)

4 Cystic fibrosis is a disease caused by recessive alleles.

F = the normal allele
f = the faulty allele that leads to cystic fibrosis

The genetic diagram below shows the possible inheritance of cystic fibrosis from one couple.

(a) Complete the genetic diagram.

(2 marks)

(b) Which of the possible offspring will be sufferers and which will be unaffected?

(1 mark)

(c) Which of the possible offspring are carriers of the disease?

(1 mark)

Reproduction

Ooo err, reproduction... Surely you knew it'd come up at some point. It can happen in two ways...

Sexual Reproduction Produces Genetically Different Cells

1) Sexual reproduction is where genes from two organisms (a father and a mother) are mixed.

2) The mother and father produce gametes — e.g. egg and sperm cells in animals.

3) The egg (from the mother) and the sperm cell (from the father) then fuse (join) together.

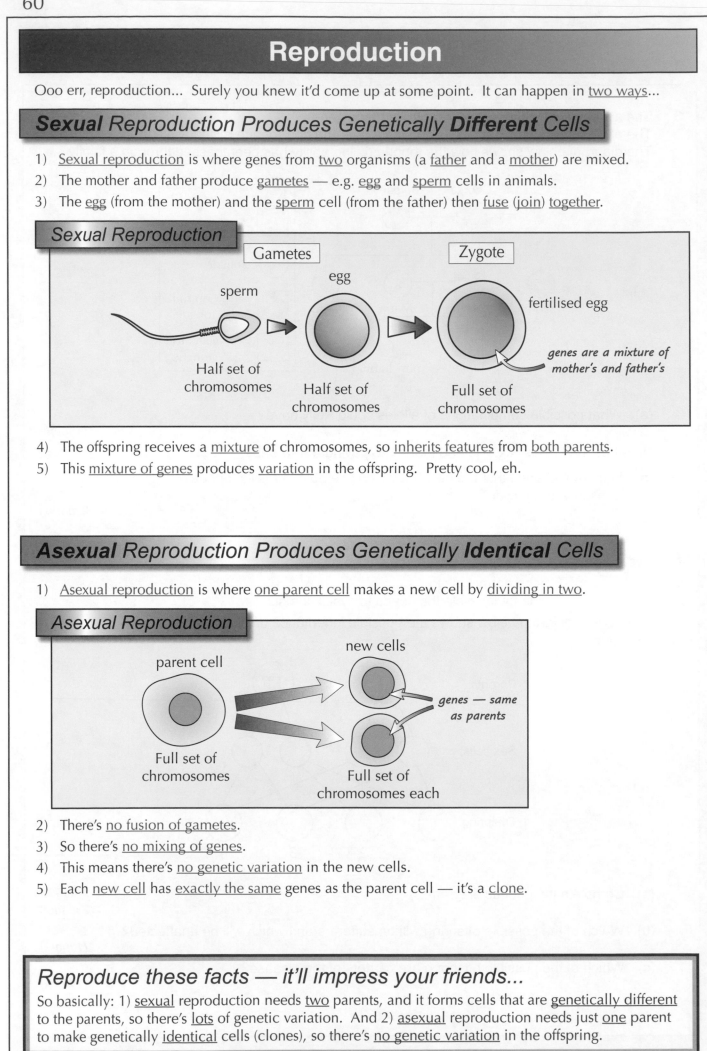

Sexual Reproduction

Gametes

Zygote

sperm

egg

fertilised egg

Half set of chromosomes

Half set of chromosomes

Full set of chromosomes

genes are a mixture of mother's and father's

4) The offspring receives a mixture of chromosomes, so inherits features from both parents.

5) This mixture of genes produces variation in the offspring. Pretty cool, eh.

Asexual Reproduction Produces Genetically Identical Cells

1) Asexual reproduction is where one parent cell makes a new cell by dividing in two.

Asexual Reproduction

parent cell

new cells

Full set of chromosomes

Full set of chromosomes each

genes — same as parents

2) There's no fusion of gametes.

3) So there's no mixing of genes.

4) This means there's no genetic variation in the new cells.

5) Each new cell has exactly the same genes as the parent cell — it's a clone.

Reproduce these facts — it'll impress your friends...

So basically: 1) sexual reproduction needs two parents, and it forms cells that are genetically different to the parents, so there's lots of genetic variation. And 2) asexual reproduction needs just one parent to make genetically identical cells (clones), so there's no genetic variation in the offspring.

Cloning

We can clone plants and animals in several <u>different ways</u>.

Plants Can Be Cloned from Cuttings and by Tissue Culture

1) Gardeners take <u>cuttings</u> from good parent plants and plant them to make <u>copies</u> with the <u>same genes</u> (<u>clones</u>).

2) Taking cuttings is <u>quick</u> and <u>cheap</u>.

3) <u>Tissue culture</u> is where you take <u>a few plant cells</u> and grow them into <u>new plants</u> — <u>clones</u> of the parent plant.

You Can Make Animal Clones Using Embryo Transplants

Farmers can produce <u>cloned offspring</u> from their best bull and cow — using <u>embryo transplants</u>.

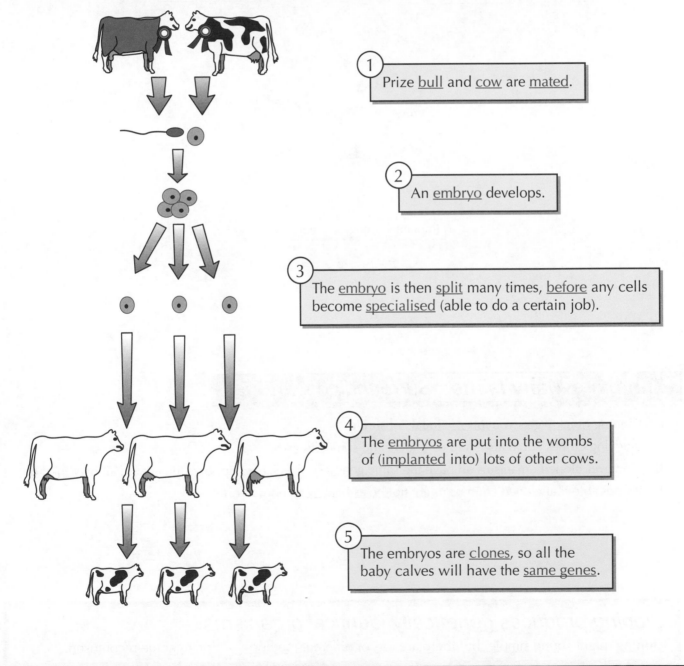

1 Prize <u>bull</u> and <u>cow</u> are <u>mated</u>.

2 An <u>embryo</u> develops.

3 The <u>embryo</u> is then <u>split</u> many times, <u>before</u> any cells become <u>specialised</u> (able to do a certain job).

4 The <u>embryos</u> are put into the wombs of (<u>implanted</u> into) lots of other cows.

5 The embryos are <u>clones</u>, so all the baby calves will have the <u>same genes</u>.

Cloning

Genetically identical organisms can also be made through adult cell cloning.

Adult Cell Cloning is Another Way to Make a Clone

1) Adult cell cloning involves taking an unfertilised egg cell and removing the nucleus.

2) The nucleus from an adult body cell (e.g. a skin cell) is put into the 'empty' egg cell.

3) An electric shock makes the egg cell divide.

4) When the embryo is a ball of cells, it's implanted into the womb of an adult female.

5) The embryo grows into a clone of the original adult body cell.

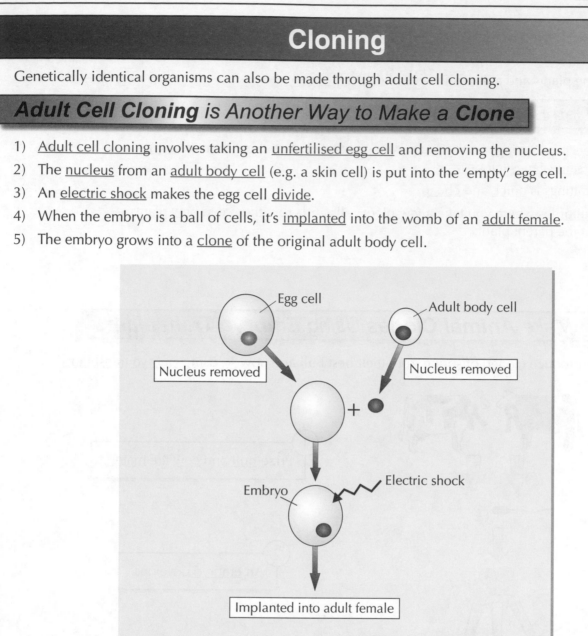

There are Many Issues Surrounding Cloning

1) Cloning quickly gets you lots of "ideal" offspring.

2) Studying clones could also help us understand some diseases.

3) However cloned organisms all have the same genes, so if a disease appears they could all be wiped out.

4) It's possible that cloned animals might not be as healthy as normal ones.

Cloning produces genetically identical organisms

Cloning might sound simple, but there are lots of different methods — don't get them confused.

Genetic Engineering

Scientists can now <u>change</u> an organism's <u>genes</u> to alter its characteristics.

Genetic Engineering Uses Enzymes to Cut and Paste Genes

1) A useful gene is "<u>cut</u>" from one organism's chromosome using <u>enzymes</u>.

2) <u>Enzymes</u> are then used to <u>cut</u> another organism's chromosome and then to <u>insert</u> the useful gene.
   For example:

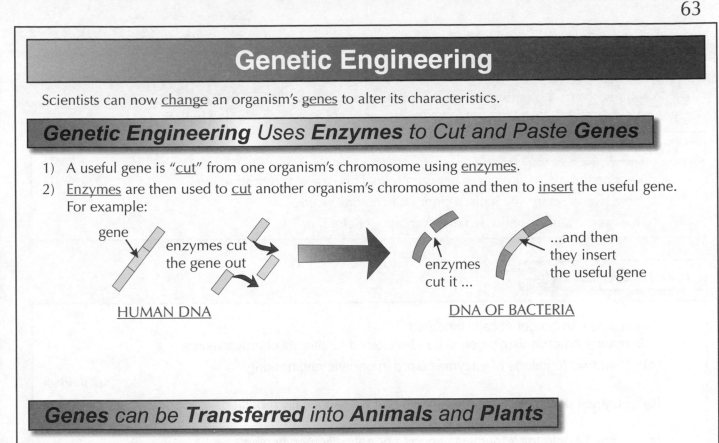

gene
enzymes cut
the gene out

enzymes
cut it ...

...and then
they insert
the useful gene

HUMAN DNA

DNA OF BACTERIA

Genes can be Transferred into Animals and Plants

1) <u>Useful genes</u> can be transferred into <u>animals</u> and <u>plants</u>
   at the <u>very early stages</u> of their development.

2) This means they'll develop <u>useful characteristics</u>.

3) <u>Genetically modified</u> (<u>GM</u>) <u>crops</u> have had their genes modified (changed).
   E.g. to make them <u>resistant to viruses</u>, <u>insects</u> or <u>herbicides</u> (chemicals used to kill weeds).

But People Disagree About Genetic Engineering...

1) Genetic engineering could <u>solve</u> many <u>problems</u> e.g. treating <u>diseases</u>,
   more efficient <u>food production</u>.

2) But not everyone thinks it's a <u>good idea</u>.

3) There are <u>worries</u> about the <u>long-term effects</u> of genetic engineering.

There Are **Pros** and **Cons** With **GM Crops**

Pros

1) GM crops can <u>increase the yield</u> of a crop, making <u>more food</u>.

2) GM crops can include extra <u>nutrients</u> to <u>prevent deficiency diseases</u> (see page 31).

Cons

1) Growing GM crops could affect the <u>number of flowers and insects</u> that live by the crops.

2) Some people are worried that GM crops are not <u>safe to eat</u>.

Warm-Up and Exam Questions

By doing these warm-up questions, you'll soon find out what you know and what you don't.
Once you've finished, take the time to go back over the bits you've struggled with.

Warm-Up Questions

1) Describe the main differences between sexual and asexual reproduction.
2) Name two ways in which plant clones can be produced.
3) Give two advantages and two disadvantages of cloning.

Exam Questions

1 Organisms can be genetically modified.
This means an organism's genes can be altered to alter its characteristics.

  (a) Give **two** functions of enzymes used in genetic engineering.

(2 marks)

  (b) Suggest **one** useful way that plants can be genetically modified.

(1 mark)

  (c) Some people think that it is wrong to genetically modify plants.
Give **two** different objections that people might have.

(2 marks)

2 In 1997 scientists at the Roslin Institute announced the birth of Dolly the sheep,
the first mammal to be cloned using adult cell cloning.

Explain how an animal can be cloned using adult cell cloning.

(4 marks)

3 Tick the boxes next to the statements which are **true**.

☐ The female human gametes are called sperm.

☐ A human gamete contains half a set of chromosomes.

☐ Two gametes fuse together to form a zygote during fertilisation.

☐ A zygote contains half a set of chromosomes.

☐ The zygote inherits half of its chromosomes from its father.

(3 marks)

4 Embryo transplants can be used to produce clones of prize bulls and cows. Circle the correct
words in the sentences below to describe the process once an embryo has been created.

  (a) The embryo is split many times before any cells become

  specialised.
  damaged.

(1 mark)

  (b) The embryos are then

  fertilised in
  implanted into

  the wombs of lots of cows.

(1 mark)

  (c) As the embryos are clones, they will all have the

  same
  different

  genes.

(1 mark)

Classification — The Five Kingdoms

It seems to be a basic human need to want to put things into groups —
that's the case in biology anyway...

Classification is Organising Living Organisms into Groups

1) Biologists <u>classify</u> organisms into groups based on how <u>closely related</u> they are to one another.

2) All living things are divided into <u>five kingdoms</u>:

Plants...

- Are <u>autotrophs</u> (they <u>make their own food</u>).
- Have <u>chlorophyll</u> (the green stuff in leaves).
- Are <u>multicellular</u> (have <u>lots</u> of cells).
- Have <u>cell walls</u>.

Animals...

- Are <u>heterotrophs</u> (they have to <u>move about</u> and <u>find things to eat</u>, e.g. plants).
- Are <u>multicellular</u>.
- <u>Don't</u> have <u>cell walls</u>.
- <u>Don't</u> have <u>chlorophyll</u>.

Fungi...

- Are <u>saprophytes</u> (they feed off <u>dead organisms</u> — nice).
- Are <u>multicellular</u>.
- Have a <u>cell wall</u>.
- <u>Don't</u> have <u>chlorophyll</u>.

Protoctists...   *E.g. algae*

- Are <u>unicellular</u> (have only <u>one cell</u>).
- Have a <u>nucleus</u>.

Prokaryotes...   *E.g. bacteria*

- Are <u>unicellular</u>.
- <u>Don't</u> have a <u>nucleus</u>.

3) Sometimes it's <u>hard to classify</u> organisms. E.g. <u>viruses</u> are <u>non-living</u>, so they can't be put in <u>any kingdom</u>.

More on Classification

There's a lot more to learn about classification, you know...

Kingdoms are Divided into Smaller Groups

Kingdoms are <u>divided</u> into smaller and smaller groups of organisms that have <u>common features</u>:

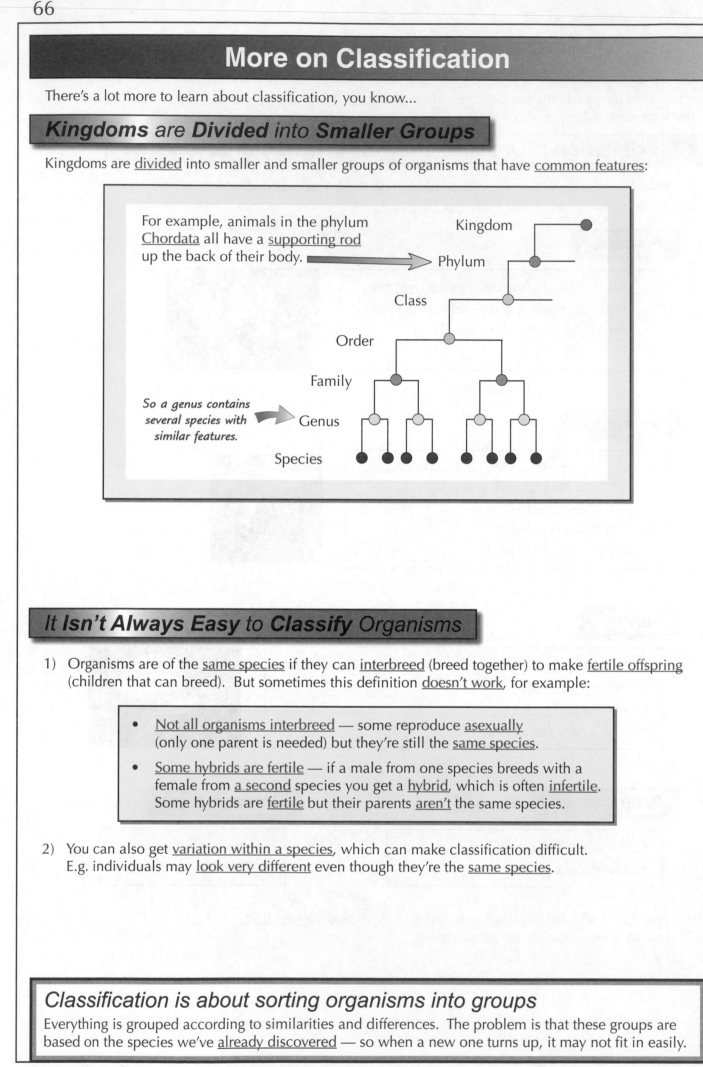

For example, animals in the phylum <u>Chordata</u> all have a <u>supporting rod</u> up the back of their body.

So a genus contains several species with similar features.

Kingdom

Phylum

Class

Order

Family

Genus

Species

It Isn't Always Easy to Classify Organisms

1) Organisms are of the <u>same species</u> if they can <u>interbreed</u> (breed together) to make <u>fertile offspring</u> (children that can breed). But sometimes this definition <u>doesn't work</u>, for example:

> • <u>Not all organisms interbreed</u> — some reproduce <u>asexually</u> (only one parent is needed) but they're still the <u>same species</u>.
>
> • <u>Some hybrids are fertile</u> — if a male from one species breeds with a female from <u>a second</u> species you get a <u>hybrid</u>, which is often <u>infertile</u>. Some hybrids are <u>fertile</u> but their parents <u>aren't</u> the same species.

2) You can also get <u>variation within a species</u>, which can make classification difficult. E.g. individuals may <u>look very different</u> even though they're the <u>same species</u>.

Classification is about sorting organisms into groups

Everything is grouped according to similarities and differences. The problem is that these groups are based on the species we've <u>already discovered</u> — so when a new one turns up, it may not fit in easily.

Adaptations

Organisms survive in many <u>different environments</u> because they have <u>adapted</u> to them. That means they have <u>special features</u> that <u>suit</u> the place they live.

Desert Animals Need to Lose Heat

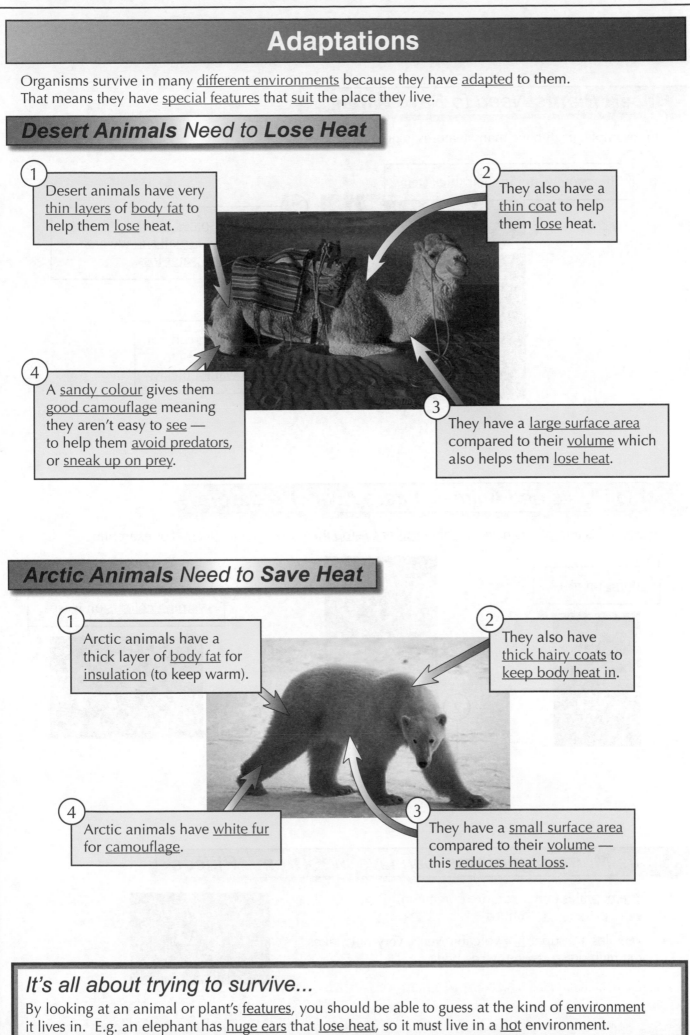

1 Desert animals have very <u>thin layers</u> of <u>body fat</u> to help them <u>lose</u> heat.

2 They also have a <u>thin coat</u> to help them <u>lose</u> heat.

4 A <u>sandy colour</u> gives them <u>good camouflage</u> meaning they aren't easy to <u>see</u> — to help them <u>avoid predators</u>, or <u>sneak up on prey</u>.

3 They have a <u>large surface area</u> compared to their <u>volume</u> which also helps them <u>lose heat</u>.

Arctic Animals Need to Save Heat

1 Arctic animals have a thick layer of <u>body fat</u> for <u>insulation</u> (to keep warm).

2 They also have <u>thick hairy coats</u> to <u>keep body heat in</u>.

4 Arctic animals have <u>white fur</u> for <u>camouflage</u>.

3 They have a <u>small surface area</u> compared to their <u>volume</u> — this <u>reduces heat loss</u>.

It's all about trying to survive...

By looking at an animal or plant's <u>features</u>, you should be able to guess at the kind of <u>environment</u> it lives in. E.g. an elephant has <u>huge ears</u> that <u>lose heat</u>, so it must live in a <u>hot</u> environment.

Adaptations

Desert Plants Need to Save Water...

...for example, cacti have many features to help them save water:

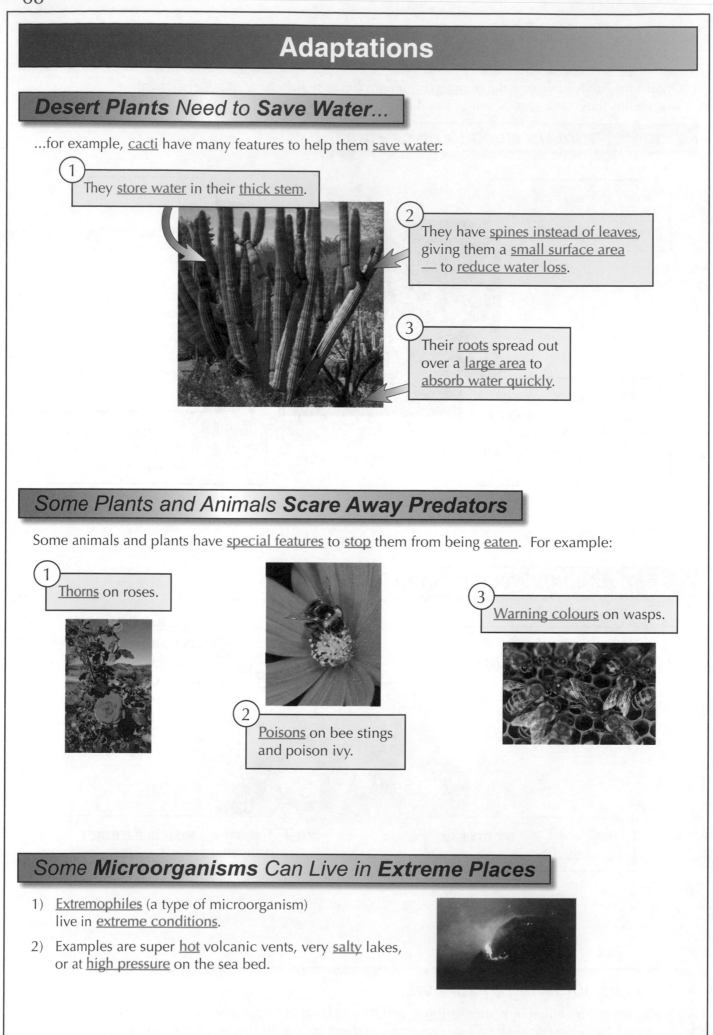

① They store water in their thick stem.

② They have spines instead of leaves, giving them a small surface area — to reduce water loss.

③ Their roots spread out over a large area to absorb water quickly.

Some Plants and Animals Scare Away Predators

Some animals and plants have special features to stop them from being eaten. For example:

① Thorns on roses.

② Poisons on bee stings and poison ivy.

③ Warning colours on wasps.

Some Microorganisms Can Live in Extreme Places

1) Extremophiles (a type of microorganism) live in extreme conditions.

2) Examples are super hot volcanic vents, very salty lakes, or at high pressure on the sea bed.

Variation

You'll probably have noticed that not everyone's the same. There are reasons for this.

There Are **Differences** *Within* **Species**

1) <u>Different species</u> look... well... <u>different</u> — my dog definitely doesn't look like a daisy.

2) But even organisms of the <u>same species</u> will look a bit <u>different</u>
   e.g. different people have <u>different hair colour</u>.

3) These differences are called the <u>variation</u> within a species.

4) There are <u>two</u> types of variation:

① *Genetic* Variation

1) All plants and animals have <u>characteristics</u> (features) that are similar to their <u>parents'</u>.

2) This is because an organism's <u>characteristics</u> are controlled by <u>genes</u> (see page 54)
   passed on from their <u>parents</u> (<u>inherited</u>).

3) These genes are passed on in <u>sex cells</u> (<u>gametes</u>), which the offspring (children) develop
   from (see page 60).

4) Most animals and quite a lot of plants get <u>some</u> genes from the <u>mother</u> and <u>some</u> from the <u>father</u>.

5) This mixing of genes from two parents causes <u>genetic variation</u>.

6) <u>Some</u> characteristics are determined <u>only</u> by genes, e.g. <u>blood group</u> in humans.

② *Environmental* Variation

<u>Any difference</u> that's caused by the <u>environment</u> an organism lives in is called <u>environmental variation</u>.

> <u>Example:</u>
> 1) A plant grown on a nice sunny windowsill would grow <u>healthy</u> and <u>green</u>.
> 2) But the same plant grown in darkness would grow <u>tall and spindly</u>
>   and its leaves would turn <u>yellow</u>.

Most Characteristics are Due to **Both Environment** *and* **Genes**

1) <u>INTELLIGENCE</u> — your <u>maximum IQ</u> might be determined by your <u>genes</u>, but whether
   you get to it depends on your environment, e.g. your <u>upbringing</u> and <u>school</u> life.

2) <u>BODY MASS</u> — your <u>natural weight</u> is determined by your genes, but it can be changed
   if you <u>diet</u>, or <u>eat loads of junk food</u>.

3) <u>HEIGHT</u> — your <u>maximum height</u> is determined by your genes, but whether you get to it
   depends on your environment. E.g. if you don't get enough food when you're little,
   you won't be as tall as you could have been.

Evolution

THEORY OF EVOLUTION: More than 3 billion years ago, life on Earth began as simple organisms from which all the more complex organisms evolved.

Natural Selection Explains How Evolution Occurs

Charles Darwin came up with the idea of natural selection. It works like this...

1) Living things show genetic variation — they're not all the same.

2) The resources living things need to survive are limited, e.g. food.

3) Individuals must compete for these resources to survive.

4) Some individuals of a particular species will have features that give them a better chance of survival than others. For example, giraffes with longer necks will be able to reach food that giraffes with shorter necks can't.

5) Those individuals will then have a better chance of reproducing and passing on their genes.

6) This means that more individuals in the next generation will have the features that help the organisms to survive.

Evolution can Occur Due To Mutations

1) A mutation is a change in an organism's DNA.

2) Most mutations have no effect, but sometimes they can be helpful by producing a useful characteristic.

3) This characteristic may give the organism a better chance of surviving and reproducing.

4) If so, the helpful mutation is more likely to be passed on to future generations by natural selection.

5) Over time, the helpful mutation will become more common in a population.

6) For example, some species of bacteria have become resistant to antibiotics due to a mutation (see page 49).

There is Good Evidence for Evolution

The Fossil Record

1) Fossils are the remains of organisms preserved in rocks.

2) The fossil record is a record of these organisms put into date order for when they existed.

3) It shows species getting more and more complex as time goes on.

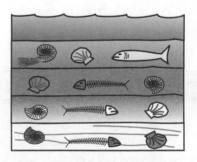

DNA

1) All living things evolved from the same simple life forms, so they have some similarities in their DNA.

2) The more closely related two species are, the more similar their DNA is.

3) Scientists can use the similarities and differences in DNA to work out how life has evolved.

More About Evolution

Nowadays there's lots of evidence for evolution by natural selection
that Charlie Darwin didn't have at the time.

Not Everyone Agreed with Darwin...

Darwin's idea wasn't accepted at the time — for various reasons...

1) It went against common religious beliefs that life on Earth was made by a "Creator" (God).
2) Darwin couldn't explain how new characteristics appeared or were passed on to offspring.
3) There wasn't enough evidence yet to convince many scientists.

...and Lamarck had Different Ideas

1) There were different scientific hypotheses about evolution around at the same time, such as Lamarck's hypothesis.
2) Lamarck argued that if a characteristic was used a lot by an organism then it would become more developed during its lifetime.
3) He believed these developed characteristics would be passed on to the next generation.

Similar Observations Can Lead to Different Hypotheses

1) Often scientists come up with different hypotheses to explain similar observations.
2) Scientists might develop different hypotheses because they have different beliefs, or they have been influenced by different people, or they just think differently.
3) The only way to find out whose hypothesis is right is to find evidence to support or disprove each one.
4) For example, Lamarck and Darwin both had different hypotheses to explain how evolution happens:

There's more about how science works on page 1.

> 1) Lamarck's theory was eventually rejected because experiments didn't support his hypothesis.
> 2) The discovery of genetics supported Darwin's idea.
> 3) Genes provided an explanation of how organisms born with helpful characteristics can pass them on.

5) There's so much evidence for Darwin's idea that it's now an accepted hypothesis (a theory).

Darwin's isn't the only theory of evolution — but it's the best so far

This is a good example of how scientific theories come about — someone observes something and tries to explain it. Their theory will then be tested by other scientists using evidence — if the theory passes these tests, it gains in credibility. If not, it's rejected. Natural selection hasn't been rejected yet.

Evolutionary Relationships

Everything evolved from the same simple life forms. So it makes sense that everything alive today is related. Classification (see pages 65-66) helps us to understand this.

All **Organisms** are **Related**... even if Only **Distantly**

Looking at the <u>similarities</u> and <u>differences</u> between organisms means we can:

1 Understand How Things Are **Related** (Evolutionary Relationships)

1) Species with <u>similar characteristics</u> often have <u>similar genes</u> because they share a <u>recent common ancestor</u>.

2) This means they are <u>closely related</u>.

3) <u>Evolutionary trees</u> show common ancestors and relationships between organisms.

4) The more <u>recent</u> the common ancestor, the more <u>closely related</u> the two species.

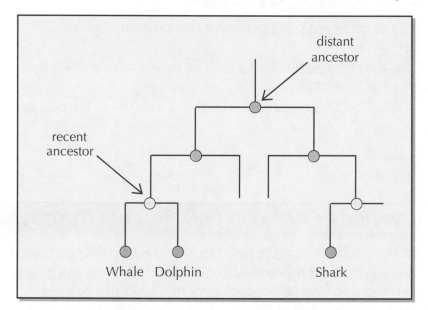

Whales and dolphins have a recent common ancestor
— so they are closely related.

2 Understand How Things **Interact** (Ecological Relationships)

If we see organisms in the <u>same environment</u> with <u>similar characteristics</u> (e.g. dolphins and sharks) it suggests they might be in <u>competition</u> (e.g for the same food source).

Warm-Up and Exam Questions

Practising answering questions is the key to success. So what are you waiting for...

Warm-Up Questions

1) Give two reasons why the definition of a species doesn't always work.
2) Why is a small body surface area compared to its volume an advantage for an animal living in cold conditions?
3) Give an adaptation that a wasp has developed to help deter predators.
4) A pair of identical twins have green eyes. Twin A has a scar above her eye. Twin B weighs half a stone more than twin A. Which of these characteristics are due to:
   a) genes only
   b) the environment only
   c) genes and the environment?

Exam Questions

1   Look at the section of an evolutionary tree shown below.

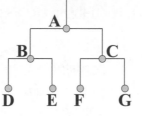

(a) Which species is the most recent common ancestor of Species **F** and Species **G**? Circle the correct answer.

A   B   C   D

(1 mark)

(b) Would you expect Species **D** to look more similar to Species **E** than Species **F**? Give a reason for your answer.

(2 marks)

2   Cacti are members of the plant kingdom.
   (a) Give **three** features that all members of the plant kingdom have in common.

(3 marks)

   (b) Explain how the features of a cactus help it to survive in desert conditions.

(3 marks)

3   Charles Darwin developed the theory of evolution by natural selection.
   (a) Explain how natural selection occurs.

(4 marks)

   (b) Give **three** reasons why Darwin originally had trouble getting his ideas accepted.

(3 marks)

   (c) Jean-Baptiste Lamarck had different ideas to Darwin about how evolution occurred.
      (i) Describe Lamarck's hypothesis about evolution.

(2 marks)

      (ii) Explain why Darwin's ideas were accepted over Lamarck's.

(2 marks)

Competition and Environmental Change

If the environment changes, an organism might not have the things it needs to survive.

Organisms **Compete** for **Resources** to **Survive**

1) <u>Resources</u> are things organisms need from their <u>environment</u> and from <u>other organisms</u> to <u>live</u> and <u>breed</u>:

Plants Need:
1) <u>light</u>
2) <u>space</u>
3) <u>water</u>
4) <u>nutrients</u> from the soil

Animals Need:
1) <u>space (territory)</u>
2) <u>food</u>
3) <u>mates</u>

2) Organisms <u>compete with other species</u> (and members of their own species) for the <u>same resources</u>.

Environmental Changes are Caused by Different Things

1) The <u>environment</u> in which plants and animals live <u>changes all the time</u>.
2) These changes are caused by <u>living</u> and <u>non-living</u> factors such as:

Living Factors — More or less:
1) <u>infectious diseases</u>
2) <u>predators</u>
3) <u>prey</u> or <u>food</u>
4) <u>competitors</u> (other organisms that need the same things)

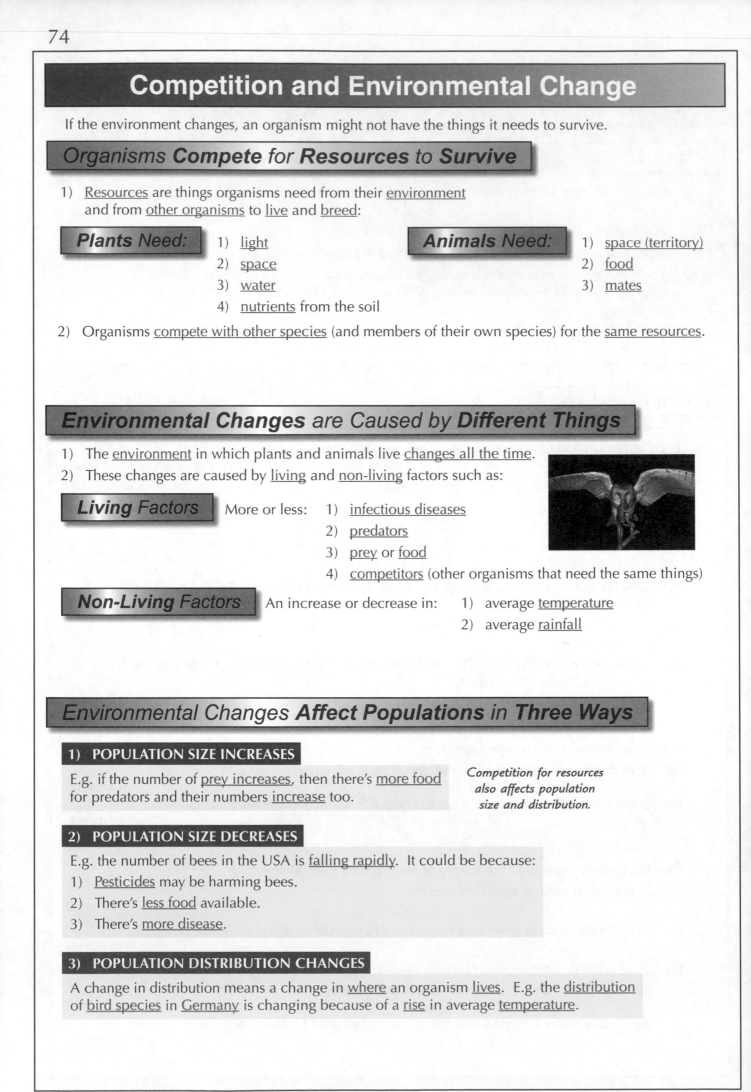

Non-Living Factors — An increase or decrease in:
1) average <u>temperature</u>
2) average <u>rainfall</u>

Environmental Changes **Affect Populations** in **Three Ways**

1) POPULATION SIZE INCREASES

E.g. if the number of <u>prey increases</u>, then there's <u>more food</u> for predators and their numbers <u>increase</u> too.

Competition for resources also affects population size and distribution.

2) POPULATION SIZE DECREASES

E.g. the number of bees in the USA is <u>falling rapidly</u>. It could be because:
1) <u>Pesticides</u> may be harming bees.
2) There's <u>less food</u> available.
3) There's <u>more disease</u>.

3) POPULATION DISTRIBUTION CHANGES

A change in distribution means a change in <u>where</u> an organism <u>lives</u>. E.g. the <u>distribution</u> of <u>bird species</u> in <u>Germany</u> is changing because of a <u>rise</u> in average <u>temperature</u>.

Measuring Environmental Change

It's difficult to <u>measure accurately</u> just how much our environment is changing. But there are some <u>useful indicators</u> that can be used...

Living Indicators Can Show Environmental Change...

1) Some <u>organisms</u> are very <u>sensitive to changes</u> in their environment e.g. they <u>can't live</u> in some conditions.
2) These organisms are <u>indicator species</u>.

Lots of Lichen = Clean Air

1) <u>Sulfur dioxide</u> pollution comes from <u>cars</u> and <u>power stations</u>.
2) <u>Lichens can't live</u> where there's <u>lots</u> of <u>sulfur dioxide</u> in the air.
3) So if there are <u>lots of lichen</u> around, the air is <u>clean</u>.

Mayfly Larvae = Clean Water

1) <u>Sewage</u> in a <u>river</u> leads to <u>less oxygen</u> in the water.
2) <u>Mayfly larvae can't live</u> where there's <u>not much oxygen</u> in the water.
3) So if you find <u>mayfly larvae</u> in a river, the <u>water is clean</u>.

Sludgeworms = Polluted Water

1) <u>Sludgeworms live</u> in water <u>without much oxygen</u>.
2) So if you find <u>sludgeworms</u> in a river, the <u>water is dirty</u>.

Mayfly larvae and sludgeworms are invertebrates.

Phytoplankton = Polluted Water

1) <u>Phytoplankton</u> (microscopic organisms that live in water) can also show <u>water pollution</u>.
2) Their <u>numbers increase</u> when <u>rivers</u> and <u>lakes</u> are polluted by things like <u>fertilisers</u> and <u>sewage</u>.
3) So if you find <u>lots of phytoplankton</u> in a river, it indicates that the water has been <u>polluted</u>.

...and Non-Living Indicators

1) Scientists use <u>satellites</u> to measure the <u>temperature</u> of the <u>sea surface</u>.
2) They measure <u>rainfall</u> using <u>rain gauges</u>, to find out how much the average rainfall changes <u>year on year</u>.
3) They use <u>dissolved oxygen meters</u> to measure <u>how much oxygen</u> there is in water. E.g. <u>not much oxygen</u> in the water means it's <u>polluted</u>.

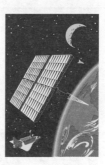

Pyramids of Biomass

<u>Biomass</u> means the mass of <u>living material</u>. A pyramid of biomass is a <u>diagram</u> that helps us to <u>understand</u> what's going on in a <u>food chain</u>.

Energy And **Biomass** *Are* **Lost In Food Chains**

There's <u>less energy</u> and <u>less biomass</u> every time you move <u>up</u> a level in a food chain:

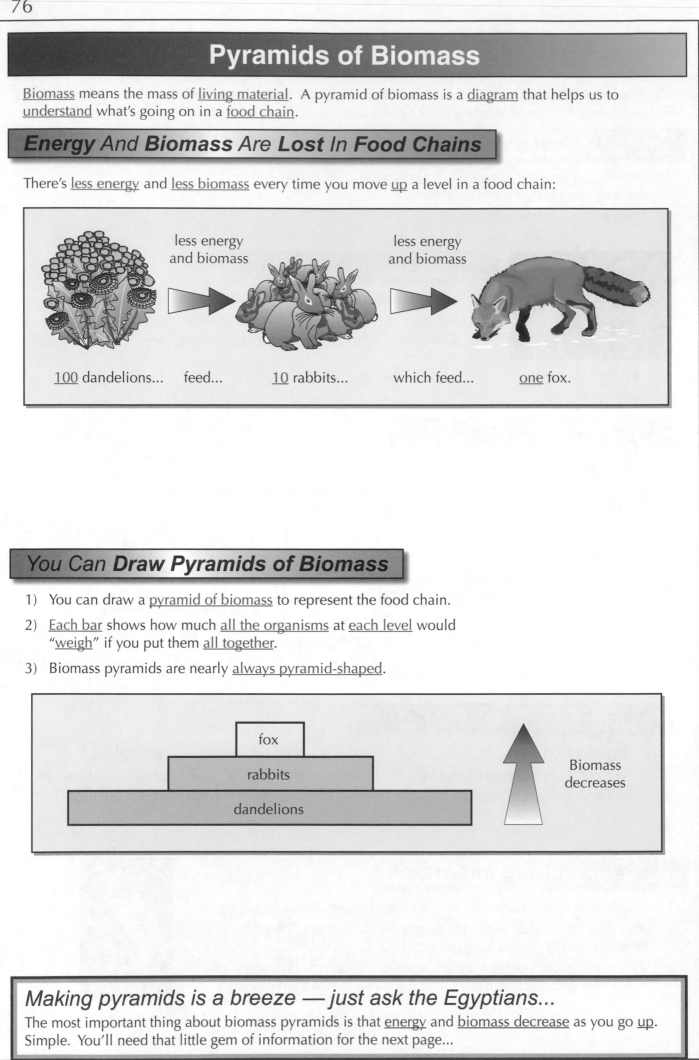

less energy and biomass

less energy and biomass

<u>100</u> dandelions... feed... <u>10</u> rabbits... which feed... <u>one</u> fox.

You Can **Draw Pyramids of Biomass**

1) You can draw a <u>pyramid of biomass</u> to represent the food chain.

2) <u>Each bar</u> shows how much <u>all the organisms</u> at <u>each level</u> would "<u>weigh</u>" if you put them <u>all together</u>.

3) Biomass pyramids are nearly <u>always pyramid-shaped</u>.

fox

rabbits

dandelions

Biomass decreases

Making pyramids is a breeze — just ask the Egyptians...

The most important thing about biomass pyramids is that <u>energy</u> and <u>biomass decrease</u> as you go <u>up</u>. Simple. You'll need that little gem of information for the next page...

Energy Transfer

Energy moves through food chains — some of it's used, and some of it is lost.

All That Energy Just Disappears Somehow...

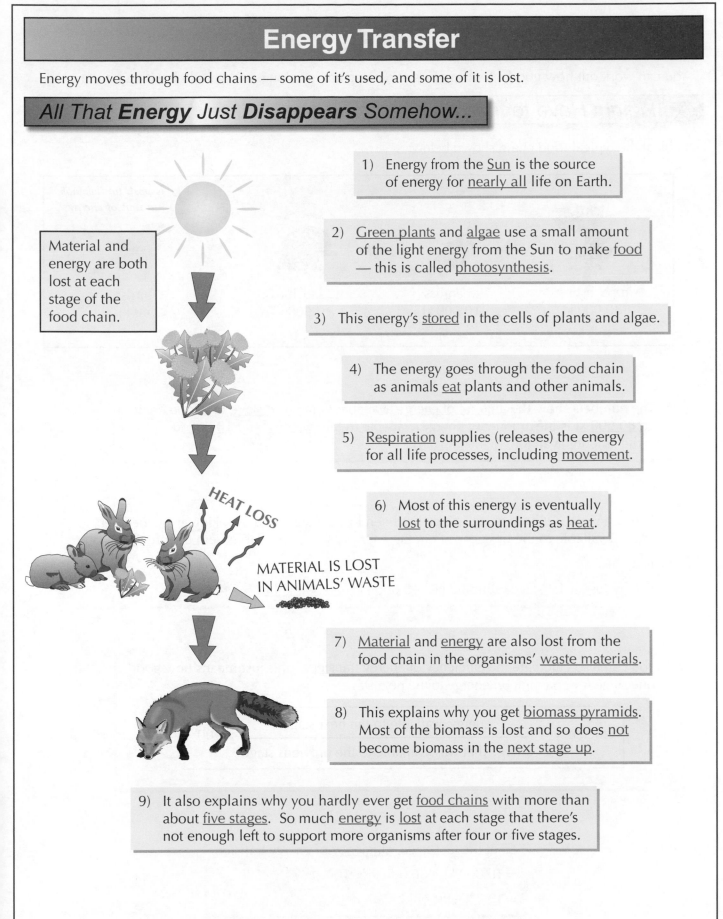

Material and energy are both lost at each stage of the food chain.

HEAT LOSS

MATERIAL IS LOST
IN ANIMALS' WASTE

1) Energy from the <u>Sun</u> is the source of energy for <u>nearly all</u> life on Earth.

2) <u>Green plants</u> and <u>algae</u> use a small amount of the light energy from the Sun to make <u>food</u> — this is called <u>photosynthesis</u>.

3) This energy's <u>stored</u> in the cells of plants and algae.

4) The energy goes through the food chain as animals <u>eat</u> plants and other animals.

5) <u>Respiration</u> supplies (releases) the energy for all life processes, including <u>movement</u>.

6) Most of this energy is eventually <u>lost</u> to the surroundings as <u>heat</u>.

7) <u>Material</u> and <u>energy</u> are also lost from the food chain in the organisms' <u>waste materials</u>.

8) This explains why you get <u>biomass pyramids</u>. Most of the biomass is lost and so does <u>not</u> become biomass in the <u>next stage up</u>.

9) It also explains why you hardly ever get <u>food chains</u> with more than about <u>five stages</u>. So much <u>energy</u> is <u>lost</u> at each stage that there's not enough left to support more organisms after four or five stages.

Energy is lost at each stage of a food chain

The main points to take from this page are that: 1) energy enters the food chain by photosynthesis, 2) energy is transferred through feeding, and 3) energy is lost as heat and in waste materials.

Energy Efficiency

You can work out how good a food chain is at passing energy along, and you do it with a bit of maths.

You Might Have to Interpret Data on Energy Flow

Look at the typical food chain shown below:

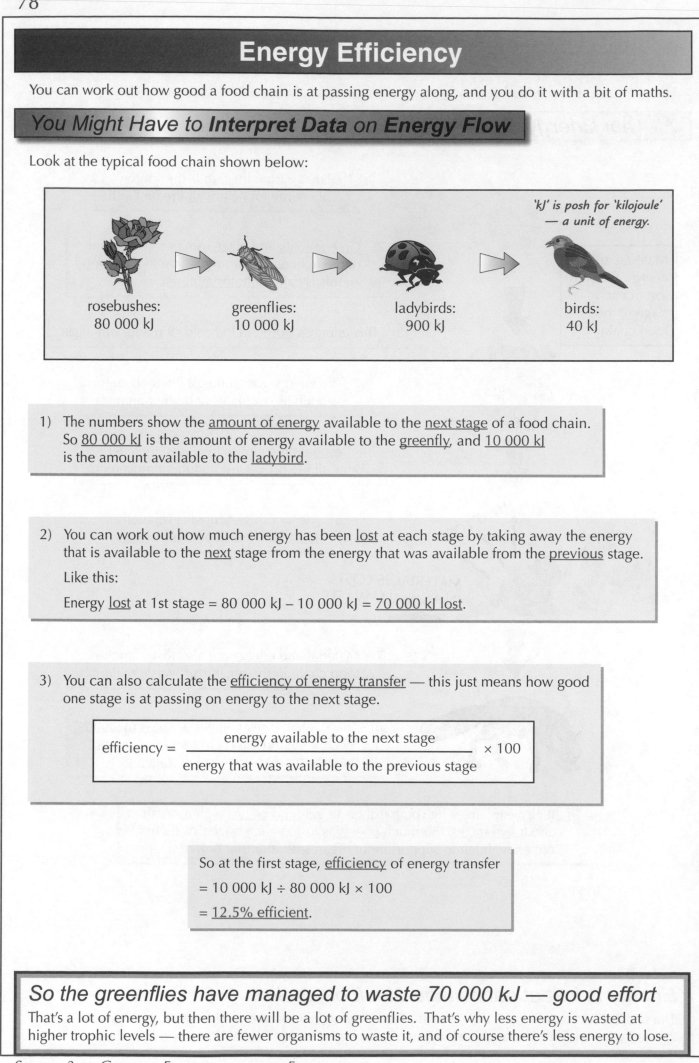

'kJ' is posh for 'kilojoule' — a unit of energy.

rosebushes: 80 000 kJ → greenflies: 10 000 kJ → ladybirds: 900 kJ → birds: 40 kJ

1) The numbers show the <u>amount of energy</u> available to the <u>next stage</u> of a food chain. So <u>80 000 kJ</u> is the amount of energy available to the <u>greenfly</u>, and <u>10 000 kJ</u> is the amount available to the <u>ladybird</u>.

2) You can work out how much energy has been <u>lost</u> at each stage by taking away the energy that is available to the <u>next</u> stage from the energy that was available from the <u>previous</u> stage.

   Like this:

   Energy <u>lost</u> at 1st stage = 80 000 kJ – 10 000 kJ = <u>70 000 kJ lost</u>.

3) You can also calculate the <u>efficiency of energy transfer</u> — this just means how good one stage is at passing on energy to the next stage.

$$\text{efficiency} = \frac{\text{energy available to the next stage}}{\text{energy that was available to the previous stage}} \times 100$$

So at the first stage, <u>efficiency</u> of energy transfer

= 10 000 kJ ÷ 80 000 kJ × 100

= <u>12.5% efficient</u>.

So the greenflies have managed to waste 70 000 kJ — good effort

That's a lot of energy, but then there will be a lot of greenflies. That's why less energy is wasted at higher trophic levels — there are fewer organisms to waste it, and of course there's less energy to lose.

Decay

If things didn't decay, we'd be living in a world of rubbish. It's a good job then that microorganisms break stuff down. But they're fussy blighters — they prefer to work in certain conditions.

Materials are Returned to the Environment by Decay

1) <u>Living things</u> are made of <u>materials</u> they <u>take</u> from the world around them.

2) Materials are <u>returned</u> to the environment in <u>waste products</u> or when <u>dead</u> organisms <u>decay</u>.

3) Materials decay because they're <u>broken down</u> (digested) by <u>microorganisms</u>.

4) Most microorganisms work best in <u>warm</u>, <u>moist</u> conditions with plenty of <u>oxygen</u>.

5) <u>Compost bins</u> recreate these <u>ideal conditions</u> (see below).
(Microorganisms decay kitchen waste in <u>compost bins</u>.)

6) So all the important <u>materials</u> are <u>recycled</u> — they return to the soil,
ready to be <u>used</u> by <u>plants</u>.

7) In a <u>stable community</u> the materials <u>taken out</u> of the soil are <u>balanced</u>
by those that are put <u>back in</u> — there's a constant <u>cycle</u> happening.

Compost Bins Create the Ideal Conditions For Microorganisms

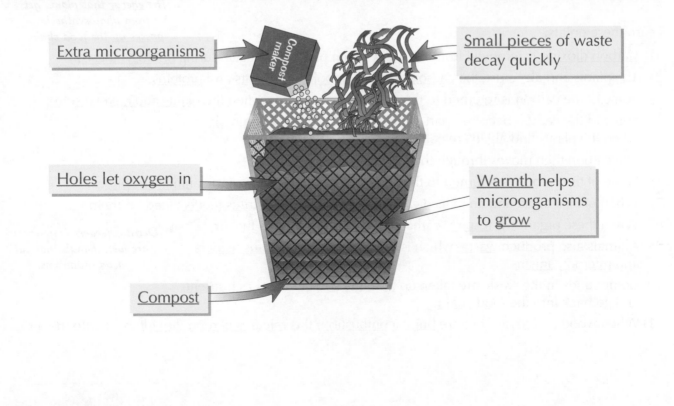

Extra microorganisms

Compost maker

Small pieces of waste decay quickly

Holes let oxygen in

Warmth helps microorganisms to grow

Compost

Microorganisms decay material by digesting it

If you're feeling environmentally friendly, kitchen compost bins are the way to go. Lots of stuff you throw away every week could be turned into compost — and used to grow your mum's roses.

The Carbon Cycle

As you've seen, all the nutrients in our environment are constantly being recycled — there's a nice balance between what goes in and what goes out again. This page is all about the recycling of carbon.

The Carbon Cycle Shows How Carbon is Recycled

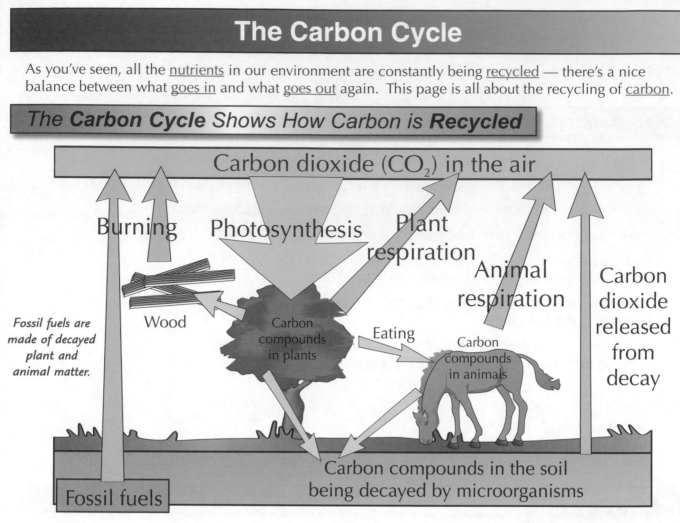

Carbon dioxide (CO_2) in the air

Burning   Photosynthesis   Plant respiration

Animal respiration

Carbon dioxide released from decay

Fossil fuels are made of decayed plant and animal matter.

Wood

Carbon compounds in plants

Eating

Carbon compounds in animals

Fossil fuels

Carbon compounds in the soil being decayed by microorganisms

The energy that plants get from photosynthesis passes up the food chain.

Learn these points:

1) Carbon dioxide is removed from the air by green plants and algae during photosynthesis.

2) The plants and algae use the carbon to make carbohydrates, fats and proteins.

3) Some of the carbon is returned to the air as carbon dioxide when the plants and algae respire.

4) Some of the carbon becomes part of the fats and proteins in animals when the plants and algae are eaten.

5) The carbon then moves through the food chain.

6) Some of the carbon is returned to the air as carbon dioxide when the animals respire.

7) When plants, algae and animals die, microorganisms and detritus feeders feed on them.

8) When these organisms respire, carbon dioxide is returned to the air.

Detritus feeders (e.g. worms) are just animals that eat dead organisms.

9) Animals also produce waste, which is broken down by detritus feeders and microorganisms.

10) Compounds in the waste are taken up from the soil by plants as nutrients and go back into the food chain.

11) When wood and fossil fuels are burnt (combustion) this releases carbon dioxide back into the air.

What goes around comes around...

Carbon is very important for living things — it's the basis for all the fats, proteins and carbohydrates in our bodies. There isn't an endless supply of it though — which is why it needs to be recycled.

The Nitrogen Cycle

Nitrogen, just like carbon, is always being <u>recycled</u>. So the nitrogen we use to make proteins might once have been in the <u>air</u>. And before that it might have been in a <u>plant</u>... or a nice, little <u>hedgehog</u>...

Nitrogen is Recycled in the Nitrogen Cycle

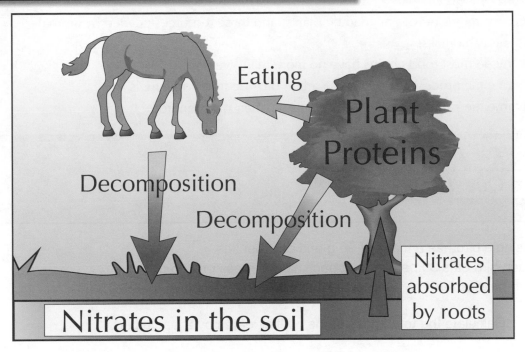

1) Nitrogen is <u>needed</u> for making <u>proteins</u> for growth, so plants and animals have to get it somehow.

2) <u>Plants</u> get their nitrogen from compounds in the <u>soil</u> called <u>nitrates</u>.

3) <u>Nitrogen compounds</u> are then passed along <u>food chains</u> and <u>webs</u> as animals feed on plants (and each other).

4) <u>Decomposers</u> (bacteria and fungi in the soil) <u>break down</u> the nitrogen compounds in <u>dead</u> plants and animals and <u>animal waste</u>. This returns the nitrogen compounds to the soil.

5) This means that the nitrogen in the dead organisms gets <u>recycled</u> — and can be <u>used again</u> by living organisms.

Some nitrogen cycles look different, but the basics are the same

<u>Nitrogen</u> is a pretty <u>boring</u> gas, colourless and with no taste or smell. But it's <u>vital</u> to living things, as it's used to make the <u>proteins</u> we're made of — it gets <u>recycled</u> when decomposers break stuff down.

Warm-Up and Exam Questions

Right, now you've got to grips with how energy and material move through a food chain, have a go at these practice questions. If there's anything you're struggling with, go back and read that bit again.

Warm-Up Questions

1) Give three resources needed by plants, and three resources needed by animals.
2) What is biomass?
3) Why do most food chains have no more than five trophic levels?
4) Name the process that releases carbon dioxide from fossil fuels.
5) Name the soil compounds that plants get their nitrogen from.

Exam Questions

1   A single bird has a mass of 90 g and eats beetles.
    Each bird eats 30 beetles that each have a mass of 12.5 g.
    The beetles feed on cabbages that together have a mass of 925 g.

    (a) Calculate the total mass of the beetles eaten by a single bird.
    (1 mark)

    Study the pyramid diagrams shown then answer the questions that follow.

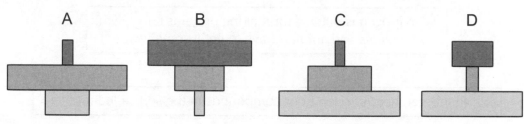

    (b) Which diagram is most likely to represent a pyramid of biomass
        for these organisms? Give a reason for your answer.
    (1 mark)

    (c) The cabbages are the first level in the food chain.
        Where does their energy initially come from?
    (1 mark)

    (d) Calculate the mass lost between the first and second levels.
        Show your working.
    (2 marks)

2   Peter believes that the river running through his local park has been polluted by sewage.

    (a) Describe how he could use a **living indicator** to measure
        the environmental change.
    (2 marks)

    (b) Describe how he could use a **non-living indicator** to measure
        the environmental change.
    (2 marks)

Exam Questions

3   All living organisms contain material taken from their surrounding environment.
    These materials are eventually recycled back into the environment. Some gardeners
    try to speed up this recycling process by producing compost in a compost bin.

    (a) Describe how materials in living organisms are recycled
         back to the environment.

         (3 marks)

    (b) Suggest **two** ways in which a compost bin could provide
         a suitable environment for the decay of materials.

         (2 marks)

4   Complete the following sentences about the nitrogen cycle by filling in the gaps.

    (a) Organisms need nitrogen for making ....

         (1 mark)

    (b) Nitrogen compounds are passed along food chains by ....

         (1 mark)

    (c) Nitrogen compounds are broken down by bacteria and ....
         acting as decomposers.

         (1 mark)

5   The diagram below shows a simplified version of the carbon cycle.

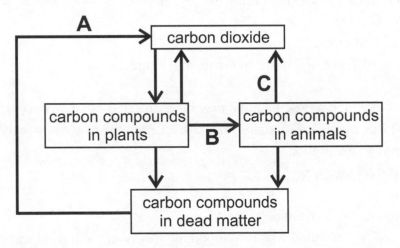

    (a) Name the process that is occurring at:

         (i)   stage A.

                (1 mark)

         (ii)   stage B.

                (1 mark)

         (iii) stage C.

                (1 mark)

    (b) Describe the likely effects on the carbon cycle
         if large areas of forest are cut down.

         (1 mark)

    (c) Name the only process in the carbon cycle that removes
         carbon dioxide from the air.

         (1 mark)

Revision Summary for Section 3

There's a lot to remember from this section and not everyone agrees about some of the topics, like cloning and genetic engineering. It's good know all sides of the story, as well as all the facts. So, here are some questions to help you figure out what you know. If you get any wrong, go back and learn the stuff.

1) Where in the cell are chromosomes found?

2) How many copies of each chromosome are found in body cells?

3)* Draw a genetic diagram for the possible inheritance of an allele for loving Aston Villa (the football club). The allele is dominant and one parent has the alleles AA and the other has Aa. Give the characteristics the offspring could have.

4) Is the allele for cystic fibrosis dominant or recessive?

5) Which two chromosomes are the sex chromosomes?

6) The table below compares sexual and asexual reproduction. Complete the table by ticking each statement that is true for sexual or asexual reproduction.

	Sexual reproduction	Asexual reproduction
Reproduction involves two parents.		
Offspring are clones of the parent.		
There is variation in the offspring.		
There is no fusion of gametes.		

8) How would you make a plant clone using tissue culture?

9) Give two pros of GM crops.

10) Give two cons of GM crops.

11) Give two characteristics of organisms in the animal kingdom.

12) What is a species?

13) Name four ways in which a desert animal may be adapted to its environment.

14) State three ways that plants and animals might be adapted to scare away predators.

15) What is environmental variation?

16) How long ago did life begin on Earth?

17) What are mutations?

18) What are evolutionary relationships?

19) Give the name of the individual who developed the theory of natural selection.

20) Give two examples of non-living factors that can cause environmental changes.

21) Why do organisms compete?

22) What does lots of lichen growing somewhere indicate?

23) Name an organism that can be used as an indicator of water pollution.

24) What does each bar on a pyramid of biomass show?

25) Give two ways that energy is lost from a food chain.

26) Describe the conditions in which microorganisms work best.

27) Give one way that carbon dioxide from the air enters a food chain.

28) Give three ways that carbon compounds in a food chain become carbon dioxide in the air again.

29) Where do plants get their nitrogen from?

30) What role do decomposers play in the nitrogen cycle?

* Answers on page 240.

Atoms and Elements

Atoms are the building blocks of <u>everything</u> — and they're <u>really, really tiny</u>.

Atoms have a Small **Nucleus** Surrounded by **Electrons**

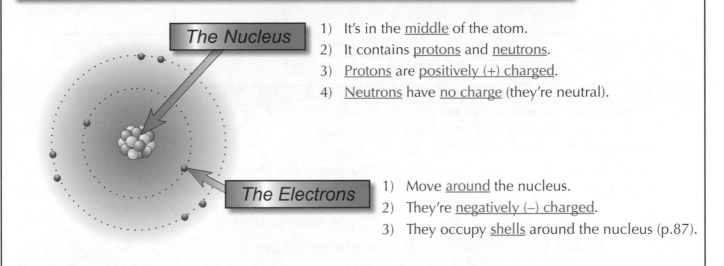

The Nucleus

1) It's in the <u>middle</u> of the atom.
2) It contains <u>protons</u> and <u>neutrons</u>.
3) <u>Protons</u> are <u>positively (+) charged</u>.
4) <u>Neutrons</u> have <u>no charge</u> (they're neutral).

The Electrons

1) Move <u>around</u> the nucleus.
2) They're <u>negatively (–) charged</u>.
3) They occupy <u>shells</u> around the nucleus (p.87).

Number of Protons **Equals** Number of Electrons

1) Atoms have <u>no charge</u> overall. They're neutral.
2) The <u>charge</u> on the electrons is the <u>same</u> size as the charge on the <u>protons</u> — but <u>opposite</u>.
3) This means the <u>number</u> of <u>protons</u> always equals the <u>number</u> of <u>electrons</u> in an <u>atom</u>.
4) If some electrons are <u>added or removed</u>, the atom becomes <u>charged</u> and is then an <u>ion</u>.

Elements Consist of **One Type** of Atom Only

1) Atoms can have different numbers of protons, neutrons and electrons.
   It's the number of <u>protons</u> in the nucleus that decides what <u>type</u> of atom it is.
2) For example, an atom with <u>one proton</u> in its nucleus is <u>hydrogen</u>.
   An atom with <u>two protons</u> is <u>helium</u>.
3) If a substance only contains <u>one type</u> of atom it's called an <u>element</u>.
4) There are about <u>100 different elements</u> — quite a lot of everyday substances are elements:

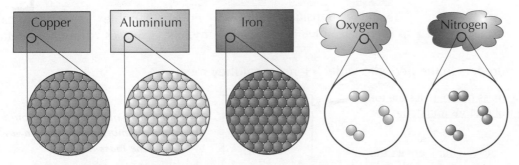

So <u>all the atoms</u> of a particular <u>element</u> (e.g. nitrogen) have the <u>same number</u> of protons...

...and <u>different elements</u> have atoms with <u>different numbers</u> of protons.

Number of protons = number of electrons

You need to <u>know these facts</u> — then you'll have a better chance of understanding the rest of Chemistry.

The Periodic Table

The periodic table is a chemist's best friend — start getting to know it now...

Atoms Can be Represented by Symbols

Atoms of each element are given a <u>one or two letter symbol</u>. E.g.

| C = carbon | O = oxygen | Mg = magnesium | Na = sodium | Fe = iron |

The Periodic Table Puts Elements with Similar Properties Together

1) Elements with <u>similar properties</u> are put into <u>columns</u>.
These <u>vertical columns</u> are called <u>groups</u>.

2) All of the elements in a <u>group</u> have the <u>same number</u> of <u>electrons</u> in their <u>outer shell</u>.

3) If you know the <u>properties</u> of <u>one element</u>, you can <u>predict</u> properties of <u>other elements</u> in that group.
For example, the <u>Group 1</u> elements include lithium (Li), sodium (Na) and potassium (K).
They're all <u>metals</u> and they <u>react the same way</u> with water and oxygen.

4) The elements in the final column (<u>Group 0</u>) are the <u>noble gases</u>.

5) Noble gases all have <u>eight electrons</u> in their <u>outer shell</u>, apart from helium (which has two).
This means that they're <u>unreactive</u>.

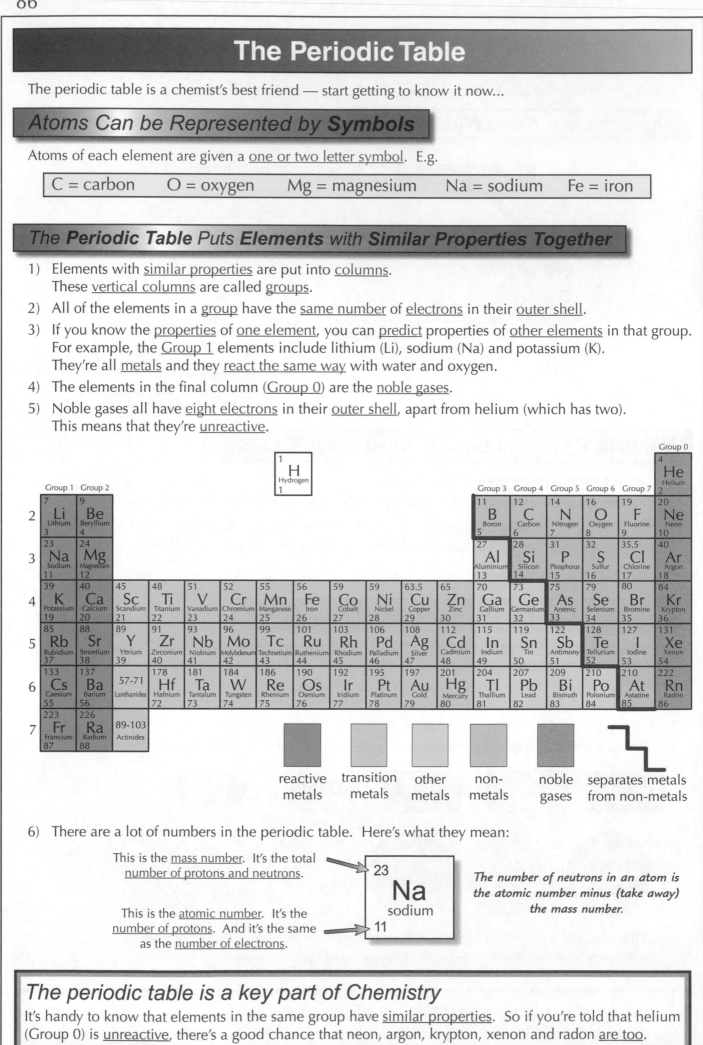

6) There are a lot of numbers in the periodic table. Here's what they mean:

This is the <u>mass number</u>. It's the total <u>number of protons and neutrons</u>.

23
Na
sodium
11

The number of neutrons in an atom is the atomic number minus (take away) the mass number.

This is the <u>atomic number</u>. It's the <u>number of protons</u>. And it's the same as the <u>number of electrons</u>.

The periodic table is a key part of Chemistry

It's handy to know that elements in the same group have <u>similar properties</u>. So if you're told that helium (Group 0) is <u>unreactive</u>, there's a good chance that neon, argon, krypton, xenon and radon <u>are too</u>.

Electron Shells

Electrons may be super-small, but they're super-important in Chemistry (and in the Universe generally).

Electron Shells are what Chemistry is All About

You saw on page 85 that electrons are in shells around atoms. This fact is the basis for the whole of chemistry.

If they just whizzed round the nucleus any old how and didn't care about shells, there'd be no chemical reactions. No nothing in fact — because nothing would happen. The atoms would just sit there.

But amazingly, they do sit in shells (if they didn't, we wouldn't even be here to wonder about it). The electron arrangement of each atom determines the whole of its chemical behaviour. Electron arrangements explain practically the whole Universe. Pretty amazing.

Electrons Always Follow the Same Pattern when Filling Shells

It's really important that you know these electron shell rules:

Electron Shell Rules:

1) Electrons always occupy shells (sometimes called energy levels).

2) The inner shells are always filled first — these are the ones closest to the nucleus.

3) Only a certain number of electrons are allowed in each shell:

    •   1st shell — 2

    •   2nd shell — 8

    •   3rd shell — 8

4) Atoms are much happier when they have full electron shells — like the noble gases in Group 0.

5) In most atoms the outer shell is not full and this makes the atom want to react to fill it.

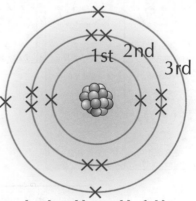

3rd shell still filling

2, 8, 8 — just three numbers to remember (in the right order)

Remember — the inside shells always fill up before the outside ones. So there's no way you'd have one electron in the first shell and six in the second shell — you'd have to have two in the first shell. There'd be five electrons left to go in the second. There's more to help you with this on the next page.

Electron Shells

You can use the electron shell rules from the previous page to work out the electronic structures for the first 20 elements.

Follow the Rules to **Work Out** Electronic Structures

You can work out the electronic structures for the first 20 elements.
For a quick example, take nitrogen. Follow the steps...

> 1) The periodic table tells us nitrogen has seven protons... so it must have seven electrons.
>
> 2) Follow the 'Electron Shell Rules' from the previous page. The first shell can only take 2 electrons and the second shell can take a maximum of 8 electrons.
>
> 3) So the electronic structure for nitrogen must be 2, 5.

Now you try it for argon. (See below for the answer.)

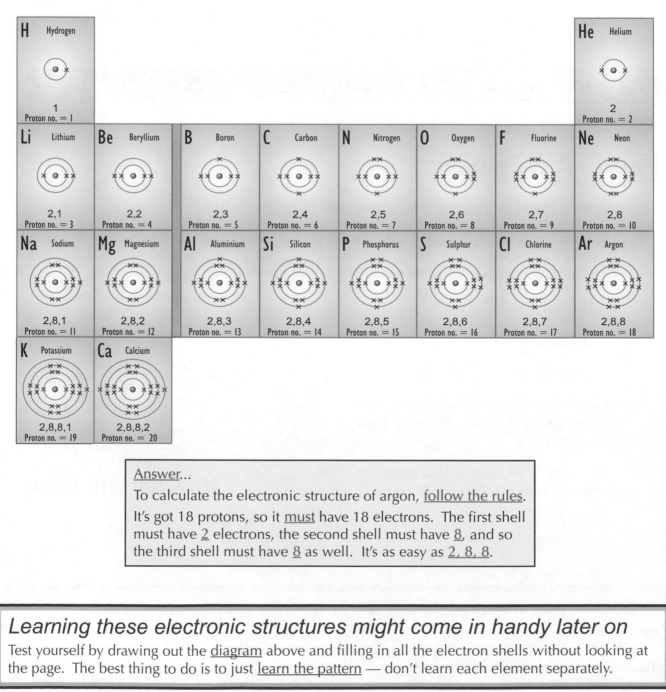

> Answer...
>
> To calculate the electronic structure of argon, follow the rules.
> It's got 18 protons, so it must have 18 electrons. The first shell must have underline{2} electrons, the second shell must have underline{8}, and so the third shell must have underline{8} as well. It's as easy as 2, 8, 8.

Learning these electronic structures might come in handy later on

Test yourself by drawing out the diagram above and filling in all the electron shells without looking at the page. The best thing to do is to just learn the pattern — don't learn each element separately.

Compounds

Elements don't just stay solo — they link up with other elements to make <u>compounds</u>.

Atoms *Join Together* to Make *Compounds*

1) When <u>different elements react</u>, atoms join together with other atoms to form <u>compounds</u>. In a compound the atoms are joined by <u>chemical bonds</u>.

2) <u>Making bonds</u> involves atoms giving away, taking or sharing <u>electrons</u>.

3) A compound which is formed from a <u>metal</u> and a <u>non-metal</u> is made up of <u>ions</u>. This is what happens when the compound forms:

- The <u>metal</u> atoms <u>lose</u> electrons to form <u>positive ions</u>.

- The non-metal atoms <u>gain</u> electrons to form <u>negative ions</u>.

- The <u>opposite charges</u> (positive and negative) of the ions mean that they're strongly <u>attracted</u> to each other.

- This is called <u>IONIC bonding</u>.

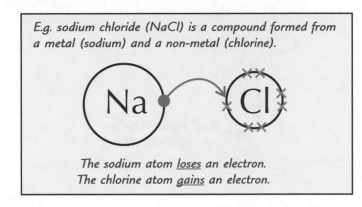

E.g. sodium chloride (NaCl) is a compound formed from a metal (sodium) and a non-metal (chlorine).

The sodium atom *loses* an electron.
The chlorine atom *gains* an electron.

4) A compound formed from <u>non-metals</u> is made up of <u>molecules</u>. This is what happens when the compound forms:

- Each atom <u>shares</u> an <u>electron</u> with another atom — this is called a <u>COVALENT</u> bond.

- Each atom has to make enough covalent bonds to <u>fill up</u> its <u>outer shell</u>.

E.g. hydrochloric acid (HCl) is a compound formed from two non-metals (hydrogen and chlorine).

A hydrogen atom bonds with a chlorine atom by sharing an electron with it.

Ionic = a metal and a non-metal, covalent = just non-metals

Make sure you understand <u>what compounds are</u> and how they form. This stuff is a bit tricky so take it <u>slowly</u> and make sure you haven't got <u>ionic</u> bonding and <u>covalent</u> bonding mixed up.

Formulas

Chemistry is _full_ of _formulas_. So you need to get to grips with what they show.

Formulas *Tell You What* Atoms *There Are*

1) You can tell what _kind of atoms_ and _how many_ there are in a substance by looking at its _molecular formula_.

2) The molecular formula is made up of _letters and numbers_.

E.g. H_2O, CH_4, HCl are all molecular formulas.

3) The _letters_ in the formula tell you the type of _atoms_ it's made up of.

4) The little _number_ at the bottom tells you _how many_ of that atom there are. For example:

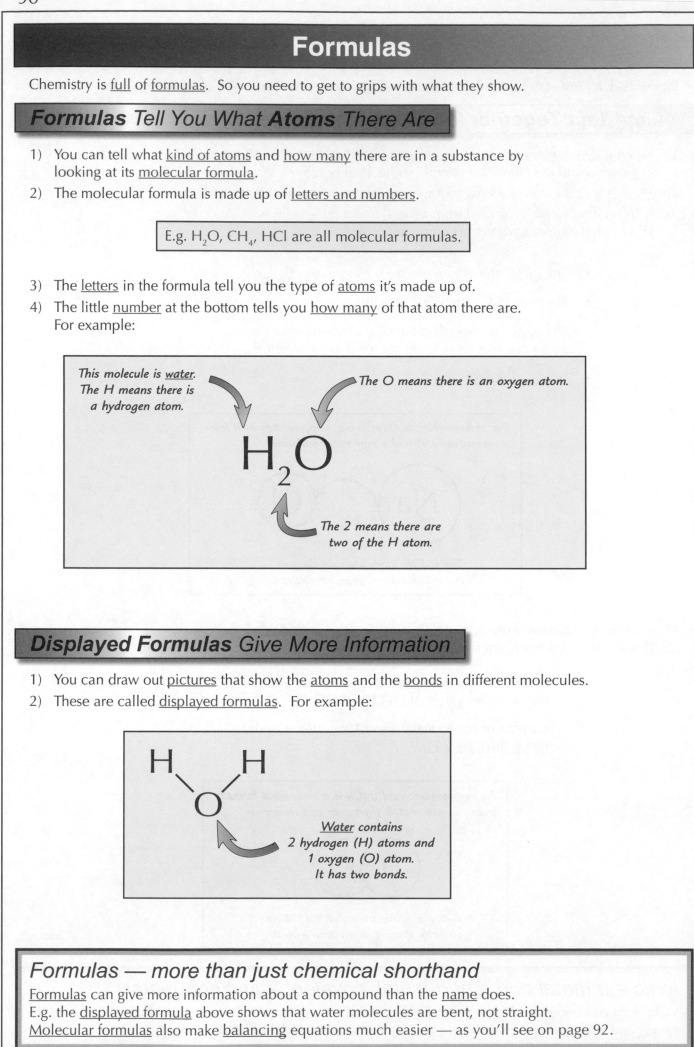

This molecule is _water_.
The H means there is
a hydrogen atom.

The O means there is an oxygen atom.

$$H_2O$$

The 2 means there are
two of the H atom.

Displayed Formulas *Give More Information*

1) You can draw out _pictures_ that show the _atoms_ and the _bonds_ in different molecules.

2) These are called _displayed formulas_. For example:

H   H
 \   /
   O

Water contains
2 hydrogen (H) atoms and
1 oxygen (O) atom.
It has two bonds.

Formulas — more than just chemical shorthand

Formulas can give more information about a compound than the _name_ does.
E.g. the _displayed formula_ above shows that water molecules are bent, not straight.
Molecular formulas also make _balancing_ equations much easier — as you'll see on page 92.

Chemical Equations

If you're going to get anywhere in chemistry you need to know about <u>chemical equations</u>...

Chemical Equations Show What Happens in a Reaction

1) In a chemical reaction chemicals <u>react together</u> to make <u>new chemicals</u>.
2) The chemicals that <u>react</u> are called <u>reactants</u>. The chemicals that are <u>made</u> are called <u>products</u>.
3) Scientists use <u>equations</u> to show what happens in chemical reactions.

Word Equations

1) In a <u>word equation</u> all the chemicals are written out as <u>words</u> — clever that.
2) If you know the reactants and the products you can <u>write out</u> the word equation.
3) You put the <u>reactants</u> on the <u>left</u> and the <u>products</u> on the <u>right</u>, then separate them with an arrow.

For example:

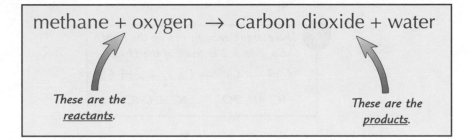

$$methane + oxygen \rightarrow carbon\ dioxide + water$$

These are the <u>reactants</u>.   *These are the <u>products</u>.*

Symbol Equations

1) These are just like word equations but the chemicals are shown using <u>molecular formulas</u>.
2) For example, the symbol equation for the word equation above is:

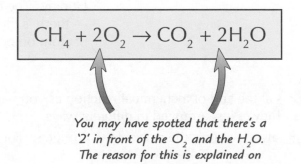

$$CH_4 + 2O_2 \rightarrow CO_2 + 2H_2O$$

You may have spotted that there's a '2' in front of the O_2 and the H_2O. The reason for this is explained on the next page...

Reactants on the left → products on the right

You need to make sure you've totally got the hang of this stuff and don't get mixed up.
For example, in the equation $2Mg + O_2 \rightarrow 2MgO$, the <u>reactants</u> are magnesium and oxygen.
They react together to make the <u>product</u>, magnesium oxide.

Balancing Equations

Both sides of a symbol equation must have the same number of each type of atom. So you have to balance them. Otherwise they'll be all wonky — you don't want that, and neither does the examiner.

Symbol Equations Need to be Balanced

1) You balance equations by putting numbers in front of the molecules so there are the same number of each type of atom on each side of the arrow.

2) But you can't change numbers in the molecular formulas. So changing O_2 to O_3 is a no-no.

3) Start by putting a number in front of one of the molecules to balance that type of atom. Then keep doing it until they all balance. For example:

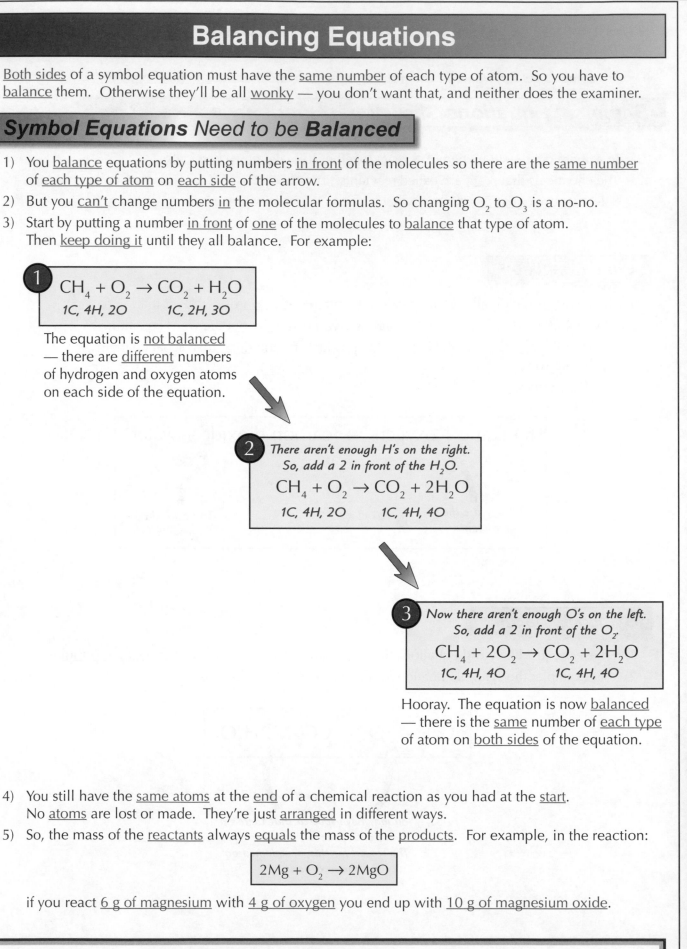

1 $CH_4 + O_2 \rightarrow CO_2 + H_2O$
1C, 4H, 2O   1C, 2H, 3O

The equation is not balanced — there are different numbers of hydrogen and oxygen atoms on each side of the equation.

2 *There aren't enough H's on the right. So, add a 2 in front of the H_2O.*
$CH_4 + O_2 \rightarrow CO_2 + 2H_2O$
1C, 4H, 2O   1C, 4H, 4O

3 *Now there aren't enough O's on the left. So, add a 2 in front of the O_2.*
$CH_4 + 2O_2 \rightarrow CO_2 + 2H_2O$
1C, 4H, 4O   1C, 4H, 4O

Hooray. The equation is now balanced — there is the same number of each type of atom on both sides of the equation.

4) You still have the same atoms at the end of a chemical reaction as you had at the start. No atoms are lost or made. They're just arranged in different ways.

5) So, the mass of the reactants always equals the mass of the products. For example, in the reaction:

$$2Mg + O_2 \rightarrow 2MgO$$

if you react 6 g of magnesium with 4 g of oxygen you end up with 10 g of magnesium oxide.

It's all about getting the balance right

Balancing equations isn't as bad as it looks. Just add a number in front of a molecule to balance one type of atom and then work out the numbers again. Keep going until the number of each type of atom on both sides is the same. It's a bit fiddly, but the numbers should end up right eventually.

Warm-Up and Exam Questions

It's easy to think you've learnt everything in the section until you try the warm-up questions. Don't panic if there are bits you've forgotten. Just go back over those bits until they're firmly fixed in your brain.

Warm-Up Questions

1) What is the definition of an element? Roughly how many different elements are there?
2) How many electrons can be held in:
   a) the first shell, and
   b) the second shell?
3) Aluminium has 13 protons. Work out the electronic structure of aluminium.
4) What does a compound formed from non-metals consist of?
5) Balance this equation for the reaction of glucose ($C_6H_{12}O_6$) and oxygen:
   $C_6H_{12}O_6 + O_2 \rightarrow CO_2 + H_2O$

Exam Questions

1   Nitrogen has 7 protons and 7 neutrons.
    (a) How many electrons does nitrogen have?
    (1 mark)

    (b) What is the chemical symbol for nitrogen?
    (1 mark)

    (c) Look at the position of nitrogen on a periodic table. Is it a metal or non-metal?
    (1 mark)

    (d) Give another element that will have similar chemical properties to nitrogen.
         Explain why you chose this element.
    (3 marks)

2   The equation for a reaction is shown below, with the masses of the reactant and products.

    equation: reactant **X** + reactant **Y** → product **Z**

    mass: 4 g   ? g   17 g

    (a) What happens to the number of atoms during a chemical reaction?
    (1 mark)

    (b) Calculate the mass of reactant **Y** involved in the reaction.
    (1 mark)

    (c) Reactant **Y** is sodium and reactant **X** is a non-metal. Put a tick (✓) in the box
         next to the type of bonding that would be present in product **Z**.

         Ionic   ☐
         Covalent   ☐
         Metallic   ☐
         Non-metallic   ☐
    (1 mark)

94

Exam Questions

3   The electronic structure of sodium is shown in the diagram:

(a)   How many protons does sodium have?

(1 mark)

(b)   Sodium is in Group 1. Give another element that would have the same
number of outer shell electrons.

(1 mark)

(c)   How many electrons does sodium need to lose so that it has a full outer shell?

(1 mark)

4   Sulfuric acid, H_2SO_4, reacts with ammonia, NH_3, to form ammonium sulfate, $(NH_4)_2SO_4$.
(a)   Write the word equation for this reaction.

(1 mark)

(b)   Write a balanced symbol equation for this reaction.

(2 marks)

(c)   In the balanced equation, how many atoms are there in the reactants?

(1 mark)

The sentences below are about chemical reactions.

A   The mass of the reactants is always equal to the mass of the products.
B   Atoms are neither created nor destroyed in a reaction.
C   The mass of the products is always less than the mass of the reactants.
D   In a written equation, the mass of all the atoms on the left of the arrow
is equal to the mass of all the atoms on the right of the arrow.

(d)   Circle the letter next to the sentence that is **not** true.

(1 mark)

5   A compound formed from a metal and a non-metal will consist of ions.

(a)   Complete the sentences below to explain how the ions are formed and why they are
strongly attracted to each other.

The metal atoms lose electrons to form .... ions.
The non-metal atoms gain electrons to form .... ions.
The .... charges of the ions mean that they're strongly attracted to
each other.

(3 marks)

(b)   Name and describe the type of bonding that occurs between
the atoms in a compound formed from non-metals.

(2 marks)

SECTION 4 — ATOMS, ELEMENTS AND COMPOUNDS

Materials and Properties

Different <u>chemicals</u> make different <u>materials</u>. And different materials can be <u>really different</u>. Sadly, "iron is <u>really different</u> to cheese" won't get you any marks. Here are some more useful ways to <u>describe materials</u>.

Different Materials Have Different **Properties**

A material's <u>properties</u> are what it's <u>like</u>. They decide what it's <u>useful for</u> and what it's <u>not</u>. Here are the most important properties:

Melting point

1) This is the temperature where the <u>solid</u> material turns to <u>liquid</u>.
2) E.g. the melting point of <u>water</u> (ice) is <u>0 degrees Celsius</u> (0 °C).

Strength

1) <u>Strength</u> is how good a material is at <u>resisting</u> a <u>force</u>.
2) You can test how strong something is by seeing how much force is needed to either <u>break</u> it or <u>permanently</u> change its <u>shape</u> (<u>deform</u> it).
3) There are <u>two</u> main types of strength:

- TENSILE STRENGTH — how much a material can resist a <u>pulling force</u>. Things like <u>ropes</u> and <u>cables</u> need a lot of tensile strength, or they'd snap.
- COMPRESSIVE STRENGTH — how much a material can resist a <u>pushing force</u>. Building materials like <u>bricks</u> need good compressive strength, or they'd be <u>squashed</u> by the weight of the bricks above them.

Stiffness

1) A <u>stiff</u> material is good at <u>not bending</u> when a force is applied to it.
2) This <u>isn't</u> the same as strength — a bendy material can still be strong if it goes back to its <u>starting shape</u> when the force is removed.
3) Some kinds of rubber are very <u>strong</u> but they <u>bend and stretch</u> very easily — they're <u>not</u> stiff.

Hardness

The hardness of a material is how <u>difficult</u> it is to <u>cut</u> into.

1) The <u>hardest</u> material found in <u>nature</u> is <u>diamond</u>.
2) The only material that can <u>cut</u> a diamond is another diamond.
3) Diamonds can cut <u>most</u> other materials — many <u>industrial drills</u> have <u>diamond tips</u>.

Density

1) Density is <u>how much stuff</u> (<u>mass</u>) there is in a certain <u>volume</u>.
2) <u>Air</u> is <u>not</u> very dense. The particles are spread out so there's <u>not many</u> in a cubic metre of air.
3) <u>Gold</u> is very <u>dense</u>. There would be <u>loads</u> of particles in a cubic metre of gold.

Diamonds — the hardest substance known to man...

Only five <u>properties</u> of materials to remember — <u>melting point</u>, <u>strength</u>, <u>stiffness</u>, <u>hardness</u> and <u>density</u>. Try to learn what each one means and the difference between the two types of strength.

Materials, Properties and Uses

Every material has a <u>different</u> set of properties, which makes it <u>perfect</u> for some jobs, and totally <u>useless</u> for others. That probably explains why <u>chocolate teapots</u> have never really caught on...

The **Uses** of a Material Depend on Its **Properties**

By looking at the <u>properties</u> of a material you can work out what it could be <u>useful</u> for.

1) <u>PLASTICS</u>
- Can be fairly <u>hard</u>, <u>strong</u> and <u>stiff</u>.
- Some are fairly <u>low density</u> (good for lightweight goods).
- Some are <u>mouldable</u> (easily made into things).

These properties make plastics good for <u>television</u> and <u>computer</u> cases as well as <u>kettles</u> and <u>toy planes</u>.

2) <u>NYLON FIBRES</u>
- Soft and flexible.
- Good <u>tensile strength</u>.

These properties make nylon fibres good for <u>ropes</u> and <u>clothing fabric</u>.

3) <u>RUBBER</u>
- <u>Strong</u> but soft and <u>flexible</u>.
- <u>Mouldable</u>.

These properties make rubber good for <u>car tyres</u>.

A **Product's Usefulness** Depends on the **Materials** It's Made From

1) The <u>effectiveness</u> of a product is <u>how good</u> it is at the job it's supposed to do.
2) How good a product is depends on the <u>materials</u> it's made from.
3) Materials also affect a product's <u>durability</u> — how long it will last.

- Really old <u>records</u> were made of a <u>mixture</u> of materials like paper, slate and wax.
- This meant they <u>broke</u> very easily.
- These days CDs are made from a plastic called <u>polycarbonate</u>.
- It's <u>tough</u> and <u>flexible</u> and should last a really <u>long time</u>.

Not rocket science — unless you're deciding what to make one out of...

Be prepared to look at the properties of a material and work out why it would be <u>good</u> for a job. Don't think that any materials are totally useless — their properties may well be <u>ideal</u> for <u>something</u>.

Properties of Metals

Even though they're <u>not</u> all exactly the <u>same</u>, <u>all metals</u> have some things in <u>common</u>.

Lots of the Elements are Metals

1) <u>Most of the elements</u> are <u>metals</u> — so they cover most of the periodic table.
   <u>Only</u> the elements on the <u>far right</u> are <u>non-metals</u>.

2) The metals in the <u>centre block</u> of the periodic table are called <u>transition metals</u>.

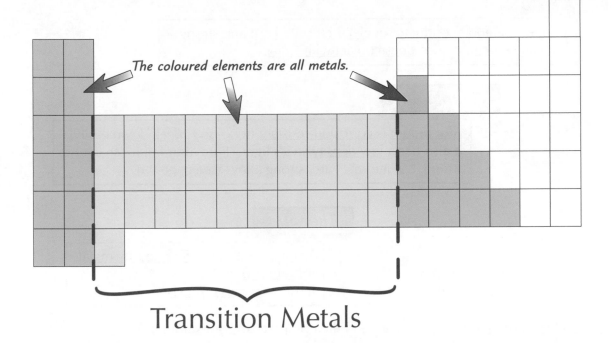

The coloured elements are all metals.

Transition Metals

Metals are Strong and Bendy and They're Great Conductors

1) All metals have some fairly similar <u>basic properties</u>:

   - Metals are <u>strong</u> (hard to break), but they can be <u>bent or hammered</u> into different shapes.
   - They're great at <u>conducting heat</u> and <u>electricity</u>.

2) This means metals have loads of <u>everyday</u> uses:

   - They're strong and can be bent so they are good for making into things like <u>bridges</u> and <u>car bodies</u>.
   - They're ideal if you're making something that heat needs to travel through, e.g. a <u>saucepan base</u>.
   - And they conduct electricity so they're great for making things like <u>electrical wires</u>.

Metals are all over the place

Watch out for <u>sneaky</u> questions about the properties of metals. You might not think you know about the properties of <u>silver</u> — but as it's a metal, you know it is <u>strong</u>, it can be <u>bent</u> and it <u>conducts</u> well.

Properties of Metals

Some metals are <u>better</u> than other metals for certain jobs — it's all down to their <u>properties</u>...

A Metal's **Exact Properties** Decide How It's Best **Used**

1) The properties on the previous page are <u>typical properties</u> of metals.
   Not all metals are the same though:

Copper

> Copper is a <u>good conductor</u> of <u>electricity</u>. It's <u>hard</u> and <u>strong</u> but can be <u>bent</u>. It also <u>doesn't react with water</u>.

Aluminium

> Aluminium is <u>corrosion-resistant</u> (it doesn't break down easily). It also has a <u>low density</u> so it's light. Pure aluminium <u>isn't</u> very strong, but it forms hard, strong alloys (see page 99).

Titanium

> Titanium is another <u>low density metal</u>. It's <u>very strong</u>. It is also <u>corrosion-resistant</u>.

2) These <u>metals</u> have <u>different uses</u> because of their properties. For example:

- <u>Copper</u> is great for <u>plumbing</u>.
  It can be <u>bent</u> to make pipes and tanks, and it <u>doesn't react with water</u>.
  Because it <u>conducts electricity</u> it's also great for making <u>electrical wires</u>.
- <u>Aluminium</u> is used to make <u>aeroplanes</u>.
  It's <u>strong</u> and can be <u>bent into shape</u>. It's also <u>light</u>.
- <u>Titanium</u> is used by doctors to make <u>replacement hips</u> for people.
  It <u>won't corrode</u> when it comes in contact with water. It's also <u>light</u> and not too bendy.

Metals are **Good** — but **Not Perfect**

1) Metals are very useful <u>structural materials</u> — they're used to make things like buildings.
2) However, some <u>corrode</u> when exposed to air and water, so they need to be <u>protected</u>. This can be done in lots of ways, e.g. by painting. If metals corrode, they lose their strength and hardness.
3) Metals can get 'tired' when they're under stress for a long time. This causes the metal to break.

Always choose your metal carefully in exams...

So, all metals <u>conduct electricity and heat</u> and can be <u>bent into shape</u>. But some have <u>extra properties</u> as well, like not corroding. If you have to choose a metal in an exam, first decide what properties are the most important for the job. The best metal to choose will be the one that has those properties.

Alloys

Pure metals often aren't quite right for certain jobs — and that's where alloys come in useful.

Impure Iron Tends to Break Easily

1) 'Iron' straight from the blast furnace is only 96% iron. The other 4% is impurities like carbon.

   A blast furnace is used to get some metals out of rocks — see page 103.

2) This impure iron is used as cast iron. It's handy for making railings (e.g. in parks).

3) It doesn't have many other uses because it's brittle (easy to break). So all the impurities are removed from most of the blast furnace iron.

Most Iron is Converted into Steel — an Alloy

1) An alloy is a mixture of two or more metals, or a mixture of a metal and a non-metal.

2) Most pure iron is changed into alloys called steels.

3) Steels are mixtures of iron and carbon. Sometimes other metals are added too.

TYPE OF STEEL	PROPERTIES	USES
Low carbon steel (0.1% carbon)	easily shaped	car bodies
High carbon steel (1.5% carbon)	very hard, inflexible	blades for cutting tools, bridges
Stainless steel (chromium added, and sometimes nickel)	corrosion-resistant	cutlery, containers for corrosive substances

Alloys are Harder Than Pure Metals

1) Alloys are useful because they are harder than pure metals such as iron and gold.

2) Many metals in use today are actually alloys. E.g.:

CUPRONICKEL = COPPER + NICKEL   This is hard and corrosion resistant. It's used to make "silver" coins.

GOLD ALLOYS ARE USED TO MAKE JEWELLERY   Pure gold is too soft. Metals such as copper, silver, and nickel are used to harden the "gold".

ALUMINIUM ALLOYS ARE USED TO MAKE AIRCRAFT   Aluminium has a low density, but it's alloyed with small amounts of other metals to make it stronger.

3) Because we understand about the properties of metals we can design alloys for specific uses.

Warm-Up and Exam Questions

The warm-up questions run quickly over the basic facts from the last few pages.
Unless you've learnt the facts first you'll find the exam questions pretty difficult.

Warm-Up Questions

1) Where are the transition metals found in the periodic table?
2) Give three useful properties of most metals.
3) What is the problem with iron from the blast furnace?
4) What is an alloy?
5) Which are harder, pure metals or alloys?

Exam Questions

1 Different materials have different properties.

(a) Explain the meaning of the term 'strength' when applied to materials.

(1 mark)

(b) What is the difference between tensile strength and compressive strength?

(2 marks)

(c) Complete the sentences below to explain why plastic is a suitable material for making the case for a television.

Plastics can be .... so the case would protect the TV well.

Plastics can be low .... so the TV wouldn't be too heavy.

Plastics can be .... so it would be easy to make the case into the right shape for the TV.

(3 marks)

2 The tensile strength of a material can be measured as the force it will withstand before it breaks. Look at the table below. It shows the cost of some metals as well as their tensile strength.

Metal	Cost / tonne (£)	Tensile strength force (MPa)
aluminium	1150	45
copper	4600	220
cast iron	180	200
steel	200	400
brass	2700	550
tungsten	24 000	1510

(a) Steel is used to make cables used in the construction of bridges. Brass is not used to make cables as it is too expensive.

Using data from the table, explain why steel is the most suitable material to make cables.

(3 marks)

(b) Aluminium is used to make aircraft. Aircraft need to be strong but aluminium is not a strong metal.

(i) Explain how aluminium can be made stronger.

(1 mark)

(ii) Using your own knowledge, suggest **two** properties of aluminium that make it suitable for making aircraft.

(2 marks)

Exam Questions

3   Titanium is a transition metal that is used in hip replacements.

   (a) Give **three** properties of titanium that make it suitable for this use.

(3 marks)

   (b) Give **one** other property of titanium.

(1 mark)

4   Most pure iron is changed into alloys called steels.
Three types of steel and their properties are listed below.

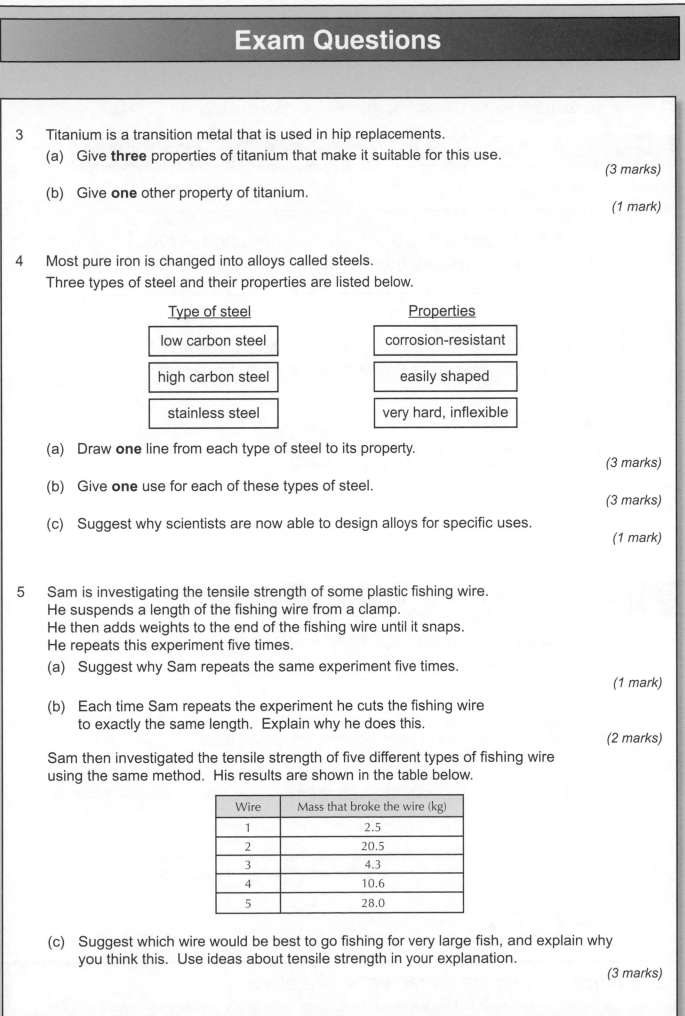

Type of steel	Properties
low carbon steel	corrosion-resistant
high carbon steel	easily shaped
stainless steel	very hard, inflexible

   (a) Draw **one** line from each type of steel to its property.

(3 marks)

   (b) Give **one** use for each of these types of steel.

(3 marks)

   (c) Suggest why scientists are now able to design alloys for specific uses.

(1 mark)

5   Sam is investigating the tensile strength of some plastic fishing wire.
He suspends a length of the fishing wire from a clamp.
He then adds weights to the end of the fishing wire until it snaps.
He repeats this experiment five times.

   (a) Suggest why Sam repeats the same experiment five times.

(1 mark)

   (b) Each time Sam repeats the experiment he cuts the fishing wire
to exactly the same length. Explain why he does this.

(2 marks)

Sam then investigated the tensile strength of five different types of fishing wire
using the same method. His results are shown in the table below.

Wire	Mass that broke the wire (kg)
1	2.5
2	20.5
3	4.3
4	10.6
5	28.0

   (c) Suggest which wire would be best to go fishing for very large fish, and explain why
you think this. Use ideas about tensile strength in your explanation.

(3 marks)

Getting Metals From Rocks

A few <u>unreactive metals</u> like <u>gold</u> are found in the Earth as the <u>metal itself</u>. But most metals are found as <u>compounds</u> in rocks. Getting the pure metal is called <u>extraction</u>.

Ores Contain **Enough Metal** to Make **Extraction** *Worthwhile*

Learn this definition:

> A <u>metal ore</u> is a <u>rock</u> which contains <u>enough metal</u>
> to make it <u>worthwhile</u> extracting the metal from it.

1) In many cases the ore is an <u>oxide</u> of the metal.

2) <u>Most metals</u> need to be extracted from their ores using a <u>chemical reaction</u>.

3) How much <u>money</u> you can make from metal extraction can <u>change</u> over <u>time</u>. For example:

- If the market <u>price</u> of a metal <u>drops</u> a lot, it <u>might not</u> be worth extracting it.
- If the <u>price increases</u> a lot then it <u>might be worth</u> extracting <u>more</u> of it.

Metals Are **Extracted** *From their Ores* **Chemically**

1) A metal can be extracted from its ore by <u>reduction</u> (see the next page) or by <u>electrolysis</u> (splitting with electricity, see pages 104-105).

2) Some ores may have to be <u>concentrated</u> before the metal is extracted — this just involves getting rid of the <u>unwanted rocky material</u>.

3) <u>Electrolysis</u> can also be used to <u>purify</u> the extracted metal (see pages 104-105).

Occasionally some metals are extracted from their
ores using displacement reactions (see page 106).

Learn how metals are extracted — ore else...

Extracting metals isn't cheap. If there's a choice of extraction methods, a company always picks the <u>cheapest</u>, unless there's a good reason not to (e.g. to increase purity). They're <u>not</u> extracting it for fun.

The Reactivity Series

There are a couple of ways to extract metals from ores. One way uses <u>carbon</u>.
It's fairly cheap — but it <u>can't</u> be used for all metals.

Some Metals can be Extracted by Reduction with Carbon

1) Some metals can be <u>extracted</u> from their ores by <u>reduction</u> using <u>carbon</u>.
2) When an ore is reduced, <u>oxygen is removed</u> from it.
E.g. the oxygen is removed from iron oxide to extract the iron.

| iron oxide | + | carbon | → | iron | + | carbon dioxide |

Position in the Reactivity Series is Important for Extraction

1) Metals can be put in a <u>list</u> of <u>how reactive</u> they are. This is known as the <u>reactivity series</u>.
2) The position of the metal in the <u>reactivity series</u> shows
whether it can be extracted by <u>reduction</u> with carbon.

- Metals <u>higher than carbon</u> in the reactivity series have to be extracted using <u>electrolysis</u>.
- Metals <u>below carbon</u> in the reactivity series can be extracted by <u>reduction</u> using <u>carbon</u>.
For example, <u>iron oxide</u> is reduced in a <u>blast furnace</u> to make <u>iron</u>.

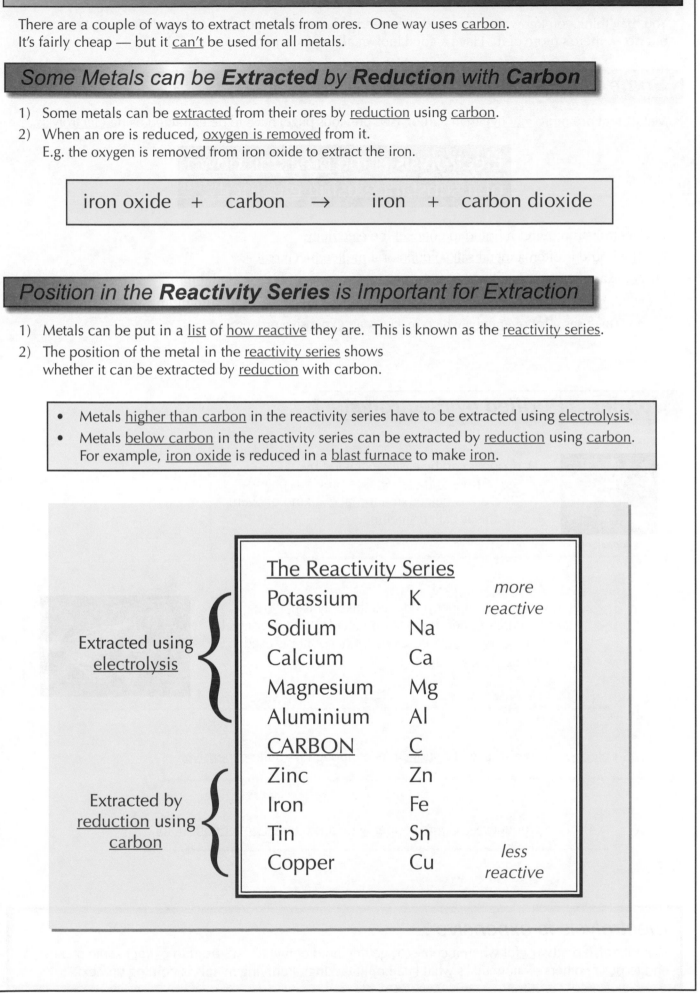

The Reactivity Series

Extracted using <u>electrolysis</u>

Potassium	K	*more reactive*
Sodium	Na	
Calcium	Ca	
Magnesium	Mg	
Aluminium	Al	
<u>CARBON</u>	<u>C</u>	

Extracted by <u>reduction</u> using <u>carbon</u>

Zinc	Zn	
Iron	Fe	
Tin	Sn	
Copper	Cu	*less reactive*

Extraction of Metals

You may think you know all you could ever need to know about how to get metals from rocks, but no — there's <u>more</u> of it. Have a good look at all the facts on this page.

Some Metals have to be Extracted by Electrolysis

Metals that are <u>more reactive</u> than carbon (see previous page) have to be extracted using <u>electrolysis</u>.

> Electrolysis is the <u>breaking down</u> of a substance using <u>electricity</u>.

1) Electrolysis requires a <u>liquid</u> to <u>conduct</u> the <u>electricity</u>.
2) The liquid is often a <u>metal salt solution</u> or a <u>molten metal oxide</u>.
3) An example of a metal that has to be extracted by electrolysis is <u>aluminium</u>.
   - A <u>high temperature</u> is needed to <u>melt</u> aluminium oxide so that <u>aluminium</u> can be extracted.
   - This uses a lot of <u>energy</u>, which makes it an <u>expensive</u> process.

Copper is Purified by Electrolysis

A copper ore

1) Copper can be easily extracted by <u>reduction with carbon</u> (see previous page). The ore is <u>heated</u> in a <u>furnace</u> (a kind of oven) — this is called <u>smelting</u>.

2) However, the copper produced this way is <u>impure</u> — and impure copper <u>doesn't</u> conduct electricity very well. This <u>isn't</u> very <u>useful</u> because a lot of copper is used to make <u>electrical wiring</u>.

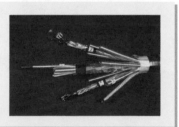

3) So <u>electrolysis</u> is also used to <u>purify</u> it, even though it's quite <u>expensive</u>.

4) This produces <u>very pure</u> copper, which is a <u>much better conductor</u>.

Electrolysis is expensive...

...but it's also pretty <u>useful</u> when it comes to getting hold of metals. It's used to <u>extract</u> some metals and to <u>purify</u> others — now that's what I call multitasking. Purifying metals is coming up next...

Extraction of Metals

Here's how electrolysis is used to <u>purify copper</u>. First though — remember that <u>ions</u> are <u>atoms</u> with <u>missing electrons</u> or <u>extra electrons</u>. If you're a bit unsure of this stuff, pop back to pages 85 and 89.

Electrolysis uses *Electricity* to move *Ions*

Here's how electrolysis can be used to get pure <u>copper</u>.

1) A <u>copper salt solution</u> is used to conduct the electricity.

2) Copper atoms from the <u>positive electrode</u> turn into Cu^{2+} ions. They go into the copper salt solution.

3) The Cu^{2+} ions move towards the <u>negative electrode</u>.

4) At the negative electrode the ions turn into <u>copper atoms</u> — making pure copper metal.

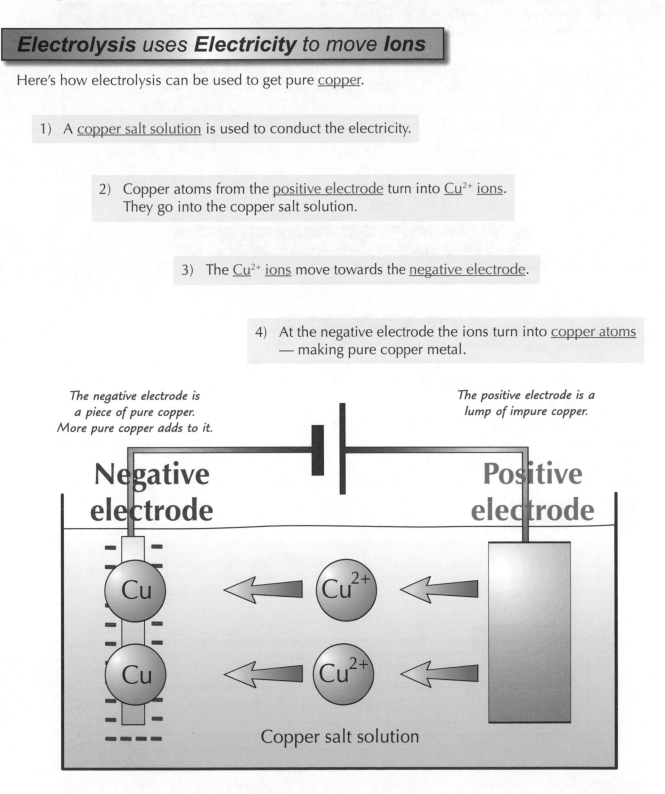

The negative electrode is a piece of pure copper. More pure copper adds to it.

The positive electrode is a lump of impure copper.

Negative electrode

Positive electrode

Cu

Cu

Cu^{2+}

Cu^{2+}

Copper salt solution

Copper is a really useful metal

The skin of the <u>Statue of Liberty</u> is made of copper — about 80 tonnes of it in fact. Its surface reacts with gases in the air to form <u>copper carbonate</u> — which is why it's that pretty shade of <u>green</u>. It was a present from France to the United States — I wonder if they found any wrapping paper big enough?

Extraction of Metals

Some more ways to extract copper here — using scrap iron, bacteria and plants.

Displacement Reactions can remove Copper From Solution

1) If you put a reactive metal into a solution of a metal compound dissolved in water, the reactive metal will replace the less reactive metal in the compound.

2) This is because the more reactive metal bonds more strongly to the non-metal bit of the compound and pushes out the less reactive metal.

3) For example, scrap iron can be used to displace (push out) copper from solution. If some iron is put in a solution of copper sulfate, the more reactive iron will "kick out" the less reactive copper from the solution. You end up with iron sulfate solution and copper metal.

copper sulfate + iron → iron sulfate + copper

Copper-rich Ores are in Short Supply

1) The supply of copper-rich ores is limited, so it's important to recycle as much copper as possible.

2) The demand for copper is growing and this may lead to shortages in the future.

3) Scientists are looking into new ways of extracting copper from low-grade ores. These are ores that only contain small amounts of copper.

4) They're also looking at ways to extract extra copper from the waste that's currently produced during extraction.

5) Examples of new methods used to extract copper are bioleaching and phytomining:

Bioleaching

This uses bacteria to separate copper from copper sulfide.
The leachate (the solution produced by the process) contains copper.
The copper can be extracted from the leachate, e.g. by filtering.

Phytomining   *Phyto just means plant — so phytomining = plant mining.*

This involves growing plants in soil that contains copper.
The plants can't use or get rid of the copper so it gradually builds up in the leaves. The plants can be harvested, dried and burned in a furnace.
The copper can be collected from the ash left in the furnace.

6) Traditional methods of copper mining are pretty damaging to the environment (p.107). These new methods of extraction have a much smaller impact, but the disadvantage is that they're slow.

Personally, I'd rather be pound rich than copper rich...

Pure copper is expensive but useful stuff. Just think where we'd be without good quality copper wire to conduct electricity — in the dark, for a start. The fact that copper-rich ore supplies are getting low means that scientists have to find new methods to extract it. It also means there's lots to learn about it.

Impacts of Extracting Metals

Metals are very useful. Just imagine if all knives and forks were made of plastic instead — they'd be snapping all over the place at dinner time. However, metal extraction uses a lot of <u>energy</u> and is <u>bad</u> for the <u>environment</u>. And that's where recycling comes in handy.

Metal Extraction can be Bad for the Environment

People have to balance the <u>social</u>, <u>economic</u> and <u>environmental</u> effects of mining the ores.

- So mining metal ores is <u>good</u> because it means that <u>useful products</u> can be made.
- It also provides local people with <u>jobs</u> and brings <u>money</u> into the area.

But...
- Mining ores is <u>bad for the environment</u> as it causes noise, damage to the landscape and loss of habitats.
- Deep mine shafts can also be <u>dangerous</u> for a long time after the mine has been abandoned.

There's more about the impacts of extracting things from the Earth on pages 118-119.

Recycling Metals is Important

1) Mining and extracting metals takes lots of <u>energy</u>. Most of that energy comes from burning <u>fossil fuels</u>.

2) Fossil fuels are <u>running out</u> so it's important to <u>use less</u> of them. Also, burning fossil fuels is causing <u>acid rain</u>, <u>global dimming</u> and <u>climate change</u> (see pages 146-149).

3) Recycling metals uses <u>much less</u> energy than mining and extracting new metal.

4) Energy doesn't come cheap, so recycling <u>saves money</u> too.

5) Also, there's a <u>fixed amount</u> of each <u>metal</u> in the Earth. Recycling means the metals are less likely to run out.

6) Recycling metal cuts down on the amount of rubbish that gets sent to <u>landfill</u>. Landfill takes up space and <u>pollutes</u> the surroundings.

Recycling metals is good for the planet — and for humans...

Recycling metals saves <u>natural resources</u> and <u>money</u> and reduces <u>environmental problems</u>. It's great. There's no limit to the number of times metals like aluminium, copper and steel can be recycled. So your humble little drink can may one day form part of an aeroplane or a mighty robot of the future.

Nanotechnology

Just time to squeeze in something really small before the end of the section...

Nanomaterials *Are Really Really Really Really* Tiny   ...smaller than that.

1) Really tiny particles are called 'nanoparticles' — they are about 1–100 nanometres across.
2) Some structures made of nanoparticles are only as big as some molecules.
3) Nanotechnology is using and controlling these very small structures.

Some Nanoparticles *are* Natural *and Some are* Man-Made

1) Some nanoparticles are made naturally. For example:

> • Seaspray — the sea produces salt particles that are nanoparticles.

2) Other types of nanoparticle are made by accident. For example:

> • During combustion — when fuels are burnt, nanoscale soot particles are produced.

3) But most types of nanoparticles are made by scientists using nanotechnology.

Nanoparticles *are Often Used to* Change *the Properties of* Materials

1) Nanoparticles can be added to materials to give them different properties. For example:

> • Nanoparticles are added to plastics in sports equipment, e.g. tennis rackets, golf clubs and golf balls.
> • They make the plastic much stronger and longer lasting.

> • Silver nanoparticles are added to fibres used to make surgical masks and bandages.
> • They give the fibres antibacterial properties (they kill bacteria).

2) Nanoparticles have a much larger surface area-to-volume ratio than larger particles of the same material.
3) This is what gives the nanoparticles different properties and makes them super useful.
4) For example silver nanoparticles can kill bacteria, but normal silver particles can't.

The Effects of Nanoparticles on Health *are Not Fully* Understood

1) The way nanoparticles affect the body isn't fully understood.
2) So it's important that any products containing nanoparticles are tested a lot to check they won't cause any harm.
3) Some people are worried that products containing nanoparticles are available before we know what the long-term impacts on human health will be.
4) Many people believe that any products that contain nanoscale particles should be clearly labelled, so that people can choose whether or not to use them.

Warm-Up and Exam Questions

You've arrived at the next set of warm-up and exam questions. It's really important to find out what you know (as well as what you think you know but actually don't). So give them a go.

Warm-Up Questions

1) What is an ore?
2) Name a metal which can be extracted from its ore by reduction with carbon.
3) Why is electrolysis expensive?
4) Explain how phytomining can be used to extract copper.
5) What is nanotechnology?

Exam Questions

1   Copper is not usually extracted from its ore by electrolysis.
   (a) Suggest why this is.

(2 marks)

   (b) A copper salt solution can be electrolysed to obtain pure copper.
        What happens to the Cu^{2+} ions in the solution during this process?

(1 mark)

2   Copper needs to be extracted from its ore before it can be used.
   (a) Why are scientists trying to find new ways to extract copper
        from low-grade ores?

(1 mark)

   (b) It is possible to extract copper from copper sulfide using bacteria.
      (i)   What is the name of this method?

(1 mark)

      (ii) Describe the process involved in this method.

(2 marks)

      (iii) Give **one** advantage of using this method rather than other methods.

(1 mark)

      (iv) Give **one** disadvantage of using this method rather than other methods.

(1 mark)

3   *In this question you will be assessed on the quality of your English,
    the organisation of your ideas and your use of appropriate specialist vocabulary.*

   *Don't panic — this isn't as scary as it looks. All it means is that you need to write in full sentences and
   use proper spelling and punctuation. You'll also need to use scientific words that relate to the question.*

   Mining ores has social, economic and environmental effects.
   Discuss the positive and negative effects of mining metal ores.

(6 marks)

Exam Questions

4   The diagram shows part of the reactivity series of metals, together with carbon.

Potassium	K	*more reactive*
Sodium	Na	
Calcium	Ca	
Magnesium	Mg	
Aluminium	Al	
<u>CARBON</u>	<u>C</u>	
Zinc	Zn	
Iron	Fe	
Tin	Sn	*less reactive*
Copper	Cu	

(a)   Name **one** metal which is extracted from its ore using electrolysis.

(1 mark)

(b)   Some metals can be extracted from their ores by reduction with carbon, producing the metal and carbon dioxide.

(i)   What does reduction mean?

(1 mark)

(ii)   Write a word equation for the reduction of zinc oxide by carbon.

(1 mark)

(c)   (i)   The block diagram below explains what happens in a displacement reaction.

A metal is put into a solution of a different metal compound.	The .... metal replaces the .... metal in the compound.

Use two of the words or phrases below to complete the block diagram.

less reactive	**displacement**	**more reactive**	**molten**

(2 marks)

(ii)   In which of these test tubes will a reaction occur? Circle the correct letter.

(1 mark)

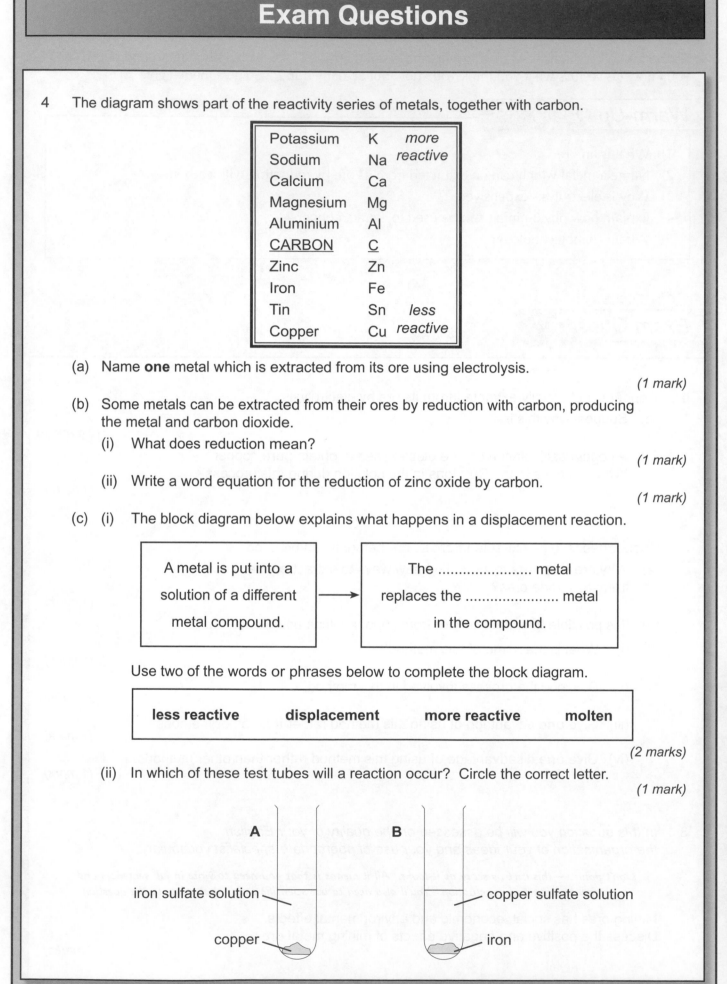

iron sulfate solution

A

copper

copper sulfate solution

B

iron

Revision Summary for Section 4

There wasn't anything too bad in this section. A few bits were even quite interesting I reckon. But you've got to make sure the facts are all firmly fixed in your brain and that you really understand it all. These questions will let you see what you know and what you don't. If you get stuck on any, you need to look at that stuff again. Keep going till you can do them all without a problem.

1) Sketch an atom. Label the nucleus and the electrons.

2) What are the symbols for: a) calcium, b) carbon, c) sodium?

3)* Which element's properties are more similar to magnesium's: calcium or iron?

4) Work out the electronic structure of sulfur.

5)* Say which of the diagrams on the right show:
   a) an element   and   b) a compound

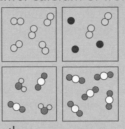

6) Name the reactants and the products in this reaction:
   methane + oxygen → carbon dioxide + water

7)* Balance this equation which shows the combustion of methane:
   $CH_4 + O_2 \rightarrow CO_2 + H_2O$.

8) What's the difference between strength and stiffness?

9) What's the hardest material found in nature?

10) Give a definition of density.

11) Name two properties of each of the following materials that make them useful:
    a) plastic b) rubber c) nylon

12) Briefly describe two problems with metals.

13) Give two examples of alloys and say what's in them.

14) Explain why zinc can be extracted by reduction with carbon but magnesium can't.

15) What is electrolysis?

16) Describe how scrap iron is used to displace copper from solution.

17) What is the name of the method where plants are used to extract metals from soil?

18) Give three reasons why it's good to recycle metal.

19) What is a nanoparticle?

20) Give two examples of uses of nanoparticles.

* Answers on page 241

The Earth's Structure

This page is mostly about how our planet is made up — then there's a bit on disasters at the bottom.

The **Earth** Has a **Crust**, **Mantle** and **Core**

The Earth is almost round and it has a layered structure.
A bit like a scotch egg. Or a peach.

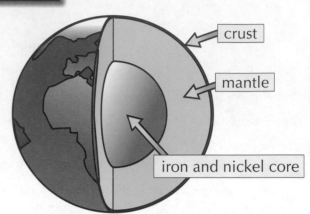

crust

mantle

iron and nickel core

1) We live on the crust. It's very thin and is surrounded by the atmosphere.

2) Below that is the mantle. The mantle is mostly solid, but it can flow very slowly.

3) Inside the mantle, radioactive decay takes place. This gives out a lot of heat, which causes the mantle to flow in convection currents (in big circles, like in a lava lamp).

4) At the centre of the Earth is the core. We think it's made of iron and nickel.

The **Earth's Surface** is Made Up of **Tectonic Plates**

1) The crust and the upper part of the mantle are cracked into a number of large pieces called tectonic plates. These plates are a bit like big rafts that 'float' on the mantle.

2) The plates move around. That's because the convection currents in the mantle make the plates drift.

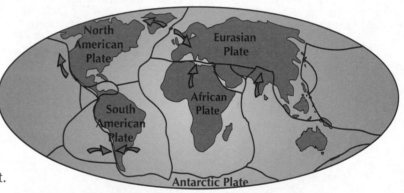

North American Plate

Eurasian Plate

African Plate

South American Plate

Antarctic Plate

3) The map shows the edges of the plates as they are now, and the directions they're moving in (red arrows).

4) Most of the plates are moving very slowly (a few centimetres a year).

5) Sometimes, the plates move very suddenly, causing an earthquake.

6) Volcanoes and earthquakes often happen where two tectonic plates meet.

Scientists Can't **Predict** Earthquakes and Volcanic Eruptions

1) Tectonic plates can stay still for a while and then suddenly jump forwards. It's impossible to know exactly when they'll move.

2) Scientists are trying to find out if there are any clues that an earthquake might happen soon — things like strain in underground rocks. Even with these clues they'll only be able to say an earthquake's likely to happen, not exactly when it'll happen.

3) There are some clues that a volcanic eruption might happen soon. For example, before an eruption, there can be mini-earthquakes near the volcano. But this can be a false alarm.

A few cm a year — that's as fast as your fingernails grow

The starter for this page is knowing the details of the Earth's structure. The main course is explaining why tectonic plates move. Then, for dessert, why not learn the facts about volcanoes and earthquakes.

Plate Tectonics

The Earth's surface is very <u>crinkly</u> — lots of mountains and valleys. Scientists used to think that these 'wrinkles' were caused by the Earth's surface shrinking as it cooled down after it was made. This theory has now been replaced by one that <u>fits the facts</u> better.

Wegener noticed some **Interesting** *things...*

1) <u>Wegener</u> noticed that the fossils found on opposite sides of the Atlantic Ocean were <u>almost the same</u>.

2) Other people had noticed this too. But they thought that there had once been <u>land bridges</u> linking the continents — so animals had been able to cross.

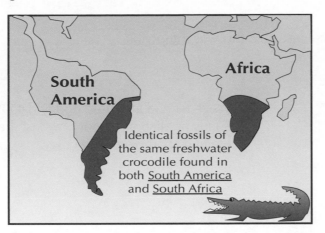

Identical fossils of the same freshwater crocodile found in both <u>South America</u> and <u>South Africa</u>

3) But Wegener had also noticed that the coastlines of Africa and South America seemed to 'match' like the pieces of a <u>jigsaw</u>. He wondered if these two continents had once been one continent which then split into two.

4) He also found <u>matching layers</u> in the rocks in different countries.

...and came up with the **Theory of Continental Drift**

- Wegener's idea was that about 300 million years ago, there had been just one '<u>supercontinent</u>'. He called this huge piece of land <u>Pangaea</u>. Pangaea broke into smaller chunks which moved apart.

- These smaller chunks make up the continents we have today. Wegener said they were still slowly '<u>drifting</u>' apart.

Plate Tectonics

Wegener's theory of continental drift (on the last page) sounded a bit weird to people at first.
But it turned out to be mostly right...

Wegener's Theory Wasn't Accepted for Many Years

Most scientists didn't believe Wegener's theory.
His explanation of how the 'drifting' happened wasn't very convincing.

1) Wegener thought that the movement of the continents
was caused by tidal forces and the Earth's spinning.

2) Other scientists said this was impossible.

3) Wegener had also used dodgy data in his calculations.
So his predictions about how fast the continents were
moving apart were a bit crazy.

But in the 1950s, Scientists Started to Believe it

1) In the 1950s, scientists investigated the ocean floor.
They found new evidence to support Wegener's theory.
He wasn't right about how the 'drifting' happened,
but his main idea was correct.

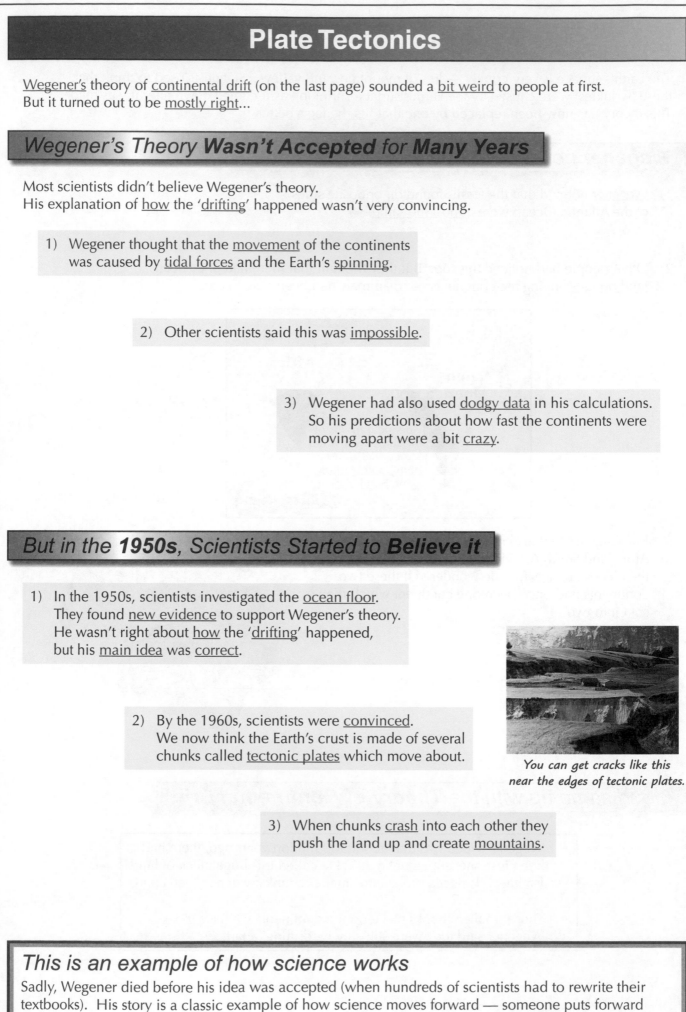

*You can get cracks like this
near the edges of tectonic plates.*

2) By the 1960s, scientists were convinced.
We now think the Earth's crust is made of several
chunks called tectonic plates which move about.

3) When chunks crash into each other they
push the land up and create mountains.

This is an example of how science works

Sadly, Wegener died before his idea was accepted (when hundreds of scientists had to rewrite their
textbooks). His story is a classic example of how science moves forward — someone puts forward
an idea, everyone else points out why it's nonsense, and in the end the good ideas are accepted.

The Three Different Types of Rock

There are three different types of rock: <u>sedimentary</u>, <u>metamorphic</u> and <u>igneous</u>.
This page is just about the sedimentary sort.

There are **Three Steps** in the Formation of **Sedimentary Rock**

<u>Sedimentary rocks</u> are formed from <u>layers of sediment</u> (bits of gravel and plant waste).

1) Over <u>millions of years</u> the layers get <u>buried</u> under more layers and the <u>weight</u> pressing down <u>squeezes out</u> the water.

2) Fluids flowing through the sediment leave behind natural mineral <u>cement</u>.

3) This cement <u>holds</u> the sediment together.

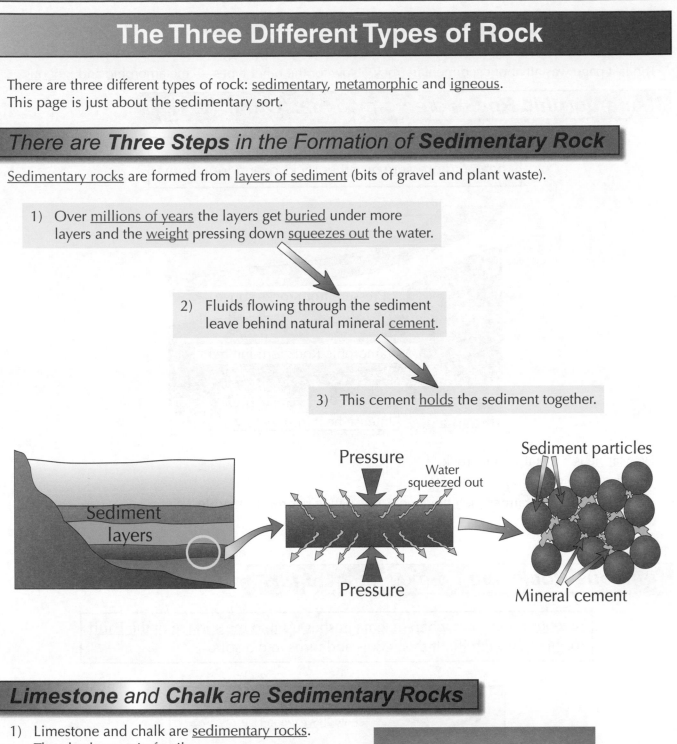

Sediment layers

Pressure

Water squeezed out

Pressure

Sediment particles

Mineral cement

Limestone and Chalk are Sedimentary Rocks

1) Limestone and chalk are <u>sedimentary rocks</u>. They both contain <u>fossils</u>.

2) Limestone and chalk are easily <u>broken up</u> into little pieces by wind, rain and waves. This is called <u>erosion</u> and it can change the shape of our landscape.

Limestone rocks that have been eroded.

Sedimentary rocks are made of particles cemented together

What you should take from this page is how sedimentary rocks are formed, and some examples of sedimentary rocks. The next page is about the other types of rocks — metamorphic and igneous.

The Three Different Types of Rock

The last page was all about <u>sedimentary rock</u>. Now for the other types — <u>metamorphic</u> and <u>igneous</u>.

Metamorphic Rocks are Formed from Other Rocks

<u>Metamorphic rocks</u> are formed by the action of
<u>heat and pressure</u> on <u>other rocks</u> over a <u>long time</u>.

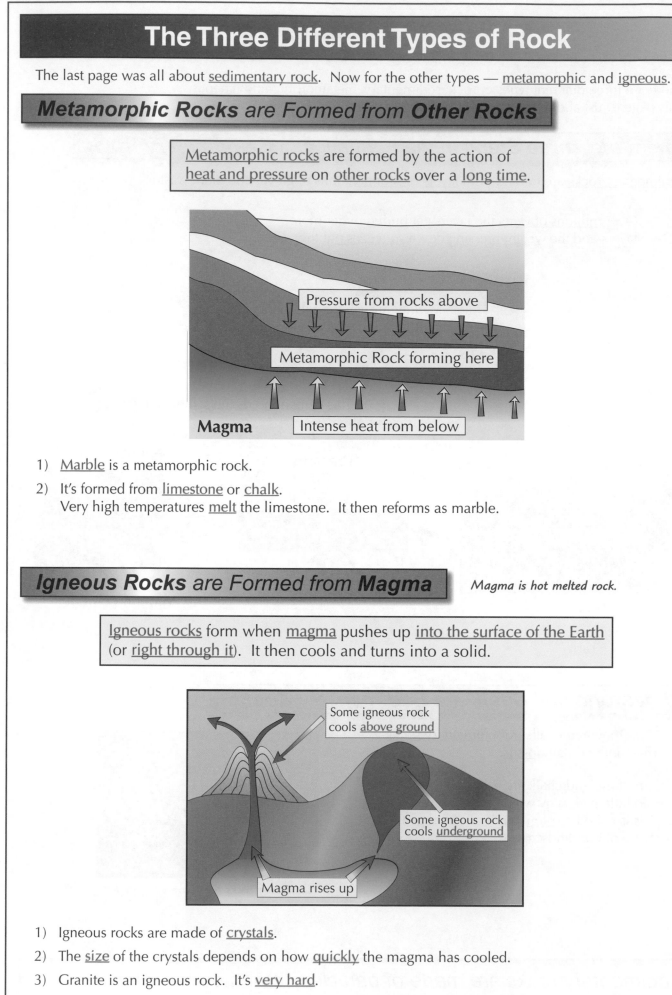

Pressure from rocks above

Metamorphic Rock forming here

Magma   Intense heat from below

1) <u>Marble</u> is a metamorphic rock.

2) It's formed from <u>limestone</u> or <u>chalk</u>.
   Very high temperatures <u>melt</u> the limestone. It then reforms as marble.

Igneous Rocks are Formed from Magma

Magma is hot melted rock.

<u>Igneous rocks</u> form when <u>magma</u> pushes up <u>into the surface of the Earth</u>
(or <u>right through it</u>). It then cools and turns into a solid.

Some igneous rock
cools <u>above ground</u>

Some igneous rock
cools <u>underground</u>

Magma rises up

1) Igneous rocks are made of <u>crystals</u>.

2) The <u>size</u> of the crystals depends on how <u>quickly</u> the magma has cooled.

3) Granite is an igneous rock. It's <u>very hard</u>.

Using Limestone

Limestone is a sedimentary rock (see page 115). It takes part in all sorts of <u>chemical reactions</u>...

Limestone *is Mainly* **Calcium Carbonate**

1) Limestone is mainly <u>calcium carbonate</u> — $CaCO_3$.
2) When it's heated it <u>thermally decomposes</u> (breaks down in the heat)
   to make <u>calcium oxide</u> and <u>carbon dioxide</u>.

> ### calcium carbonate → calcium oxide + carbon dioxide

- When <u>magnesium</u>, <u>copper</u>, <u>zinc</u> and <u>sodium carbonates</u> are heated, they decompose
  in the <u>same way</u>. E.g. magnesium carbonate → magnesium oxide + carbon dioxide
- You <u>can't</u> do some of these reactions in class — a <u>Bunsen burner</u> can't reach a
  <u>high enough temperature</u> to thermally decompose some carbonates of <u>Group 1 metals</u>.

3) Calcium carbonate also reacts with <u>acid</u> to make a <u>calcium salt</u>, <u>carbon dioxide</u> and <u>water</u>.

> ### calcium carbonate + sulfuric acid →
> ### calcium sulfate + carbon dioxide + water

- The type of <u>salt</u> produced <u>depends</u> on the type of <u>acid</u>.
  For example, a reaction with <u>hydrochloric</u> acid would make a <u>chloride</u> (e.g. $CaCl_2$).
- Other carbonates that react with acids are <u>magnesium</u>, <u>copper</u>, <u>zinc</u> and <u>sodium</u>.

Calcium Oxide *Reacts with* **Water** *to Produce* **Calcium Hydroxide**

1) When you <u>add water</u> to calcium oxide you get <u>calcium hydroxide</u>.

> ### calcium oxide + water → calcium hydroxide

2) Calcium hydroxide is an <u>alkali</u> which can be used to neutralise <u>acidic soil</u> in fields.
3) When calcium hydroxide is mixed with water it makes a <u>solution</u> called <u>limewater</u>.
   Limewater can be used as a <u>test</u> for <u>carbon dioxide</u>. If you bubble <u>gas</u> through it,
   the solution will turn <u>cloudy</u> if the gas is <u>carbon dioxide</u>. This is the reaction:

> ### calcium hydroxide + carbon dioxide → calcium carbonate + water

---

Four fun-filled chemical reactions here...

...and they all look a bit similar. So the only way to <u>learn</u> these equations is to cover the page
and <u>write them all out</u>. It's not the most fun way to spend ten minutes of your life, but it does work.

Using Limestone

Limestone gets used a lot in <u>building materials</u>. But first it has to be <u>quarried</u> (dug up) out of the ground.

Limestone is Used to Make **Cement**

1) Limestone can be <u>heated</u> with <u>clay</u> to make <u>cement</u>.
2) Cement can be mixed with <u>sand</u> and <u>water</u> to make <u>mortar</u>. <u>Mortar</u> is the stuff you stick <u>bricks</u> together with.
3) Or you can mix cement with <u>sand</u> and <u>aggregate</u> (<u>water</u> and <u>gravel</u>) to make <u>concrete</u>.

Quarrying Limestone Makes a **Right Mess** of the **Landscape**

Digging limestone out of the ground can cause <u>environmental problems</u>.

1) For a start, it makes <u>huge ugly holes</u> which change the landscape for ever.

2) <u>Quarrying</u> means blasting rocks apart with explosives. This makes lots of <u>noise</u> and <u>dust</u>.

3) Quarrying <u>destroys the homes</u> of animals and birds.

4) The limestone needs to be <u>transported away</u> from the quarry — usually in lorries. This causes more noise and pollution.

5) Waste materials produce unsightly <u>tips</u>.

Making Stuff from Limestone Causes **Pollution** Too

1) <u>Cement factories</u> make a lot of <u>dust</u>. This can cause <u>breathing problems</u> for some people.
2) <u>Energy</u> is needed to produce cement. The energy is likely to come from burning <u>fossil fuels</u>, which causes pollution.

See pages 146-149 for more on pollution caused by burning fossil fuels.

Using Limestone

You just saw the downsides of quarrying and using limestone — but it's not all bad.

On the **Plus Side** of using Limestone...

1) Limestone provides things that people want — like <u>houses</u> and <u>roads</u>. Chemicals used in making <u>dyes</u>, <u>paints</u> and <u>medicines</u> also come from limestone.

2) Limestone products are used to <u>neutralise acidic soil</u>, <u>lakes</u> and <u>rivers</u>.

3) Limestone is also used in power station chimneys to <u>neutralise sulfur dioxide</u>, which is a cause of acid rain.

4) The quarry provides <u>jobs</u> for people and brings more money into the <u>local economy</u>.

Limestone **Products** Have **Advantages** and **Disadvantages**

Limestone and concrete (made from cement) are used as <u>building materials</u>. In some cases they're <u>perfect</u> for the job, but in other cases they aren't so great.

1) Limestone is found in <u>large amounts</u> in the UK and is <u>cheaper</u> than granite or marble. It's also a fairly easy rock to <u>cut</u>.

2) Some limestone is more <u>hard-wearing</u> than marble, but it still looks <u>nice</u>.

3) However, limestone can be <u>damaged</u> by <u>acid rain</u> (see page 147).

4) Concrete can be poured into <u>moulds</u> to make blocks or panels that can be joined together. It's a <u>very quick and cheap</u> way of making buildings, <u>and it shows</u> — concrete is <u>ugly</u>.

5) Limestone, concrete and cement <u>don't rot</u> when they get wet like wood does. They can't be eaten by <u>insects</u> or <u>rodents</u> either. And to top it off, they <u>can't</u> be set on <u>fire</u>.

6) Concrete <u>doesn't corrode</u> (break down or rust) like lots of metals do. It can crack though. <u>Steel bars</u> can be used to make it stronger.

Limestone — who knew it was so useful...

Wow. It sounds like you can build <u>pretty much anything</u> with limestone, except perhaps a bouncy castle. Loads of <u>famous buildings</u> are made out of limestone so it's pretty important stuff.

Warm-Up and Exam Questions

If you still think the Earth is flat, you may want to go back and check your facts. If you think differently, and also know more interesting facts about the Earth's structure, test yourself with these...

Warm-Up Questions

1) What can happen at the boundary of two tectonic plates?
2) What was 'Pangaea'?
3) How are igneous rocks formed?
4) Apart from building materials, give two things that limestone is used for.
5) Give two advantages of limestone building materials.

Exam Questions

1   The following diagram shows the internal structure of the Earth.

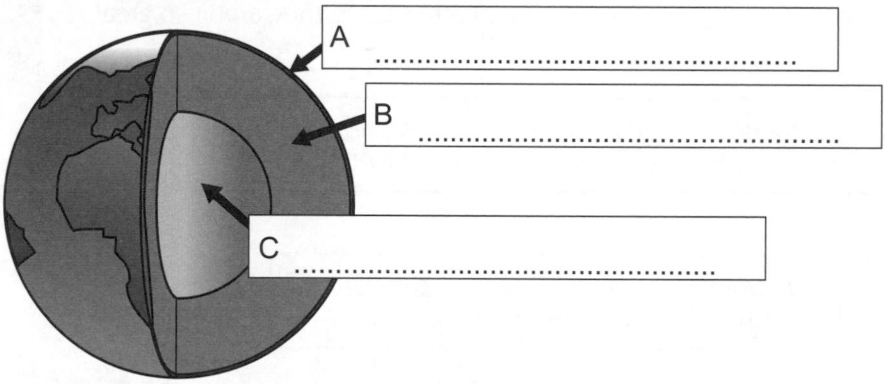

A ....

B ....

C ....

(a)   Complete the labels on the diagram.

(3 marks)

(b)   The part labelled A is cracked into many pieces.
    (i)   What are these pieces called?

(1 mark)

    (ii)   Explain the process that causes these pieces to move.

(3 marks)

2   Some metamorphic rocks, such as marble, are formed from sedimentary rocks.

(a)   Complete the sentence below to describe how metamorphic rocks are formed.

Metamorphic rocks are formed by the action of heat and .... on other rocks over a .... time.

(2 marks)

(b)   Name a sedimentary rock that marble is formed from.

(1 mark)

(c)   Describe how sedimentary rocks are formed.

(3 marks)

Exam Questions

3   Alfred Wegener came up with the theory of continental drift.

(a)   Circle the correct answers to complete the following sentences about pieces of evidence that support this theory.

(i)   The | coastlines / mountains | of South America and Africa fit together.

(1 mark)

(ii)   There are | fossils of animals / chemical elements | that couldn't have crossed the Atlantic Ocean found in both South America and Africa.

(1 mark)

(b)   Complete the sentence below by circling the letter (**A-D**) next to the correct answer.

Wegener thought the continents' movement was caused by tidal forces and the Earth's rotation,

A   and other scientists confirmed this.

B   but other scientists realised that this was impossible.

C   but other scientists didn't know if this was correct or not.

D   and other scientists showed that this was true for some continents, but not others.

(1 mark)

4   Limestone is mainly calcium carbonate, $CaCO_3$.

(a)   Calcium carbonate can be thermally decomposed.

(i)   Complete the word equation for this reaction.

calcium carbonate   →   .... + ...

(2 marks)

(ii)   Explain why you cannot carry out this reaction with all carbonates of Group 1 metals in the school lab.

(1 mark)

(b)   Limestone reacts with acid rain. Give **two** chemicals that are produced when limestone reacts with acid rain.

(2 marks)

5   Limestone is often used to make building materials.

(a)   Describe how **cement** is made from limestone.

(2 marks)

(b)   Describe how **concrete** is made from limestone.

(2 marks)

(c)   *In this question you will be assessed on the quality of your English, the organisation of your ideas and your use of appropriate specialist vocabulary.*

Outline the negative impacts of quarrying limestone and using it to produce building materials.

(6 marks)

Salt

People dig great big holes to get at salt — yep, it's that important.

Sodium Chloride (Salt) is Mined from Underneath Cheshire

1) Salt is mainly found in the <u>sea</u> or <u>underground</u>.

2) The regions of salt found underground are called <u>salt deposits</u>.

3) There are huge deposits of salt under <u>Cheshire</u>.

4) Salt can be extracted from these deposits by normal <u>mining</u> or <u>solution mining</u>.

5) In normal mining salt is brought up to the surface as solid <u>rock salt</u> (a <u>mixture</u> of salt and other materials). The salt is then <u>separated</u> out from the other materials.

6) In solution mining hot water is pumped underground. This <u>dissolves</u> the salt and the <u>salt solution</u> is <u>forced to the surface</u>.

7) When the mining is finished, it's important to <u>fill in the holes</u> in the ground. If not, the land could <u>collapse</u> and <u>slide into the holes</u> — this is called <u>subsidence</u>.

Salt — it's not just for chips

Salt's used for a lot of <u>chemical products</u> (see the next page) as well as for <u>food</u> (see page 124) and <u>gritting the roads</u>. There's plenty to learn about it — so start by trying to learn the ways salt is <u>extracted</u>.

Salt

The fancy chemical name for salt that you eat is <u>sodium chloride</u>. So its chemical formula is <u>NaCl</u>. Salt is really useful in itself, and you can get even more useful products if you electrolyse a solution of it.

Electrolysis of **Brine** gives **Hydrogen**, **Chlorine** and **NaOH**

1) <u>Concentrated sodium chloride solution</u> is also known as <u>brine</u>.

2) <u>Brine</u> can be <u>electrolysed</u> using a set-up like this one.

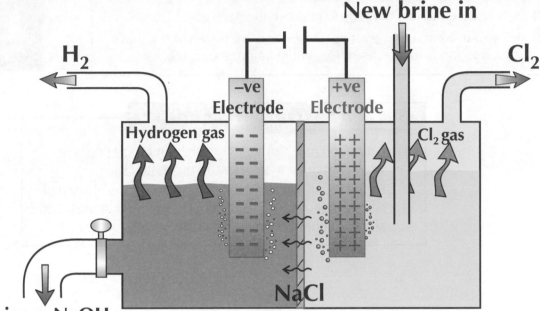

3) The <u>electrodes</u> (solids that conduct electricity) are made of an <u>inert</u> material — this just means that they <u>won't react</u>.

4) There are <u>three</u> useful products:

> • <u>Hydrogen gas</u> is given off at the negative electrode.
>
> • <u>Chlorine gas</u> is given off at the positive electrode.
>
> • <u>Sodium hydroxide</u> (NaOH) is also formed.

The **Products** of Brine Electrolysis are **Really Useful**

The products of the electrolysis of brine are important in the <u>chemical industry</u>.

> 1) <u>Hydrogen</u> is used for making <u>margarine</u>.
>
> 2) <u>Chlorine gas</u> can be used to <u>disinfect water</u>, or to make <u>plastics</u> (such as <u>PVC</u>), <u>solvents</u> or <u>hydrochloric acid</u>.
>
> 3) The <u>sodium hydroxide</u> solution can be used to make <u>soap</u>.
>
> 4) You can react the <u>sodium hydroxide</u> solution with <u>chlorine gas</u> to make <u>household bleach</u>.

Salt in the Food Industry

Salt has been used as a <u>preservative</u> and <u>flavouring</u> for thousands of years. Sailors on long journeys used to cover meat in it to keep it from rotting and the Romans even used it on their salads.

Salt is Important in Food Production

Salt is Added to Lots of Foods

1) <u>Salt</u> is added to lots of <u>foods</u> to improve the <u>flavour</u>.
2) It's also used as a <u>preservative</u>. A preservative is something that's added to foods to give them <u>longer life</u> before they go 'off'.

Salt can be Bad for Your Health

1) Eating <u>too much</u> salt may cause <u>high blood pressure</u> which can lead to <u>strokes</u> and <u>heart attacks</u>.
2) Eating too much salt could also increase the chance of getting <u>stomach cancer</u>, <u>osteoporosis</u> (weak bones) and <u>kidney failure</u>. None of which are good.

The Government Gives Out Information On Food

1) <u>Labels</u> on food often tell you <u>how much</u> salt there is in the food.
2) The labels can also tell you how much this is <u>compared</u> to the <u>maximum</u> you should eat each day.
3) The <u>Department of Health</u> and the <u>Department for Environment, Food and Rural Affairs</u> are both government departments.
4) As part of their job they:

> • Look at the health <u>risk</u> of chemicals in food to make sure they're <u>safe</u>.
> • Tell the public about how food affects their <u>health</u>.

5) Even though too much salt is unhealthy, food manufacturers may <u>still include</u> salt in their products.
6) This may be because it <u>costs</u> a lot to <u>change</u> the recipes.
7) Also, if the recipe is changed so there's <u>less salt</u>, the food may not <u>taste</u> as good or <u>last</u> as long. So <u>sales</u> of the product won't be as good.

Thanks for all your hard work — here's a bag of salt

Back in the olden days when they didn't have fridges, salt was a much more common way to stop food going off. It was also fairly expensive. At one point salt was so precious that we think people were <u>paid</u> in it. You learn something new every day — so make sure it also includes all the info on this page...

Chlorination

It's easy to take water for granted... turn on the tap, and there it is — nice clean water, thanks to <u>chlorination</u>.

Chlorine is Used in *Water Treatment*

1) In the UK, drinking water is treated to make it <u>safe</u>.

2) <u>Chlorine</u> is an important part of water treatment because:

- It <u>kills disease-causing microorganisms</u> like bacteria.
- It also stops <u>algae</u> growing and gets rid of <u>bad tastes</u> and <u>smells</u>.

3) Adding chlorine to water is called <u>chlorination</u>.

4) Since chlorination was started <u>public health</u> has improved a <u>huge amount</u>.

5) This is because chlorination helps provide <u>clean water</u> for everyone to <u>drink</u>.

Chlorine Can be *Made* from *Hydrogen Chloride*

1) Chlorine is found in compounds such as <u>salt</u> (sodium chloride) and <u>hydrogen chloride</u> (HCl).

2) But it has to be <u>separated</u> out of these compounds before it can be used to treat drinking water.

3) This is because the properties of <u>compounds</u> are <u>different</u> from the properties of the <u>elements</u> that they're made of.

4) So <u>chlorine</u> will kill microorganisms in water, but compounds that <u>contain chlorine</u> may not.

5) In fact, adding sodium chloride to water will give you nothing more than salty water — not ideal for drinking.

6) Chlorine can be made by <u>electrolysing brine</u> (see p.123).

7) It can also be made from the reaction between <u>hydrogen chloride</u> and <u>oxygen</u>. This is an <u>oxidation</u> reaction.

A compound is a substance that's made up of <u>more than one</u> element (see p.89).
E.g. hydrogen chloride is a compound that is made up of the elements hydrogen and chlorine.

There are **Disadvantages** to Chlorinating Water

Chlorination can cause <u>health problems</u>. For example:

- Water contains chemicals called <u>organic compounds</u>.
- These compounds can <u>react</u> with the chlorine to make chemicals that can cause cancer.
- But, the chance of this happening is <u>small</u>. And the <u>risks</u> caused by <u>not treating</u> the water are <u>really big</u> — thousands of people could fall ill and even die.

Chlorine means safe water to drink — but some people are worried

Chlorine is also used to make swimming pool water safer — it can lead to sore eyes, but a bit of stinging is a small price to pay for killing those disease-causing germs. As with most things in science, there are pros and cons. You have to weigh up all of the evidence and decide what's best to do.

Impacts of Chemical Production

Time to look at some bits about <u>making chemicals</u> — including the times when things <u>go wrong</u>...

Lots of Products Can be Made Using Chemistry

1) There are loads of different chemicals that are used to make lots of different things.

For example:

- chemicals are used in <u>industry</u>, e.g. <u>acids</u> and <u>alkalis</u>,

- chemicals are used in the <u>home</u>, e.g. <u>bleach</u>, <u>toiletries</u>,

- chemicals are used in <u>farming</u>, e.g. fertilisers,

- chemicals are used to make things like <u>plastics</u>, <u>metals</u> and <u>fuels</u>.

2) As there are so <u>many</u> chemicals, they <u>can't</u> all be <u>tested</u> as much as we'd like.

3) This means there's <u>not enough data</u> to tell if some chemicals are a risk to the environment or public health.

Plasticisers can Harm the Environment

See page 155 for more on plasticisers

1) PVC is a chemical that's made up of <u>carbon</u>, <u>hydrogen</u> and <u>chlorine</u>.

2) Chemicals called <u>plasticisers</u> are added to PVC to make it <u>heat</u> and <u>fire resistant</u>.

3) The plasticisers can <u>leach (leak) out</u> of the plastic and into <u>water ways</u>.

4) Plasticisers are <u>toxic</u>, and can <u>build up</u> in animals like fish and end up being eaten by humans (see next page).

Chemicals, chemicals, everything's made from chemicals...

No one's managed to convince a group of people to all drink a cup of shampoo to see how <u>harmful</u> it is. So even though they're usually ok, we don't always know the <u>full effects</u> chemicals will have.

Impacts of Chemical Production

When some chemicals get <u>into</u> the environment, the effects can <u>last</u> for <u>ages</u>.

*Some Chemicals **Stay** in the **Environment** for a **Long Time***

1) Toxic chemicals will stay in the environment if they're not <u>broken down</u>.

2) Chemicals that end up in <u>water ways</u> or are eaten by <u>animals</u> may be carried over <u>long distances</u>.

3) This means they can spread over a <u>large area</u> as the water and animals move from place to place.

4) They may also be passed along the <u>food chain</u> and cause harm to other animals and even <u>humans</u>.

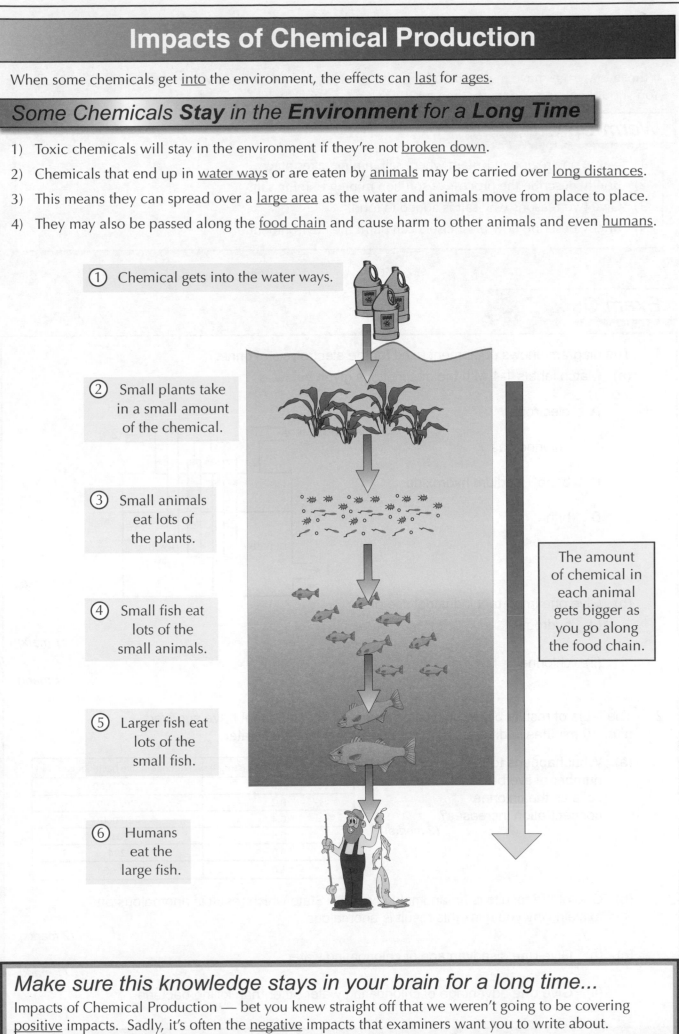

① Chemical gets into the water ways.

② Small plants take in a small amount of the chemical.

③ Small animals eat lots of the plants.

④ Small fish eat lots of the small animals.

⑤ Larger fish eat lots of the small fish.

⑥ Humans eat the large fish.

The amount of chemical in each animal gets bigger as you go along the food chain.

Make sure this knowledge stays in your brain for a long time...

Impacts of Chemical Production — bet you knew straight off that we weren't going to be covering <u>positive</u> impacts. Sadly, it's often the <u>negative</u> impacts that examiners want you to write about.

Warm-Up and Exam Questions

If those few pages have made you a bit chilly, then take a look at these warm-up questions.
You should be nice and toasty then for the exam questions below.

Warm-Up Questions

1) Name one region in Britain where salt mining takes place.
2) Briefly describe the process of solution mining to mine salt.
3) Give two reasons why salt is added to food.
4) Briefly describe how plasticisers can harm the environment.

Exam Questions

1 The diagram shows equipment used for the electrolysis of brine.
  (a) Match labels 1-4 with the descriptions given below.

      A electrode

      B chlorine gas

      C brine + sodium hydroxide

      D brine

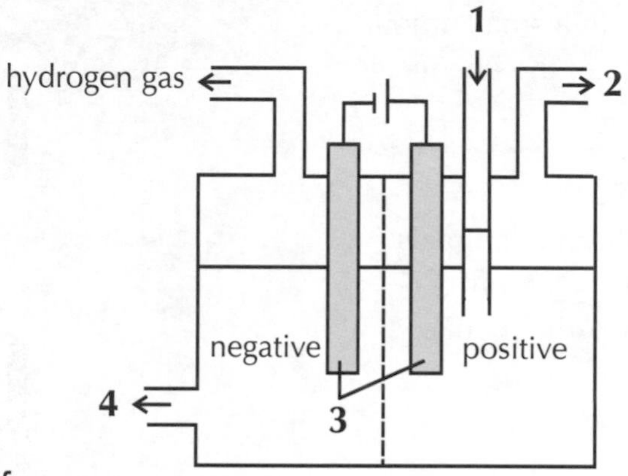

(4 marks)

  (b) Give one important industrial use of:
      (i) hydrogen

(1 mark)

      (ii) chlorine

(1 mark)

2 The table of results below shows the number of bacteria that have survived
  after 10 minutes in different concentrations of chlorinated water.

  (a) What happens to the
      number of live bacterial
      cells as the chlorine
      concentration increases?
      (2 marks)

Chlorine concentration (mg/l)	Number of live bacterial cells / l
0.0	2 010 000
0.2	207 000
0.4	20 000
0.6	2030
0.8	204
1.0	302 000

  (b) One of the results is an anomalous result. State which result is anomalous and
      explain why you think this result is anomalous.

(2 marks)

  (c) (i) Give **one** disadvantage of chlorinating water

(1 mark)

      (ii) Give **one** advantage of chlorinating water other than killing bacteria.

(1 mark)

Hazard Symbols

Look out for these symbols. So if you drink something <u>corrosive</u>, you can't say you weren't <u>warned</u>.

Watch Out For These Common *Hazard Symbols*

1) Lots of the chemicals you'll meet in Chemistry can be <u>dangerous</u> in some way.
2) The chemical containers will normally have <u>symbols</u> on them to tell you what the dangers are.

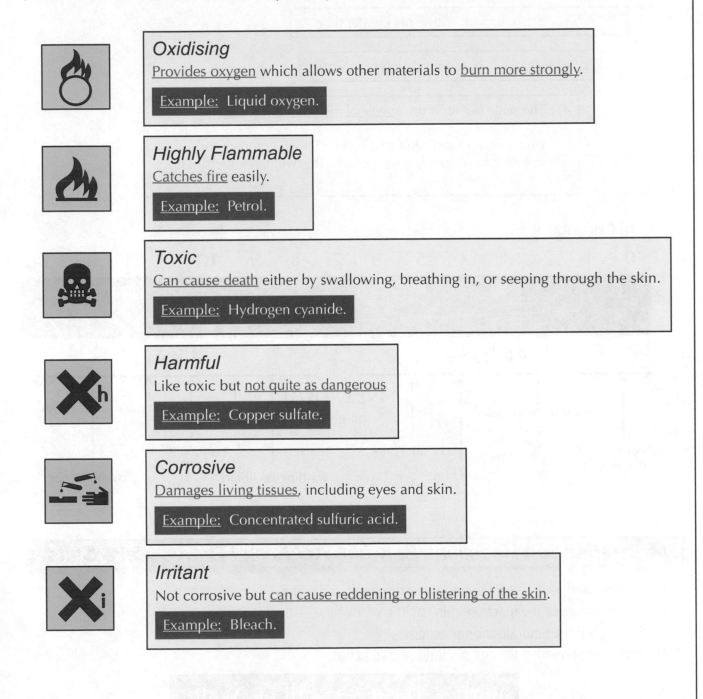

Oxidising
<u>Provides oxygen</u> which allows other materials to <u>burn more strongly</u>.

<u>Example:</u> Liquid oxygen.

Highly Flammable
<u>Catches fire</u> easily.

<u>Example:</u> Petrol.

Toxic
<u>Can cause death</u> either by swallowing, breathing in, or seeping through the skin.

<u>Example:</u> Hydrogen cyanide.

Harmful
Like toxic but <u>not quite as dangerous</u>

<u>Example:</u> Copper sulfate.

Corrosive
<u>Damages living tissues</u>, including eyes and skin.

<u>Example:</u> Concentrated sulfuric acid.

Irritant
Not corrosive but <u>can cause reddening or blistering of the skin</u>.

<u>Example:</u> Bleach.

If it's got a hazard symbol on it — use extreme caution...

Of course, just knowing that something might be hazardous isn't enough. You need to know what <u>kind</u> of hazard it is. You wouldn't need to worry much about bleach catching fire — but mixing petrol with liquid oxygen would be a very bad idea indeed. It'd probably be the last bad idea you ever had.

Acids and Bases

You've made it through most of the section. Now — your guide to the world of acids.

Substances can be *Acids*, *Bases* or *Neutral*

1) An <u>acid</u> is a substance with a pH <u>less</u> than 7.

2) A <u>base</u> is a substance with a pH <u>greater</u> than 7.

3) An <u>alkali</u> is a base that <u>dissolves in water</u>.

4) The scale below is the <u>universal indicator pH scale</u>.

Add a drop of indicator to a solution, then <u>compare</u> the colour it turns to the <u>colour chart</u>. This will tell you its pH.

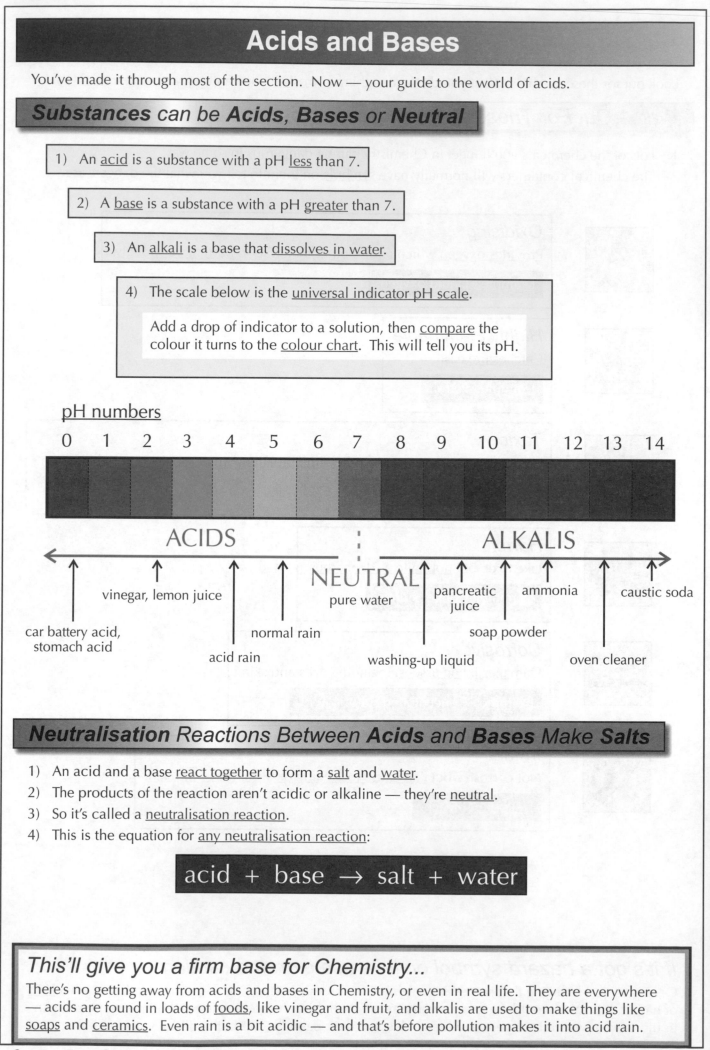

pH numbers

0 1 2 3 4 5 6 7 8 9 10 11 12 13 14

ACIDS   ALKALIS

NEUTRAL

vinegar, lemon juice   pure water   pancreatic juice   ammonia   caustic soda

car battery acid, stomach acid   normal rain   washing-up liquid   soap powder   oven cleaner

acid rain

Neutralisation Reactions Between *Acids* and *Bases* Make *Salts*

1) An acid and a base <u>react together</u> to form a <u>salt</u> and <u>water</u>.
2) The products of the reaction aren't acidic or alkaline — they're <u>neutral</u>.
3) So it's called a <u>neutralisation reaction</u>.
4) This is the equation for <u>any neutralisation reaction</u>:

$$\text{acid} + \text{base} \rightarrow \text{salt} + \text{water}$$

This'll give you a firm base for Chemistry...

There's no getting away from acids and bases in Chemistry, or even in real life. They are everywhere — acids are found in loads of <u>foods</u>, like vinegar and fruit, and alkalis are used to make things like <u>soaps</u> and <u>ceramics</u>. Even rain is a bit acidic — and that's before pollution makes it into acid rain.

Reactions of Acids

If you mix an <u>acid</u> and a <u>base</u>, exactly what you end up with depends on which acid and base you use...

Different **Acids** and **Bases** make Different **Salts**

1) Metal <u>oxides</u> and metal <u>hydroxides</u> are <u>bases</u>.
2) This means that they will <u>neutralise acids</u>.
3) So, all <u>metal oxides</u> and <u>metal hydroxides</u> will <u>react with acids</u> to form a <u>salt</u> and <u>water</u>.
4) The actual salt made depends on what <u>acid</u> is used and what <u>metal</u> is in the base.
5) If you have to <u>name</u> the <u>salt</u> that's produced, the clue is in the names of the acid and the base...

1) <u>HYDROCHLORIC ACID</u> — always produces <u>CHLORIDE SALTS</u>

Hydrochloric acid	+	Copper oxide	→	<u>Copper chloride</u> + water
Hydrochloric acid	+	Sodium hydroxide	→	<u>Sodium chloride</u> + water

2) <u>SULFURIC ACID</u> — always produces <u>SULFATE SALTS</u>

Sulfuric acid	+	Zinc oxide	→	<u>Zinc sulfate</u> + water
Sulfuric acid	+	Potassium hydroxide	→	<u>Potassium sulfate</u> + water

Metal **Carbonates** will also Neutralise Acids

1) These are very like the reactions above — they just produce <u>carbon dioxide</u> as well.
2) So when an acid reacts with a carbonate you get a <u>salt</u> and <u>water</u> and <u>carbon dioxide</u>.
3) The <u>salt produced</u> follows the same pattern as above
   — it depends on the <u>acid</u> used and the <u>metal</u> in the base.

Hydrochloric acid + Sodium carbonate	→	<u>Sodium chloride</u> + water + carbon dioxide
Sulfuric acid + Calcium carbonate	→	<u>Calcium sulfate</u> + water + carbon dioxide

Acid + Revision → Zzzzzzzz...

Make sure you understand how all these salts are <u>named</u>. Try writing down <u>different combinations</u> of acids and bases, and acids and carbonates. Then write down the salt produced by each neutralisation.

The Evolution of the Atmosphere

For 200 million years or so, the atmosphere has been about how it is now: about <u>80% nitrogen</u>, <u>20% oxygen</u>, and <u>small amounts</u> of <u>other gases</u> (mainly carbon dioxide, noble gases and water vapour). But it wasn't always like this. Here's one idea of how the past 4.5 billion years may have gone:

Phase 1 — *Volcanoes* Gave Out *Gases*

1) For ages the Earth's surface was molten. It was <u>so hot</u> that any atmosphere just '<u>boiled away</u>' into space.

2) Eventually things cooled down a bit and a <u>thin crust</u> formed, but <u>volcanoes</u> kept erupting.

3) The volcanoes gave out lots of gas — including <u>carbon dioxide</u>, <u>water vapour</u>, <u>methane</u> and <u>ammonia</u>.

4) These gases formed the early atmosphere. It was <u>mostly carbon dioxide</u>, with almost <u>no oxygen</u>. So, it was like the atmospheres of Mars and Venus today.

5) The <u>oceans</u> formed when the water vapour <u>condensed</u>.
   Condensed means it's changed from a gas into a liquid.

<u>Holiday report</u>: Not a nice place to be. Take strong walking boots and a good coat.

Phase 2 — *Green Plants* Evolved and Produced *Oxygen*

<u>Holiday report</u>: A bit slimy underfoot. Take wellies and a lot of suncream.

1) <u>Green plants</u> and <u>algae</u> grew over most of the Earth. They were happy in the <u>carbon dioxide atmosphere</u>.

2) A lot of the early carbon dioxide <u>dissolved</u> into the oceans. The <u>green plants</u> and <u>algae</u> also absorbed some of the <u>carbon dioxide</u> and <u>produced oxygen</u> by <u>photosynthesis</u>.

3) Plants and algae died and were buried under layers of <u>sediment</u> (bits of plant waste and gravel) along with the skeletons and shells of sea creatures. The <u>carbon</u> inside them became 'locked up' in <u>sedimentary rocks</u> as <u>carbonates</u> and <u>fossil fuels</u>.

4) When we <u>burn</u> fossil fuels, this 'locked up' carbon is released into the atmosphere as <u>carbon dioxide</u>.

The *Increasing Carbon Dioxide* Level Affects the *Climate* and *Oceans*

1) <u>Burning</u> fossil fuels releases carbon dioxide, and we're burning <u>more and more</u> of them...

2) ... so the carbon dioxide level is <u>increasing</u>. This is thought to be <u>changing</u> our planet.

> 1) An increase in carbon dioxide is causing <u>global warming</u> — a type of <u>climate change</u> (see page 149).
>
> 2) The oceans <u>absorb</u> carbon dioxide from the atmosphere. But the extra carbon dioxide we're releasing is making them too <u>acidic</u>. This is bad news for <u>coral</u> and <u>shellfish</u>. Also, in future, the oceans won't be able to absorb <u>any more</u> carbon dioxide.

Warm-Up and Exam Questions

Time to see just how much of that hazardous material you've managed to take in.
Here are a few warm-up questions before you get stuck into some exam questions.

Warm-Up Questions

1) What is the meaning of the hazard symbol shown on the right?
2) What name is given to the type of reaction in which
   an acid reacts with a base?
3) Which two substances are formed when sulfuric acid reacts with copper oxide?
4) Where did the gases that made up the early atmosphere come from?

Exam Questions

1   The table shows the results when three solutions,
    A-C, were tested with universal indicator.

    (a) Complete the table.

    (2 marks)

Solution	Colour	pH
A		1
B	pale green	
C	dark blue	

    (b) Which solution (A-C) is an acid?

    (1 mark)

    (c) Which solution (A-C) is an alkali?

    (1 mark)

    (d) Which solution (A-C) is salt in water?

    (1 mark)

2   Metal oxides and metal hydroxides are bases. They react with acids.
    (a) What are bases that dissolve in water called?

    (1 mark)

    (b) Complete the word equation given below for the reaction
         of a metal oxide with an acid.

         magnesium oxide + hydrochloric acid → .... + ...

    (2 marks)

    (c) Acids also react with carbonates.   Complete the word equation given below
         for the production of copper chloride from copper carbonate.

         .... + copper carbonate →

                         copper chloride + ... + ...

    (3 marks)

Exam Questions

3 The table below gives information about the Earth's atmosphere as it might have been millions of years ago, and how it is today.

Gas	Percentage composition of the atmosphere (%)	
	4500 million years ago	Today
carbon dioxide	78	0.04
X	3	77.2
Y	small amounts	20.7
argon	small amounts	0.9
sulfur dioxide	7	small amounts
water vapour	11	1
other gases	1	small amounts

(a) Use information from the table to help you answer the questions below.

(i) What is the name of gas **X**?

(1 mark)

(ii) What is the name of gas **Y**?

(1 mark)

(iii) What was the most common gas in the Earth's atmosphere 4500 million years ago?

(1 mark)

(iv) One gas is less common today than it was millions of years ago because it condensed and formed the oceans. Which gas is this?

(1 mark)

(b) Match the words for **A**, **B**, **C** and **D** with the numbers **1 - 4** in the sentences below.

A photosynthesis
B oxygen
C carbon
D carbon dioxide

Once green plants had evolved, they thrived in an atmosphere rich in ...**1**....
These plants produced ...**2**... by the process of ...**3**....
...**4**... from dead plants eventually became 'locked up' in fossil fuels.

(4 marks)

(c) Carbon dioxide is produced today by human activity.
Some of it dissolves in the oceans. Describe how this affects the oceans.

(2 marks)

Revision Summary for Section 5

There wasn't anything too bad in this section. A few bits were even quite interesting I reckon. But you've got to make sure the facts are all firmly fixed in your brain and that you really understand it all. These questions will let you see what you know and what you don't. If you get stuck on any, you need to look at that stuff again. Keep going till you can do them all without coming up for air.

1) What can be found beneath the Earth's crust?

2) A scientist places a very heavy marker on the seabed in the middle of the Atlantic ocean. She records the marker's position over a period of four years. The scientist finds that the marker moves in a straight line away from its original position. Her measurements are shown in the graph on the right.
   a) What process has caused the marker to move?
   b)* How many years did it take for the marker to move 7 cm?

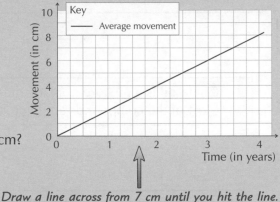

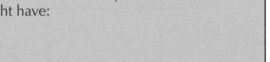

Draw a line across from 7 cm until you hit the line. Then draw a line down and read off the time where your line hits the bottom of the graph.

3) Give one reason why Wegener's theory of continental drift wasn't accepted for a long time.

4) What type of rock is chalk?

5) What type of rock is marble?

6) What products are produced when calcium carbonate reacts with an acid?

7) Name one thing calcium hydroxide is used for.

8) Name three building materials made from limestone.

9) Plans to develop a limestone quarry and a cement factory on some hills next to your town are announced. Describe the opinions that the following might have:
   a) dog owners
   b) the owner of a cafe

10) Give a use of sodium hydroxide.

11) Give two health problems that can be caused by eating too much salt.

12) Why is chlorine added to water supplies?

13) State two ways of making chlorine.

14) What can happen when long-lasting toxic chemicals get into rivers?

15) Give the meaning of this symbol: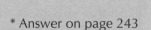

16) What do you get when you react an acid with a metal oxide?

17) Write a word equation for the reaction of hydrochloric acid with sodium carbonate.

18) Name the two main gases that make up the Earth's atmosphere today.

19) How did the oceans form?

* Answer on page 243

Fractional Distillation of Crude Oil

Crude oil is formed over millions of years from buried remains of plants and animals — it's a fossil fuel.

Crude Oil is a Mixture of Hydrocarbons

1) A mixture consists of two (or more) elements or compounds that aren't chemically bonded to each other.

2) Crude oil is a mixture of many different compounds. Most of the compounds are hydrocarbon molecules.

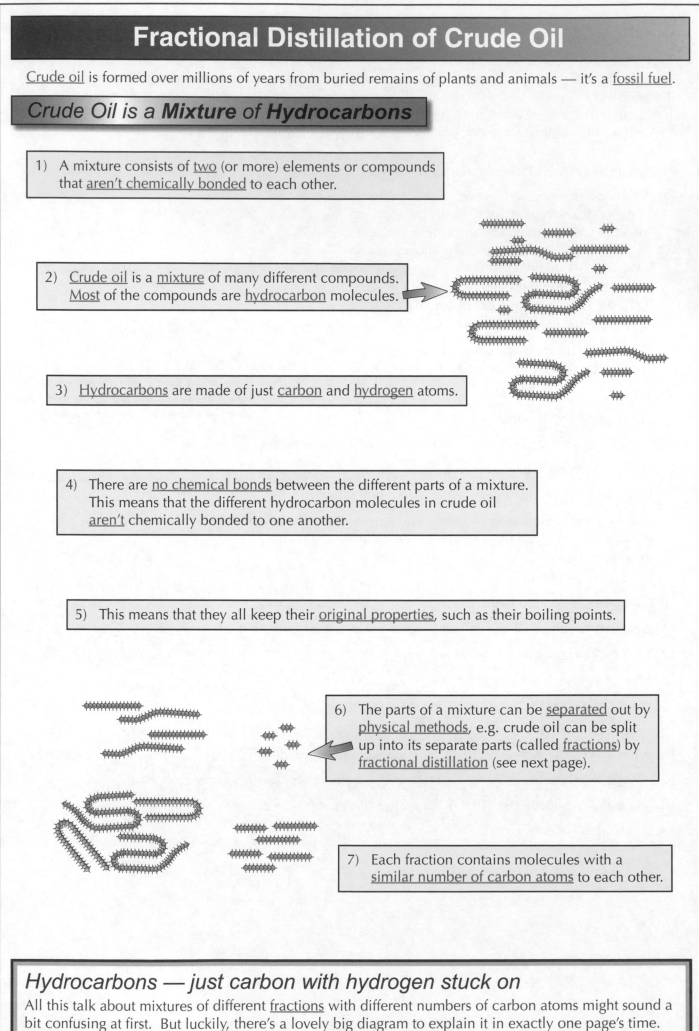

3) Hydrocarbons are made of just carbon and hydrogen atoms.

4) There are no chemical bonds between the different parts of a mixture. This means that the different hydrocarbon molecules in crude oil aren't chemically bonded to one another.

5) This means that they all keep their original properties, such as their boiling points.

6) The parts of a mixture can be separated out by physical methods, e.g. crude oil can be split up into its separate parts (called fractions) by fractional distillation (see next page).

7) Each fraction contains molecules with a similar number of carbon atoms to each other.

Hydrocarbons — just carbon with hydrogen stuck on

All this talk about mixtures of different fractions with different numbers of carbon atoms might sound a bit confusing at first. But luckily, there's a lovely big diagram to explain it in exactly one page's time.

Fractional Distillation of Crude Oil

Crude oil is not much use — it's a yucky mix of tar, oil, petrol and other stuff that needs to be separated.

Crude Oil is **Split** into **Separate Groups of Hydrocarbons**

1) The fractionating column works continuously (non-stop).
2) Heated crude oil is piped in at the bottom.
3) The oil evaporates (it forms a gas) and rises up the column.
4) The various fractions are constantly collected at the different levels where they condense (change from gas to liquid).

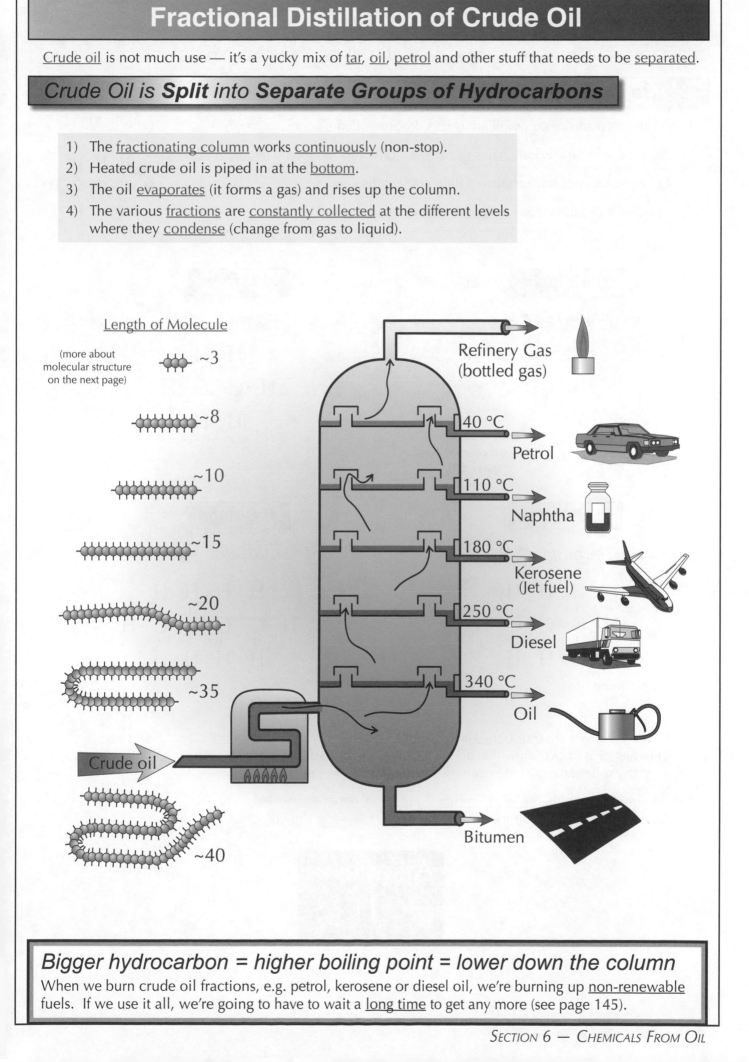

Length of Molecule

(more about molecular structure on the next page)

~3

~8

~10

~15

~20

~35

~40

Crude oil

Refinery Gas (bottled gas)

40 °C — Petrol

110 °C — Naphtha

180 °C — Kerosene (Jet fuel)

250 °C — Diesel

340 °C — Oil

Bitumen

Bigger hydrocarbon = higher boiling point = lower down the column

When we burn crude oil fractions, e.g. petrol, kerosene or diesel oil, we're burning up non-renewable fuels. If we use it all, we're going to have to wait a long time to get any more (see page 145).

Crude Oil and Alkanes

<u>Crude oil</u> is made up of different <u>alkane</u> molecules. This page is all about alkanes.

Crude Oil is Mostly Alkanes

1) All the fractions of crude oil are hydrocarbons called <u>alkanes</u>.

2) Alkanes are made up of <u>chains of carbon atoms</u> surrounded by <u>hydrogen atoms</u>.

3) Different alkanes have chains of different <u>lengths</u>.

4) The first four alkanes are <u>methane</u>, <u>ethane</u>, <u>propane</u> and <u>butane</u>.

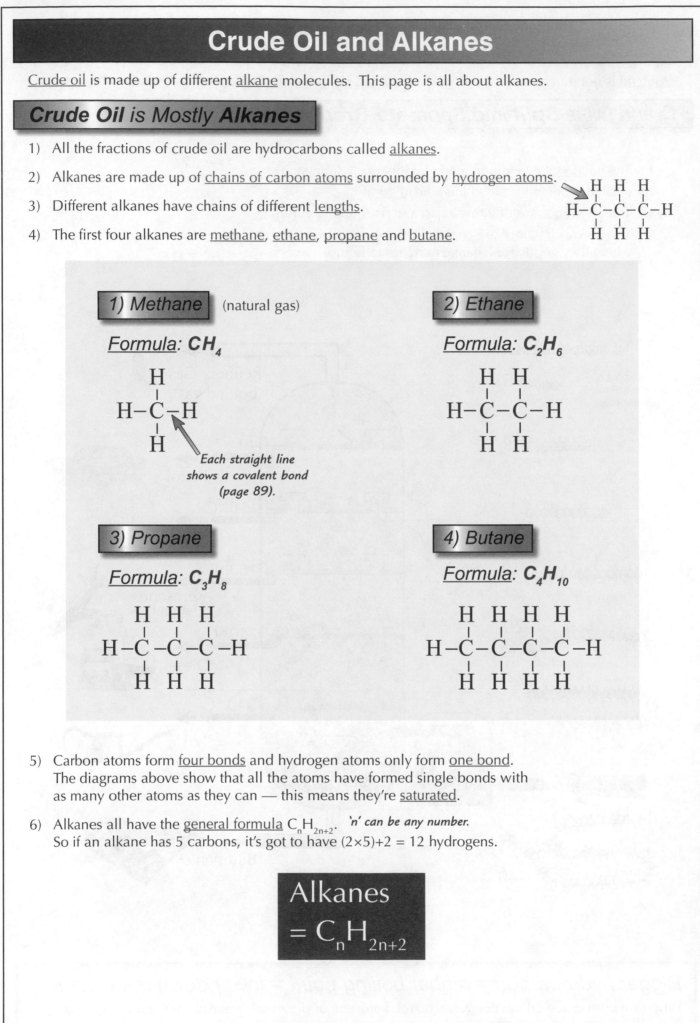

1) **Methane** (natural gas)

Formula: CH_4

Each straight line shows a covalent bond (page 89).

2) **Ethane**

Formula: C_2H_6

3) *Propane*

Formula: C_3H_8

4) *Butane*

Formula: C_4H_{10}

5) Carbon atoms form <u>four bonds</u> and hydrogen atoms only form <u>one bond</u>. The diagrams above show that all the atoms have formed single bonds with as many other atoms as they can — this means they're <u>saturated</u>.

6) Alkanes all have the <u>general formula</u> C_nH_{2n+2}. *'n' can be any number.*
So if an alkane has 5 carbons, it's got to have $(2\times5)+2 = 12$ hydrogens.

Alkanes
$= C_nH_{2n+2}$

Properties and Uses of Crude Oil

The <u>different fractions</u> of crude oil have <u>different properties</u>, and it's all down to their <u>structure</u>.

Learn *the Basic* Trends:

1) The <u>shorter</u> the molecules, the <u>less viscous</u> (gloopy) and <u>more runny</u> the hydrocarbon is.

2) The <u>shorter</u> the molecules, the <u>lower the boiling point</u> of the hydrocarbon — so they turn into a gas at a <u>lower temperature</u>.

3) Also, the <u>shorter</u> the molecules, the more <u>flammable</u> (easier to set on fire) the hydrocarbon is.

The *Uses* Of Hydrocarbons Depend on their *Properties*

1) The <u>boiling point</u> helps decide what the fraction is used for.

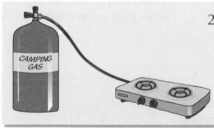

2) The <u>refinery gas fraction</u> has the shortest molecules, so it has the <u>lowest boiling point</u> — in fact it's a gas at room temperature. It's used as <u>bottled gas</u> (e.g. for camping stoves).

3) The <u>petrol</u> fraction has longer molecules, so it has a higher boiling point. Petrol is a <u>liquid</u> which is ideal for storing in the fuel tank of a car. It can flow to the engine where it's easily <u>vaporised</u> (turned to gas) to mix with the air before it is burnt.

Don't put bitumen into your petrol engine...

So <u>short-chain</u> hydrocarbons have a <u>lower boiling point</u> than <u>longer-chain</u> hydrocarbons. They're also <u>less viscous</u> and <u>easier to burn</u>. If you learn the properties of short-chain hydrocarbons, you should be able to work out the properties of longer-chain ones. These properties decide how they're used.

Cracking Crude Oil

After the distillation of crude oil (see pages 136-137), you've still got both <u>short</u> and <u>long</u> hydrocarbons. The only difference is that now they're not all mixed together.

Cracking Means *Splitting Up* Long-chain Hydrocarbons...

1) <u>Long-chain hydrocarbons</u> are <u>thick gloopy liquids</u> like <u>tar</u> which aren't very useful.

2) To make them more useful, they're <u>turned into smaller ones</u>.

3) This is called <u>cracking</u>.

4) Some of the products of cracking are useful as <u>fuels</u>, e.g. petrol for cars.

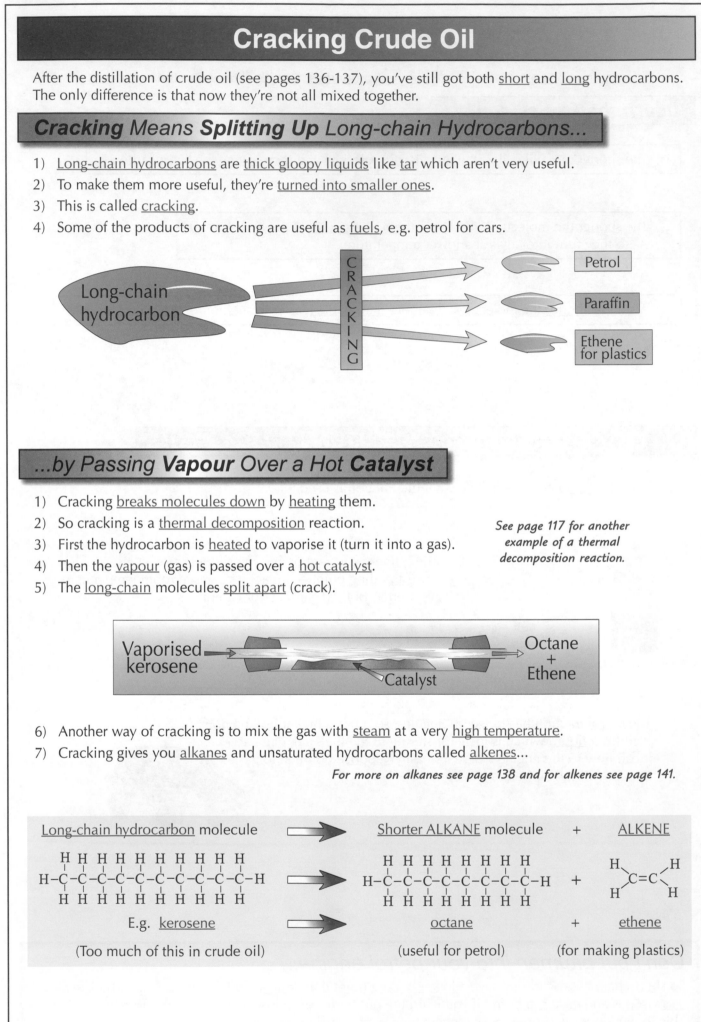

...by Passing *Vapour* Over a Hot *Catalyst*

1) Cracking <u>breaks molecules down</u> by <u>heating</u> them.

2) So cracking is a <u>thermal decomposition</u> reaction.

3) First the hydrocarbon is <u>heated</u> to vaporise it (turn it into a gas).

4) Then the <u>vapour</u> (gas) is passed over a <u>hot catalyst</u>.

5) The <u>long-chain</u> molecules <u>split apart</u> (crack).

See page 117 for another example of a thermal decomposition reaction.

6) Another way of cracking is to mix the gas with <u>steam</u> at a very <u>high temperature</u>.

7) Cracking gives you <u>alkanes</u> and unsaturated hydrocarbons called <u>alkenes</u>...

For more on alkanes see page 138 and for alkenes see page 141.

Alkenes

Alkenes are very useful. You can use them to make all sorts of stuff.

Alkenes Have a Carbon=Carbon Double Bond

1) Alkenes are hydrocarbons.
2) They have a double bond between two of the carbon atoms in their chain.
3) This means that they're unsaturated.
4) The first two alkenes are ethene (with two carbon atoms) and propene (three carbon atoms).
5) All alkenes have the general formula: C_nH_{2n}.
6) So the number after the H is always twice the number after the C.

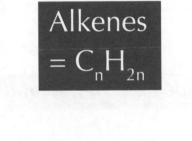

Alkenes = C_nH_{2n}

1) Ethene

Formula: C_2H_4

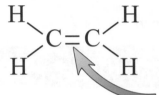

This is a double bond — so each carbon atom is still making four bonds.

2) Propene

Formula: C_3H_6

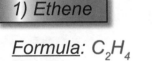

Carbon atoms always make four bonds, but hydrogen atoms only make one.

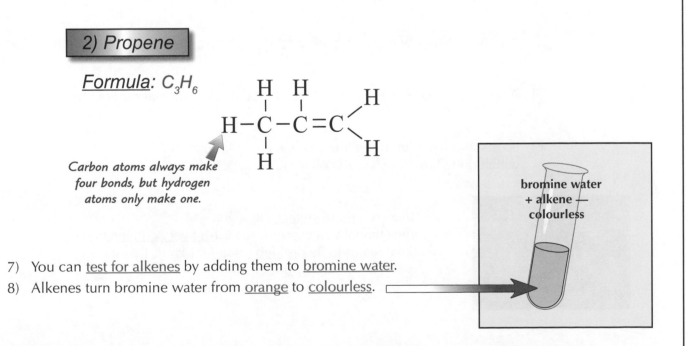

bromine water + alkene — colourless

7) You can test for alkenes by adding them to bromine water.
8) Alkenes turn bromine water from orange to colourless.

I never really liked the colour of bromine water anyway

Don't get alkenes confused with alkanes — that one letter makes all the difference. Alkenes have a C=C bond, alkanes don't. And remember — alkenes turn bromine water colourless and alkanes don't.

Alkenes and Ethanol

Ethene is a really useful alkene. You can use it to make ethanol. Ethanol is an alcohol — it's in whisky, beer and other alcoholic drinks. You can make ethanol either from ethene or from sugar.

Reacting Ethene With Steam Makes Ethanol

1) Ethene can be hydrated with steam to make ethanol.

2) This reaction needs a catalyst (a catalyst speeds up a reaction).

3) Ethene comes from crude oil, which is a non-renewable resource. So it will run out one day.

Ethanol Can Also Be Made from Renewable Resources

1) The alcohol in beer isn't made from ethene — it's made by fermentation.

2) Fermentation uses yeast to turn sugar into ethanol.

sugar → carbon dioxide + ethanol

3) This process needs a lower temperature and simpler equipment than using ethene.

4) Another advantage is that sugar is a renewable resource.

5) Also, sugar is grown as a major crop, including in many poorer countries.

6) So ethanol made from sugar is a cheap fuel in countries which don't have much crude oil for making petrol.

7) There are disadvantages though.
   The ethanol you get from sugar isn't very concentrated (strong).
   So, it needs to be distilled (as in whisky distilleries).
   It also needs to be purified.

Sugar can be made as fast as it's used up — it's renewable

Make sure you remember the differences between these two ways of making ethanol.
Try to learn the advantages and disadvantages of fermenting sugar instead of hydrating ethene.

Warm-Up and Exam Questions

Give these questions your best shot. If they show up areas where your knowledge isn't great, it's time to re-revise those pages so you can improve your confidence.

Warm-Up Questions

1) What does a mixture consist of?
2) Name the first three alkanes.
3) What sort of hydrocarbon molecules are cracked, and why are they cracked?
4) Are hydrocarbons heated or cooled to crack them?
5) What do alkenes have that alkanes don't?
6) When ethene is hydrated with steam, what substance is formed?

Exam Questions

1   Alkanes are made up of chains of carbon atoms surrounded by hydrogen atoms.

   (a)   Butane contains four carbon atoms. Give its molecular formula.

(1 mark)

   (b)   Draw the displayed formula of butane showing all of the bonds.

(1 mark)

   (c)   Suggest **two** ways that the properties of butane would be different from the properties of an alkane with twenty carbon atoms.

(2 marks)

2   Crude oil can be separated into a number of different compounds as shown in the diagram:

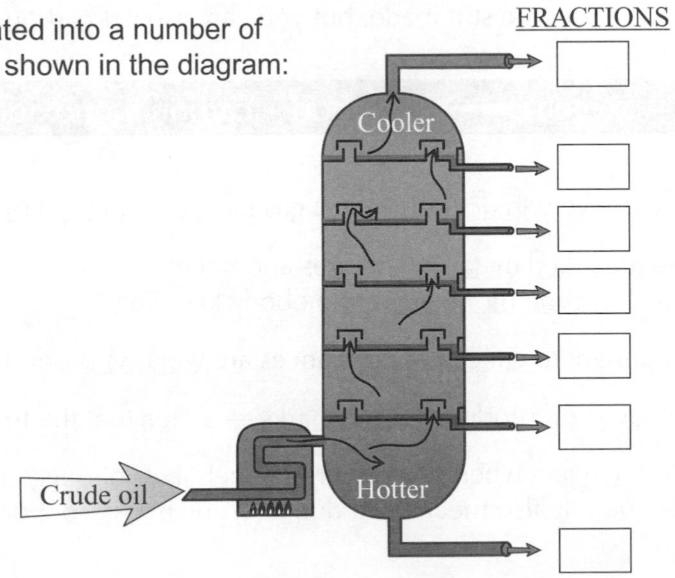

FRACTIONS

Cooler

Crude oil

Hotter

   (a)   (i)   Put an **M** in the box of the fraction with the longest hydrocarbon molecules.

(1 mark)

        (ii)   Put a **B** in the box of the fraction with the lowest boiling point.

(1 mark)

   (b)   Describe how the separation process works.

(3 marks)

Burning Fuels

We get loads of fuels from crude oil. And then we burn them.
But there's safe burning and there's dangerous burning...

Complete Combustion Happens When There's Plenty of Oxygen

1) When there's plenty of oxygen about, hydrocarbons burn to produce only carbon dioxide and water.

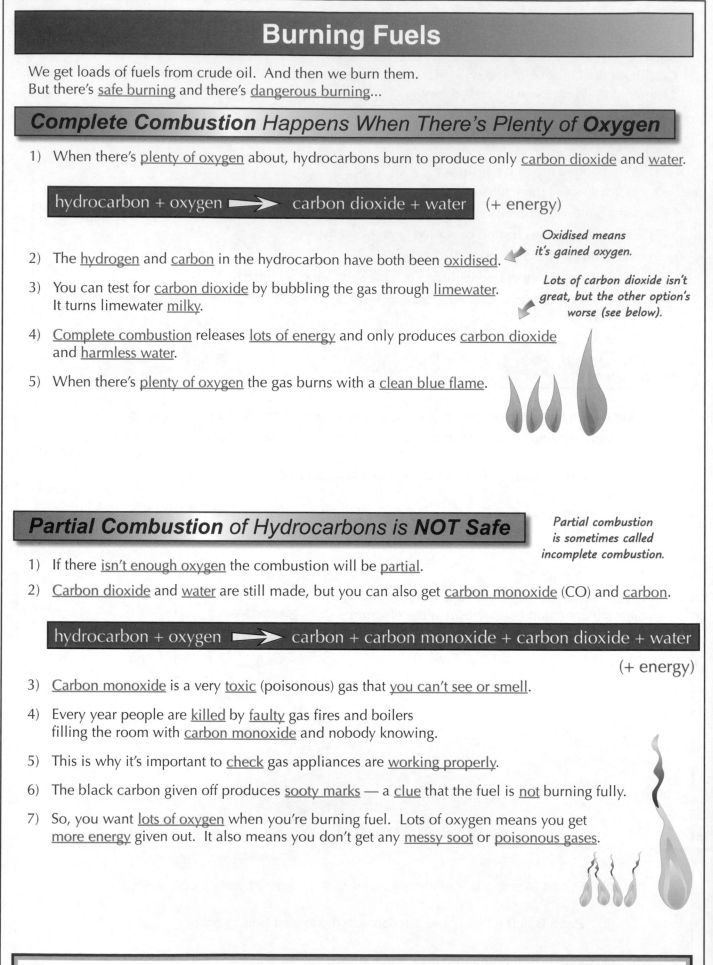

> hydrocarbon + oxygen ➡ carbon dioxide + water   (+ energy)

2) The hydrogen and carbon in the hydrocarbon have both been oxidised.

Oxidised means it's gained oxygen.

3) You can test for carbon dioxide by bubbling the gas through limewater. It turns limewater milky.

Lots of carbon dioxide isn't great, but the other option's worse (see below).

4) Complete combustion releases lots of energy and only produces carbon dioxide and harmless water.

5) When there's plenty of oxygen the gas burns with a clean blue flame.

Partial Combustion of Hydrocarbons is NOT Safe

Partial combustion is sometimes called incomplete combustion.

1) If there isn't enough oxygen the combustion will be partial.

2) Carbon dioxide and water are still made, but you can also get carbon monoxide (CO) and carbon.

> hydrocarbon + oxygen ➡ carbon + carbon monoxide + carbon dioxide + water

(+ energy)

3) Carbon monoxide is a very toxic (poisonous) gas that you can't see or smell.

4) Every year people are killed by faulty gas fires and boilers filling the room with carbon monoxide and nobody knowing.

5) This is why it's important to check gas appliances are working properly.

6) The black carbon given off produces sooty marks — a clue that the fuel is not burning fully.

7) So, you want lots of oxygen when you're burning fuel. Lots of oxygen means you get more energy given out. It also means you don't get any messy soot or poisonous gases.

Blue flame good, orange flame bad...

This is why people should get their gas fires and boilers serviced every year. Carbon monoxide really can kill people in their sleep — scary stuff. But don't let that scare you off learning this page.

Using Crude Oil as a Fuel

Nothing as <u>useful</u> as crude oil would be without its <u>problems</u>. No, that would be too good to be true.

There's a Lot to Consider When *Choosing* the *Best Fuel*

1) <u>How easily it burns</u>. Fuels like gas burn more easily than diesel.

2) The <u>amount</u> of <u>heat energy</u> it gives out.

3) <u>Ash and smoke</u> — some fuels, like coal, leave behind a lot of messy <u>ash</u>.

4) <u>Storage and transport</u> — gas needs to be stored in special <u>canisters</u>. Coal needs to be kept <u>dry</u>.
   Fuels need to be transported <u>carefully</u> as gas leaks and oil spills can be dangerous.

Crude Oil *Provides* *Important Fuels* for *Modern Life*

1) Crude oil fractions make good <u>fuels</u>. For example, they're use to fuel
   <u>cars</u>, <u>boats</u>, <u>central heating systems</u> in homes and <u>power stations</u>.

2) So, the extraction and use of crude oil is a <u>massive industry</u>.

3) Often, there are <u>alternatives</u> to using crude oil fractions as fuel.
   E.g. electricity can be generated by <u>nuclear</u> power or <u>wind</u> power, there
   are <u>ethanol</u>-powered cars, and <u>solar</u> energy can be used to heat water.

4) But things tend to be <u>set up</u> for using oil fractions. For example, cars are designed
   for <u>petrol or diesel</u> and it's <u>readily available</u>. So crude oil fractions are often the
   <u>easiest and cheapest</u> thing to use.

5) Crude oil fractions are often <u>more reliable</u> too — e.g. solar and wind power won't
   work without the right weather conditions.

But it Might **Run Out** One Day...

1) Most scientists think that oil will <u>run out</u> — it's a <u>non-renewable fuel</u>. It can't be made again.

2) But no one knows exactly when it'll run out.

3) <u>New oil reserves</u> are discovered from time to time and <u>technology</u> is constantly improving.
   So, it's now possible to extract oil that was once too <u>difficult</u> or <u>expensive</u> to extract.

4) Some people think we should <u>stop</u> using oil for things like transport <u>now</u>. This is because there
   are alternative fuels. They think the oil should be saved for things that it's <u>really</u> needed for,
   like making some medicines.

5) It will take time to <u>develop</u> alternative fuels that will meet all our energy needs (see page 150 for
   more info). It'll also take time to <u>adapt things</u> so that the fuels can be used on a wide scale.
   E.g. we might need different kinds of car engines, or special storage tanks built.

6) One alternative is to generate energy from <u>renewable</u> sources — these are sources that <u>won't
   run out</u>. Examples of renewable energy sources are <u>wind power</u>, <u>solar power</u> and <u>tidal power</u>.

7) So however long oil does last for, it's a good idea to start <u>saving</u> it and finding <u>alternatives</u> now.

Environmental Problems

We <u>burn fuels</u> all the time to release the energy stored inside them.

Crude Oil is **NOT** the **Environment's** Best Friend

1) <u>Oil spills</u> can happen as the oil is being transported by tanker.
   They are <u>really bad</u> for the local environment.
   <u>Birds</u> get covered in the stuff and are <u>poisoned</u> as they try to clean themselves.
   Other creatures, like <u>sea otters</u> and <u>whales</u>, are poisoned too.

2) You have to <u>burn oil</u> to release the energy from it.
   But burning oil is thought to be a major cause of <u>acid rain</u> (see p.147),
   <u>global warming</u> (see p.148-149) and <u>global dimming</u> (see below).

Burning Fossil Fuels Releases Gases and Particles

1) <u>Power stations</u> burn huge amounts of fossil fuels to make <u>electricity</u>.
   <u>Cars</u> also burn a lot of fossil fuels.

Pure hydrogen can also be used as a fuel (see page 150). It only produces water vapour when burnt.

2) When fuels are burnt, the carbon and hydrogen are oxidised
   to <u>carbon dioxide</u> and <u>water vapour</u> (see page 144).

3) If the fuel contains <u>sulfur</u> impurities, <u>sulfur dioxide</u> is released when the fuel is burnt.

4) Oxides of <u>nitrogen</u> will also form if the fuel burns at a <u>high temperature</u>.

5) Partial combustion releases <u>solid particles</u> (called particulates) of <u>soot</u> (carbon).
   <u>Unburnt fuel</u> and <u>carbon monoxide</u> (a poisonous gas) are also released (see page 144).

Particles Cause Global Dimming

1) Scientists have been measuring how much <u>sunlight</u> reaches the Earth's surface.

2) In some areas <u>a lot less</u> light has been reaching the surface
   — they have called this <u>global dimming</u>.

3) Scientists think that it's caused by <u>particles</u> of soot and ash that are produced
   when <u>fossil fuels</u> are burnt. These particles <u>reflect</u> sunlight back into space.

Revision and pollution — the two problems with modern life...

Eeee... <u>cars</u> and <u>fossil fuels</u> — they're nothing but trouble. But at least this topic is kind of interesting,
what with its relevance to <u>everyday life</u> and all. Just think... you could see this kind of stuff on TV.

Acid Rain

I sometimes wonder if anything could be worse than <u>rain</u>. The answer is yes — <u>acid rain</u> could.

Sulfur Dioxide Causes Acid Rain

1) <u>Sulfur dioxide</u> (SO_2) is one of the gases that causes acid rain.

2) When the <u>sulfur dioxide</u> mixes with <u>clouds</u> it forms dilute <u>sulfuric acid</u>. This then falls as <u>acid rain</u>.

3) <u>Oxides of nitrogen</u> also mix with clouds to form <u>dilute nitric acid</u>. This fall as <u>acid rain</u> too.

4) <u>Acid rain</u> causes <u>lakes</u> to become <u>acidic</u>. This means that many plants and animals <u>die</u>.

5) Acid rain kills <u>trees</u> and damages <u>limestone buildings</u> and ruins <u>stone statues</u>. It's shocking.

You can Reduce Acid Rain by Reducing Sulfur Emissions

1) Most of the sulfur can be <u>removed</u> from fuels <u>before</u> they're burnt.

2) Petrol and diesel are starting to be replaced by <u>low-sulfur</u> versions.

3) <u>Power stations</u> now have <u>Acid Gas Scrubbers</u> to take the sulfur dioxide <u>out</u> of the waste gases before they're released into the atmosphere.

4) The other way of reducing acid rain is simply to <u>reduce</u> our usage of <u>fossil fuels</u>.

Acid rain — bad for the trees

But good for you, because acid rain might get you some <u>nice easy marks</u> in the exam.
Make sure you remember the names of the <u>gases</u> that <u>cause</u> acid rain, and where they <u>come from</u>.

Carbon Dioxide and Human Activity

From driving around in cars to chopping down trees, we're messing with the natural carbon dioxide level.

Carbon Dioxide Keeps the Earth Warm

1) Gases in the atmosphere like carbon dioxide, methane and water vapour help to keep the Earth warm.

2) These gases trap most of the heat that would normally escape out into space, and send it back to the Earth.

Energy from the Sun

CO_2 and Methane

Heat trapped by gases

There's more on this topic on pages 217-218

Human Activity Affects the Carbon Dioxide Level

The amount of carbon dioxide in the atmosphere is increasing because of human activity.

1) People are cutting down large areas of forest.
This increases the level of carbon dioxide in the atmosphere because living trees use carbon dioxide for photosynthesis.
So removing these trees means less carbon dioxide is removed from the atmosphere.

2) Burning fossil fuels is another way humans are releasing carbon dioxide into the atmosphere.

Carbon Dioxide and Human Activity

Carbon dioxide helps keep us <u>warm</u>. Making <u>more</u> carbon dioxide makes us <u>warmer</u>.

Increasing Carbon Dioxide Causes Climate Change

1) The extra carbon dioxide produced by human activity has caused the average <u>temperature</u> of the Earth to <u>increase</u>.

2) This is known as <u>global warming</u>.

3) Global warming is a type of <u>climate change</u> and causes other types of climate change, e.g. changing rainfall patterns. It could also cause severe <u>flooding</u> due to the polar ice caps melting.

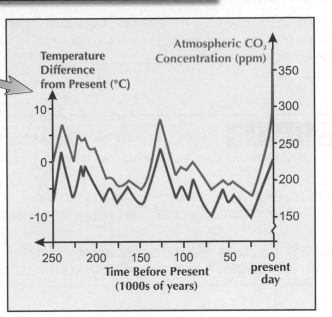

We Could Remove Carbon Dioxide from the Air

There are a couple of ways we could do this:

Iron Seeding

1) <u>Iron</u> is needed by plants for <u>photosynthesis</u>. Adding it to the ocean makes more plants called <u>phytoplankton</u> grow there.

2) These plants <u>absorb</u> carbon dioxide to use for <u>photosynthesis</u>. This could help to remove some of the extra carbon dioxide.

Photosynthesis is the way plants make their food.

3) The problem is that we can't control what plants grow and some are <u>poisonous</u>.

Converting Carbon Dioxide into Hydrocarbons

1) Scientists are looking into the idea of <u>changing</u> carbon dioxide into <u>hydrocarbons</u>.

2) This could be done using a <u>high temperature</u> and <u>pressure</u>.

3) This would <u>remove</u> some of the extra carbon dioxide. But you need energy to do this. So, it'd have to be '<u>green</u>' energy (e.g. wind power) and not just more fossil fuels.

It's a threat to the Earth as we know it...

The possible effects of global warming are <u>pretty scary</u>. What we really need are some extra-clever scientists with some amazing planet-saving ideas... Well what do you know. As well as the ones on this page, there's a whole page of ideas I prepared earlier coming up right about... Now.

Alternative Fuels

It's not all doom and gloom... There are more ways we can help to <u>reduce</u> our carbon dioxide emissions.

Alternative Fuels are Being Developed

Some <u>alternative fuels</u> have already been developed.
Many of them are <u>renewable</u> fuels so, unlike fossil fuels, they won't run out.
However, they all have <u>pros and cons</u>. For example:

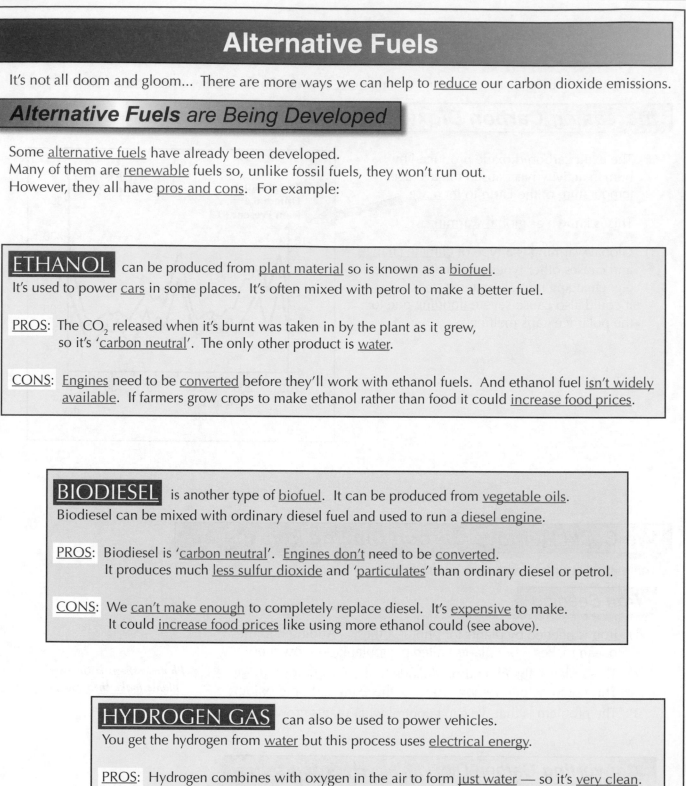

ETHANOL can be produced from <u>plant material</u> so is known as a <u>biofuel</u>.
It's used to power <u>cars</u> in some places. It's often mixed with petrol to make a better fuel.

<u>PROS</u>: The CO_2 released when it's burnt was taken in by the plant as it grew,
so it's '<u>carbon neutral</u>'. The only other product is <u>water</u>.

<u>CONS</u>: <u>Engines</u> need to be <u>converted</u> before they'll work with ethanol fuels. And ethanol fuel <u>isn't widely available</u>. If farmers grow crops to make ethanol rather than food it could <u>increase food prices</u>.

BIODIESEL is another type of <u>biofuel</u>. It can be produced from <u>vegetable oils</u>.
Biodiesel can be mixed with ordinary diesel fuel and used to run a <u>diesel engine</u>.

<u>PROS</u>: Biodiesel is '<u>carbon neutral</u>'. <u>Engines don't</u> need to be <u>converted</u>.
It produces much <u>less sulfur dioxide</u> and '<u>particulates</u>' than ordinary diesel or petrol.

<u>CONS</u>: We <u>can't make enough</u> to completely replace diesel. It's <u>expensive</u> to make.
It could <u>increase food prices</u> like using more ethanol could (see above).

HYDROGEN GAS can also be used to power vehicles.
You get the hydrogen from <u>water</u> but this process uses <u>electrical energy</u>.

<u>PROS</u>: Hydrogen combines with oxygen in the air to form <u>just water</u> — so it's <u>very clean</u>.

<u>CONS</u>: You need a <u>special, expensive engine</u>. Hydrogen <u>isn't widely available</u>. You still need to use <u>energy</u> from <u>another source</u> to make it. Also, hydrogen's hard to <u>store</u>.

Library books — renewable but not very good as a fuel...

<u>Alternative fuels</u> are the shining light at the end of a long tunnel of problems caused by burning fuels (and I mean long). But <u>nothing's perfect</u>, so get learning those <u>disadvantages</u>...

Warm-Up and Exam Questions

Have a go at these questions. If there are any that you really struggle with... well, you know what to do — have a look back at the section then have another go.

Warm-Up Questions

1) What kind of combustion occurs when there's plenty of oxygen?
2) Explain why using crude oil fractions to generate electricity is more reliable than using solar or wind power.
3) How do gases like carbon dioxide and methane help to keep the earth warm?
4) Describe how iron seeding removes CO_2 from the atmosphere.

Exam Questions

1   When fossil fuels like petrol are burnt, they produce carbon dioxide, sulfur dioxide and particulate matter.
   (a)   Name the atmospheric environmental problem caused by increased levels of carbon dioxide.
(1 mark)

   (b)   (i)   Describe how acid rain is formed.
(3 marks)

         (ii)   Give **one** effect of acid rain.
(1 mark)

   (c)   One advantage of burning ethanol is that it produces no sulfur.
Give **two** disadvantages of using ethanol as a fuel compared to petrol.
(2 marks)

2   Scientists are developing 'fuels for the future'. One example could be hydrogen.
   (a)   Give **one** advantage of using hydrogen as a fuel.
(1 mark)

   (b)   Give **two** disadvantages of using hydrogen as a fuel in a car compared with using petrol or diesel.
(2 marks)

   (c)   Scientists are also looking into making hydrocarbons from carbon dioxide.
This could be used to remove carbon dioxide from the air.
Circle the correct answers to complete the following sentences about this process.

It would need a [high / low] temperature and pressure.

It would **not** reduce the amount of carbon dioxide in the air if the energy for the process came from [wind power / fossil fuels] .
(2 marks)

Exam Questions

3   Some environmental problems are caused by human activities.
   (a) Complete the sentences below by circling the correct letter (A-D).

   (i) Global warming happens when:
        A   more of the Sun's heat is reflected into space than is absorbed by the Earth.
        B   oceans absorb more and more CO_2.
        C   there is more CO_2 and methane in the atmosphere.
        D   we use a greater proportion of renewable energy sources.

        (1 mark)

   (ii) Global dimming may be caused by:
        A   too much methane in the atmosphere.
        B   soot particles from burning fossil fuels, which reflect sunlight back into space.
        C CO_2 particles from burning fossil fuels, which reflect sunlight back into space.
        D   the absorption of infrared radiation by CO_2.

        (1 mark)

   (b) The graph below shows how the percentage of carbon dioxide in the atmosphere (% CO_2)
        changed over the last 300 years.
        Use the information on the graph to answer the following questions.

   (i) What was the % CO_2
        in 1700?
        (1 mark)

   (ii) In what year did the % CO_2
        reach 0.029%?
        (1 mark)

   (iii) Describe what happened to
        the % CO_2 after this year.
        (1 mark)

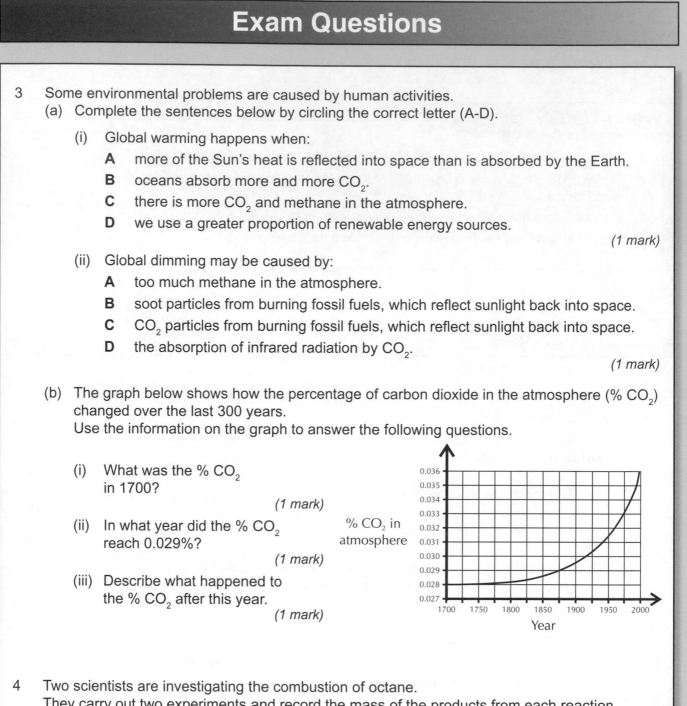

% CO_2 in atmosphere

Year

4   Two scientists are investigating the combustion of octane.
     They carry out two experiments and record the mass of the products from each reaction.
     Their results are shown in the table below.

Product	Experiment 1 (mass in grams)	Experiment 2 (mass in grams)
carbon	4.2	0
carbon monoxide	189.0	0
carbon dioxide	462.0	774.4
water	356.4	356.4
total	1011.6	

   (a) Calculate the total mass of products produced in experiment 2.

        (1 mark)

   (b) Using the results of the experiments, state what kind of combustion
        is occurring in each experiment and explain your answer.

        (4 marks)

   (c) Write the word equation for the reaction shown in experiment 1.

        (1 mark)

Using Alkenes to Make Polymers

Polymers really are pretty useful things... But before you get stuck into the exciting world of <u>polymers</u>, it'll be a good idea to take a look back at page 141 and brush up on your <u>alkenes</u>.

Alkenes Can Be Used to Make Polymers

1) Probably the most useful thing you can do with alkenes (see page 141) is <u>polymerisation</u>.

2) This means joining together lots of <u>small alkene molecules</u> (<u>monomers</u>) to form <u>very large molecules</u> (<u>polymers</u>).

3) For example, many <u>ethene</u> molecules can be joined up to produce <u>poly(ethene)</u>.

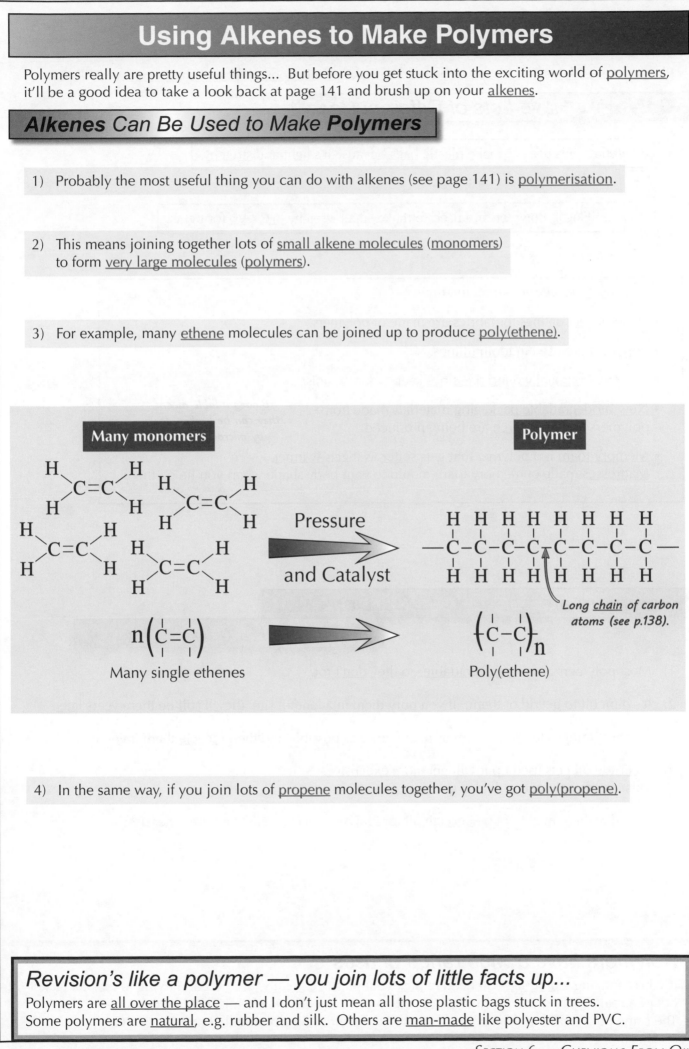

Many monomers

Polymer

Pressure and Catalyst

Long *chain* of carbon atoms (see p.138).

Many single ethenes

Poly(ethene)

4) In the same way, if you join lots of <u>propene</u> molecules together, you've got <u>poly(propene)</u>.

Revision's like a polymer — you join lots of little facts up...

Polymers are <u>all over the place</u> — and I don't just mean all those plastic bags stuck in trees. Some polymers are <u>natural</u>, e.g. rubber and silk. Others are <u>man-made</u> like polyester and PVC.

Uses of Polymers

Plastics are <u>really useful</u>. They can be used to make <u>novelty football pencil sharpeners</u> and all sorts.

Polymers Have Lots of Different Uses

1) Poly(ethene) is used to make <u>plastic bags</u> because it's <u>light</u> and <u>stretchy</u>.

2) <u>Elastic</u> polymers are used to make super-stretchy <u>LYCRA</u>® for tights.

3) <u>New uses</u> are developed all the time:

- <u>Waterproof</u> coatings for fabrics are made of polymers.

- <u>Polymers</u> are used in <u>tooth fillings</u>.

- Polymer <u>hydrogel wound dressings</u> keep wounds moist.

- <u>New biodegradable packaging</u> materials made from polymers and <u>cornstarch</u> are being produced.

  Biodegradable means they can be broken down by microorganisms.

- <u>Memory foam</u> is a polymer that gets <u>softer</u> as it gets <u>warmer</u>. <u>Mattresses</u> made of memory foam mould to your body shape when you lie on them.

Polymers are Cheap, but Most Don't Rot
— They're Hard to Get Rid Of

1) Most polymers aren't <u>biodegradable</u>, so they <u>don't rot</u>.

2) It's difficult to get rid of them. If you bury them in a landfill site, they'll <u>still</u> be there <u>years later</u>.

3) The best thing is to <u>re-use</u> them as many times as possible and then <u>recycle</u> them if you can.

4) As <u>crude oil</u> gets <u>used up</u> it will get more <u>expensive</u>. This means polymers will also get <u>more expensive</u>.

5) One day there might not be <u>enough</u> oil for fuel AND plastics AND all the other uses.

Polymers have a wide range of uses

If you're making a <u>product</u>, you need to <u>pick</u> your plastic <u>carefully</u>. It's no good trying to make a jacket out of a really stiff polymer — imagine trying to walk any distance in a jacket like that. The same goes for things like kettles — there's no point using a plastic that melts at 50 °C.

Structure and Properties of Polymers

This lovely page explains how the <u>properties</u> of a polymer are affected by the <u>way it's made</u>.

A Polymer's **Properties** Decide its **Uses**

Its **Properties** Depend on How the Molecules are **Arranged**...

1) A polymer's properties don't just depend on the <u>chemicals</u> it's made from.

2) They also depend on how the molecules are <u>arranged</u> and <u>held together</u>.

> If the polymer chains are packed <u>close together</u>, the material will have a <u>**high density**</u>.
> If the polymer chains are <u>spread out</u>, the material will have a <u>low density</u>.

Density is how much stuff there is in a certain volume.

...And How They're **Held Together**

The <u>forces</u> between the different chains of the polymer <u>hold it together</u>.

1) <u>Chains</u> held together by <u>weak forces</u> are free to <u>slide</u> over each other.

2) This means the polymer can be <u>stretched easily</u>, and will have a <u>low melting point</u>.

3) Chains held together with <u>stronger bonds</u> between the polymer chains can't slide over each other.

4) These polymers have <u>higher melting points</u> and <u>can't be easily stretched</u>.

5) So, the <u>stronger</u> the bonds or forces between the polymer chains, the more <u>energy</u> is needed to break them apart, and the <u>higher</u> the <u>melting point</u>.

polymer chain

polymer chain   bond

Polymers Can be **Changed** to Give Them **Different Properties**

You can <u>alter</u> polymers to change their <u>properties</u>.

1) Polymers can be changed to <u>increase</u> their <u>chain length</u>.
   - Polymers with <u>short</u> chains are <u>easy</u> to shape and have <u>lower</u> melting points.
   - <u>Longer</u> chain polymers are <u>stiffer</u> and have <u>higher</u> melting points.

2) Polymers can be made stronger by adding <u>cross-linking agents</u>.
   - These agents <u>bond</u> the chains together, making the polymer <u>stiffer</u>, <u>stronger</u> and more <u>heat-resistant</u>.

polymer chain

cross-linking agent

3) <u>Plasticisers</u> can be added to a polymer to make it <u>softer</u> and easier to shape.
   - Plasticisers work by getting in <u>between</u> the polymer chains and <u>reducing</u> the forces between them.

Choose your polymers wisely...

The <u>molecules</u> that make up a polymer and the way they are <u>arranged</u> both affect the <u>properties</u> of the polymer. I know there's a lot of diagrams of lines on this page, but this stuff is pretty important.

Warm-Up and Exam Questions

These warm-up questions should ease you in gently before you move onto the exam questions. Unless you've learnt the facts you'll find the exam questions tougher than leather sandwiches.

Warm-Up Questions

1) How is poly(ethene) made?
2) Butene is an alkene containing four carbon atoms. What would a polymer made from butene be called?
3) Explain why burying plastics is not a good way to dispose of them.
4) What can a plastic's melting point tell you about the bonds between its polymer chains?

Exam Questions

1   Polymers are long-chain molecules formed from smaller monomers.

(a) Complete this equation for the formation of poly(propene).

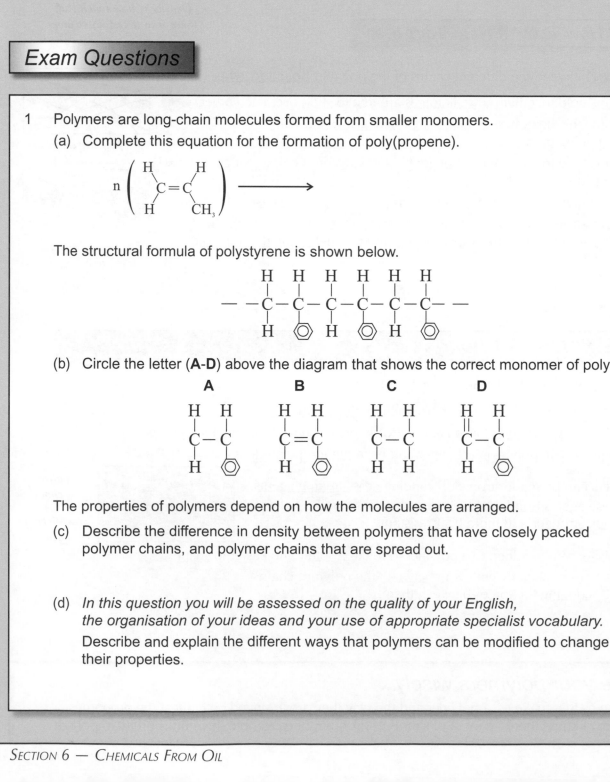

(1 mark)

The structural formula of polystyrene is shown below.

(b) Circle the letter (**A-D**) above the diagram that shows the correct monomer of polystyrene.

(1 mark)

The properties of polymers depend on how the molecules are arranged.

(c) Describe the difference in density between polymers that have closely packed polymer chains, and polymer chains that are spread out.

(1 mark)

(d) *In this question you will be assessed on the quality of your English, the organisation of your ideas and your use of appropriate specialist vocabulary.*

Describe and explain the different ways that polymers can be modified to change their properties.

(6 marks)

Plant Oils

If you squeeze a <u>walnut</u> really hard, some <u>walnut oil</u> will ooze out, which you could use to make <u>walnut mayonnaise</u>. Much better to just buy some oil from the shop though.

We Can *Extract Oils* from *Plants*

olive mush

weight

olive oil

1) Some <u>fruits</u> and <u>seeds</u> contain a lot of <u>oil</u>. E.g. avocados, olives and Brazil nuts.

2) These oils can be extracted (removed) and used for <u>food</u> or for <u>fuel</u>.

3) <u>Olive oil</u> is a good example. To get the oil out, the plant material is <u>crushed</u>.

4) The next step is to <u>press</u> the crushed plant material between metal plates and squash the oil out (look at the picture).

5) After this, <u>water</u> and other <u>impurities</u> can be removed from the oil.

Vegetable Oils Are Used in *Food*

1) Vegetable oils provide a lot of <u>energy</u>.
2) They also provide some of the <u>nutrients</u> that our bodies need.
3) For example, oils from seeds contain <u>vitamin E</u>.

Vegetable Oils Have Benefits for *Cooking*

1) Vegetable oils have <u>higher boiling points</u> than water. This means they can be used to cook foods at higher temperatures and at <u>faster</u> speeds.

2) Cooking with vegetable oil gives food a <u>different flavour</u>. This is down to the oil's own flavour.

3) It's also because the oil '<u>carries</u>' the flavours of the food, making them seem <u>stronger</u>.

4) Using oil to cook food <u>increases</u> the <u>energy</u> we get from eating it. This is because vegetable oil is high in energy.

Don't be silly, that's nut oil, it's a walnut...

Plant oils are pretty fab. How would you fry up your bacon if it wasn't for good old sunflower oil? That's how you get it nice and crispy and stop it sticking to the pan. It's also jam packed full of <u>nutrients</u> and <u>energy</u> so that should keep hunger locked up till tea time.

Plant Oils

Oils aren't just good for cooking — you can fuel a car with them as well...

Vegetable Oils Can Be Used to Produce Fuels

1) Vegetable oils such as rapeseed oil and soybean oil can be turned into <u>fuels</u>.

2) Vegetable oils provide a lot of <u>energy</u> so they're really good for using as fuels.

3) A very useful fuel made from vegetable oils is called <u>biodiesel</u>.

4) Biodiesel is quite like ordinary <u>diesel</u> fuel — it burns in the same way, so you can use it in a diesel engine.

See page 150 for more about biodiesel.

Unsaturated Oils Contain Carbon=Carbon Double Bonds

1) Oils and fats contain <u>long-chain molecules</u> with lots of <u>carbon</u> atoms.

2) Oils and fats can be <u>saturated</u> or <u>unsaturated</u>.

3) Unsaturated oils contain <u>double bonds</u> between some of the carbon atoms in their carbon chains.

4) So, an unsaturated oil will turn bromine water from orange to <u>colourless</u>.

5) Saturated oils <u>don't</u> contain any carbon=carbon double bonds.

6) So saturated oils <u>won't</u> change bromine water.

bromine water + unsaturated oil — colourless

This is like the test for alkenes (see p.141).

Vegetable Oils in Foods Can Affect Health

1) Vegetable oils are normally <u>unsaturated</u>.

2) Animal fats are normally <u>saturated</u>.

3) In general, <u>saturated fats</u> are less healthy than <u>unsaturated fats</u>. This is because <u>saturated</u> fats <u>increase</u> the amount of <u>cholesterol</u> in the blood. Cholesterol can block up the arteries and increase the risk of <u>heart disease</u>.

4) Natural <u>unsaturated</u> fats such as olive oil and sunflower oil <u>decrease</u> blood cholesterol.

5) But, <u>cooking</u> food in any oil, saturated or unsaturated, makes it more <u>fattening</u>.

Double bond — hero of the good fats...

This is tricky stuff. Basically... there are saturated and unsaturated fats, which are <u>mostly</u> bad and good for you (in that order). Remember that <u>unsaturated fats</u> have <u>double bonds</u> and how to test for this.

(Pssst they turn bromine water colourless.)

Emulsions

Emulsions are all over the place in foods, cosmetics and paint. And in exams...

Emulsions Can Be Made from Oil and Water

1) Oils don't dissolve in water. So far so good...

2) But, you can mix an oil with water to make an emulsion.

3) Emulsions are made up of lots of droplets of one liquid suspended in another liquid.

4) You can have an oil-in-water emulsion (oil droplets suspended in water) or a water-in-oil emulsion (water droplets suspended in oil).

Suspended just means the droplets of one liquid are hanging in the other liquid.

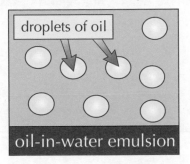

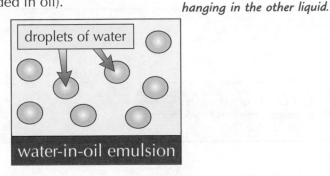

5) Emulsions are thicker than oil and thicker than water. E.g. mayonnaise is an emulsion of sunflower oil and vinegar — it's thicker than both the sunflower oil and the vinegar.

6) Emulsions have lots of uses in food because of their properties — e.g. as salad dressings and in sauces.

There's more about the properties of materials on page 95.

7) For example, a salad dressing made by shaking olive oil and vinegar together forms an emulsion. This coats salad better than plain oil or plain vinegar.

8) Whipped cream and ice cream are emulsions with an extra ingredient — air. Air is whipped into cream to make it fluffy and frothy. It's mixed into ice cream to make it softer and easier to scoop out of the tub.

9) Emulsions also have non-food uses. Most moisturising lotions are emulsions. They feel smooth and are easy to rub into the skin. Lots of paints are emulsions too.

Emulsifiers Stop Emulsions From Separating Out

1) Mixtures of oil and water (emulsions) naturally want to separate out.

2) Emulsifiers can be added to emulsions to make them more stable and stop them from separating out.

3) Emulsifiers also give emulsions a longer shelf-life.

4) Emulsifiers let food companies make food that's lower in fat but still has a good texture.

Texture is how something feels.

5) One down side is that some people are allergic to certain emulsifiers. For example, egg yolk is often used as an emulsifier. People who are allergic to eggs need to check the ingredients carefully.

Emulsion paint — spread mayonnaise all over the walls...

Emulsions like salad cream have to be made from shaking up two liquids — tiny droplets of one liquid are 'suspended' or 'hanging' in the other liquid. They are definitely NOT dissolved in the other liquid.

Warm-Up and Exam Questions

Here we go again... Yet another lovely page of questions to test your mad chemistry skills. Start with the warm-up questions and once you're happy you've nailed 'em have a crack at the exam questions.

Warm-Up Questions

1) Why are vegetable oils suitable for use as fuels?
2) Name a fuel made from vegetable oils.
3) Why are natural unsaturated fats typically healthier than saturated fats?
4) What is an emulsion?

Exam Questions

1   Oils that are extracted from plants are often used for cooking.

   (a) Describe the process used to extract oils from plants.

   (3 marks)

   (b) Give **three** benefits of using vegetable oils for cooking.

   (3 marks)

   Mayonnaise contains oil, water and emulsifiers.
   The diagram below shows an emulsifier molecule.
   It has one end that is attracted to water and another end that is attracted to oil.

   attracted   attracted
   to water   to oil

   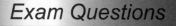

   (c) Using the information in the diagram above, answer the following questions
        about diagrams 1 and 2 below.

   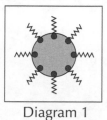   

   Diagram 1   Diagram 2

   (i)   Which diagram (1 or 2) shows an oil droplet suspended in water?

   (1 mark)

   (ii) Which diagram (1 or 2) shows a water droplet suspended in oil?

   (1 mark)

   (d) Give **one** effect of including emulsifiers in mayonnaise.

   (1 mark)

Revision Summary for Section 6

Cracking alkanes, making mayonnaise, acid rain — can they really belong in the same section, I almost hear you ask. Whether you find the topics easy or hard, interesting or dull, you could do with learning it all before the exam. Try these questions and see how much you really know:

1) What is crude oil made up of? What does fractional distillation do to crude oil?

2) What's the general formula for an alkane?

3) Is a short-chain hydrocarbon more viscous than a long-chain hydrocarbon? Is it more flammable?

4) What is "cracking"?

5) What's the name of the alkene with two carbon atoms?

6) What is the general formula for alkenes?

7) Write the word equation for the fermentation of sugar.

8) What two things are produced during complete combustion of hydrocarbons?

9) Explain how partial combustion can be harmful to humans.

10) Give three things you might want to consider when deciding on the best fuel to use.

11) What happens to wildlife if crude oil is spilled from a tanker?

12) What causes acid rain?

13) List two ways in which humans are increasing carbon dioxide in the atmosphere.

14) What are the pros and cons of using biodiesel as a fuel in cars?

15) What are polymers?

16) List four uses of polymers.

17) Give one problem with using polymers.

18) How does the arrangement of polymer chains affect the density of a material?

19) A polymer is easily stretched and has a low melting point.
   What can you say about the forces holding the polymer chains together?

20) Give an example of a fruit or seed that vegetable oil can be extracted from.

21) Do unsaturated oils contain any double bonds?

22) Give an example of an emulsion.

23) Why are emulsifiers needed?

Heat and Temperature

When it starts to get a bit cold, on goes the heating to warm things up a bit.
Heating is all about the <u>transfer of energy</u>.

Temperature is a Measure of *Hotness*

1)   The <u>hotter</u> something is, the <u>higher its temperature</u>.

2)   The <u>colder</u> something is, the <u>lower its temperature</u>.

3)   Temperature is <u>measured</u> in <u>°C</u> (degrees Celsius).

Energy Flows from *Hot* to *Cold*

**If two things have <u>DIFFERENT TEMPERATURES</u>,
heat <u>ENERGY WILL FLOW</u> between them.**

1)   <u>Energy</u> will <u>flow</u> from <u>hot objects</u> to <u>cooler</u> ones.

2)   This makes the hot objects <u>cool down</u> until they're
     at the <u>same temperature</u> as the <u>air in the room.</u>

3)   And it makes <u>cold</u> objects <u>warm up</u> until they reach
     <u>room temperature</u>.

4)   <u>Warm radiators</u> heat the <u>cold air</u> in your room
     — they'd be <u>no use</u> if heat didn't <u>flow</u>.

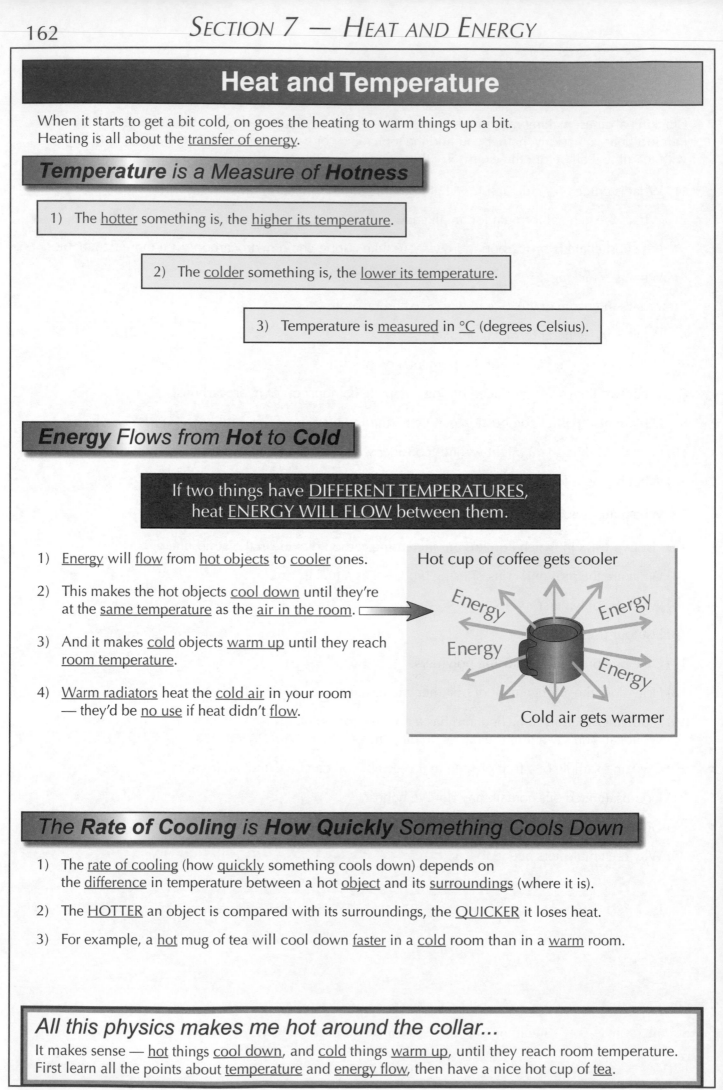

Hot cup of coffee gets cooler

Energy   Energy   Energy   Energy

Cold air gets warmer

The *Rate of Cooling* is *How Quickly* Something Cools Down

1)   The <u>rate of cooling</u> (how <u>quickly</u> something cools down) depends on
     the <u>difference</u> in temperature between a hot <u>object</u> and its <u>surroundings</u> (where it is).

2)   The <u>HOTTER</u> an object is compared with its surroundings, the <u>QUICKER</u> it loses heat.

3)   For example, a <u>hot</u> mug of tea will cool down <u>faster</u> in a <u>cold</u> room than in a <u>warm</u> room.

All this physics makes me hot around the collar...

It makes sense — <u>hot</u> things <u>cool down</u>, and <u>cold</u> things <u>warm up</u>, until they reach room temperature.
First learn all the points about <u>temperature</u> and <u>energy flow</u>, then have a nice hot cup of <u>tea</u>.

Kinetic Theory

Yikes — bit of a scary title. But don't panic, it's only a fancy name for 'how particles move'. Phew.

Kinetic Theory Can Explain the Three States of Matter

The three states of matter are solid (e.g. ice), liquid (e.g. water) and gas (e.g. water vapour).
The particles in solids, liquids and gases are all the same — but have different amounts of energy.

Solids

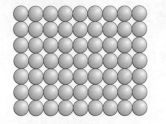

a) Strong forces of attraction (a pull) hold the particles close together.

b) The particles are arranged in a pattern.

c) The particles don't have much energy so they can only vibrate a little.

Vibrate just means they jiggle about.

If you heat the solid, eventually it will melt and become a liquid.

Liquids

a) There are weaker forces of attraction between the particles.

b) The particles are close together, but can move past each other.

c) They have more energy than the particles in a solid — they move in all directions at low speeds.

If you heat the liquid, eventually it will boil and become a gas.

Gases

a) There are almost no forces of attraction between the particles.

b) The particles have more energy than those in liquids and solids.

c) They are free to move in any direction and move at high speeds.

When you heat something, you give its particles more energy. This means the particles will vibrate or move faster. This is what eventually causes solids to melt and liquids to boil.

The state of a substance depends on the energy of its particles

So, the more energy something has, the faster it moves about. Makes sense. But if you cool something down enough it stops moving altogether. The temperature this happens at is the same for everything and it's called 'absolute zero' (−273°C). Now that's seriously cool.

Conduction

Mmmm... I do like being toasty warm. But keeping the heat where you want it is easier said than done — there are several ways that heat is 'lost'. <u>Conduction</u> is up first.

Conduction Happens Mainly in Solids

1) In a <u>solid</u>, the particles are held <u>tightly together</u>.

2) So when one particle <u>vibrates</u> (shakes), it <u>bumps into</u> other particles nearby.

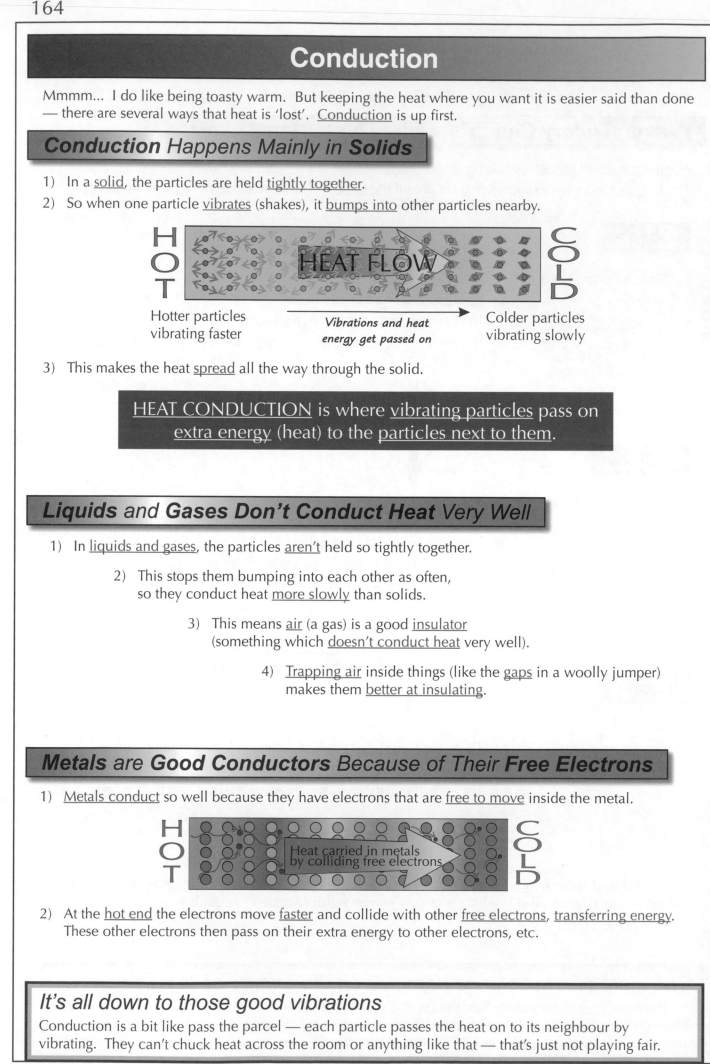

Hotter particles vibrating faster

Vibrations and heat energy get passed on

Colder particles vibrating slowly

3) This makes the heat <u>spread</u> all the way through the solid.

> <u>HEAT CONDUCTION</u> is where <u>vibrating particles</u> pass on <u>extra energy</u> (heat) to the <u>particles next to them</u>.

Liquids and Gases Don't Conduct Heat Very Well

1) In <u>liquids and gases</u>, the particles <u>aren't</u> held so tightly together.

2) This stops them bumping into each other as often, so they conduct heat <u>more slowly</u> than solids.

3) This means <u>air</u> (a gas) is a good <u>insulator</u> (something which <u>doesn't conduct heat</u> very well).

4) <u>Trapping air</u> inside things (like the <u>gaps</u> in a woolly jumper) makes them <u>better at insulating</u>.

Metals are Good Conductors Because of Their Free Electrons

1) <u>Metals conduct</u> so well because they have electrons that are <u>free to move</u> inside the metal.

Heat carried in metals by colliding free electrons

2) At the <u>hot end</u> the electrons move <u>faster</u> and collide with other <u>free electrons</u>, <u>transferring energy</u>. These other electrons then pass on their extra energy to other electrons, etc.

It's all down to those good vibrations

Conduction is a bit like pass the parcel — each particle passes the heat on to its neighbour by vibrating. They can't chuck heat across the room or anything like that — that's just not playing fair.

Convection

Oh goody — another way heat can be lost. This page is all about <u>convection</u>.

Convection Happens in Liquids and Gases

1) Heating up a <u>fluid</u> (<u>liquid</u> or <u>gas</u>) gives the particles <u>more energy</u> so they <u>move around faster</u>.

2) The <u>warmer</u> part of the fluid <u>rises</u> above the <u>colder</u> parts.

3) As the <u>warm</u> part <u>rises</u>, <u>cooler</u> fluid <u>falls</u> and <u>takes its place</u>.

4) This carries on so you have a <u>circular</u> flow of fluid — called a <u>convection current</u>.

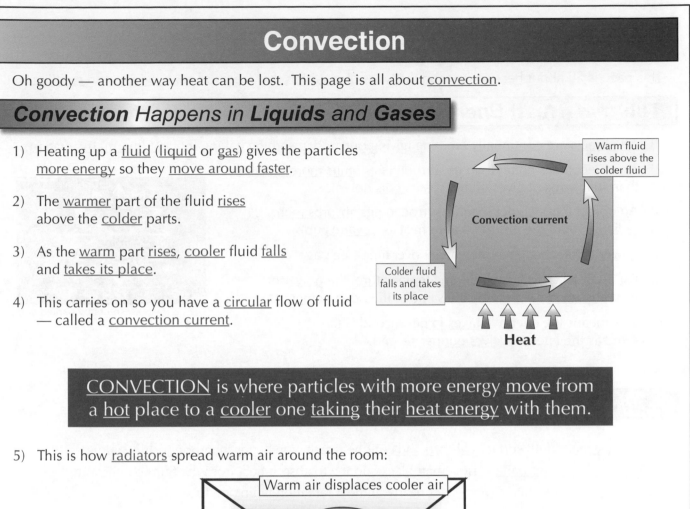

Warm fluid rises above the colder fluid

Convection current

Colder fluid falls and takes its place

Heat

<u>CONVECTION</u> is where particles with more energy <u>move</u> from a <u>hot</u> place to a <u>cooler</u> one <u>taking</u> their <u>heat energy</u> with them.

5) This is how <u>radiators</u> spread warm air around the room:

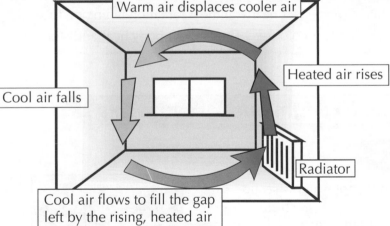

Warm air displaces cooler air

Cool air falls

Heated air rises

Cool air flows to fill the gap left by the rising, heated air

Radiator

Convection Can't Happen in Solids

1) Convection <u>can't happen in solids</u> because the <u>particles can't move</u>.

2) To <u>stop convection</u>, you need to <u>stop the liquid or gas moving</u>.

3) <u>Clothes</u>, <u>blankets</u> and <u>wall insulation</u> all work by <u>trapping pockets of air</u> which can't move.

Remember: most 'radiators' heat rooms by convection
Heat transfer by radiation is coming up on the next page though. Handy that, almost like I planned it.

Heat Radiation

This page is all about <u>heat energy</u> and the types of <u>materials</u> that are good at <u>absorbing</u> and <u>emitting</u> it.

Thermal (Heat) Energy can be Transferred by Radiation

1) <u>All objects</u> are <u>continually</u> emitting (giving out) and absorbing (taking in) <u>heat (thermal) radiation</u>.

2) An object that's <u>hotter</u> than its surroundings <u>emits more radiation</u> than it <u>absorbs</u> (it gives off heat as it <u>cools</u> down).

3) An object that's <u>cooler</u> than its surroundings <u>absorbs more radiation</u> than it <u>emits</u> (it takes in heat as it <u>warms</u> up).

4) <u>Power</u> is the change in the energy over time (see page 196).

5) For an object to stay at the <u>same temperature</u>, the <u>power</u> of heat <u>absorbed</u> needs to be the <u>same</u> as the power <u>emitted</u>.

6) This means the energy it <u>takes in</u> per second is the same as the energy it <u>gives out</u> per second.

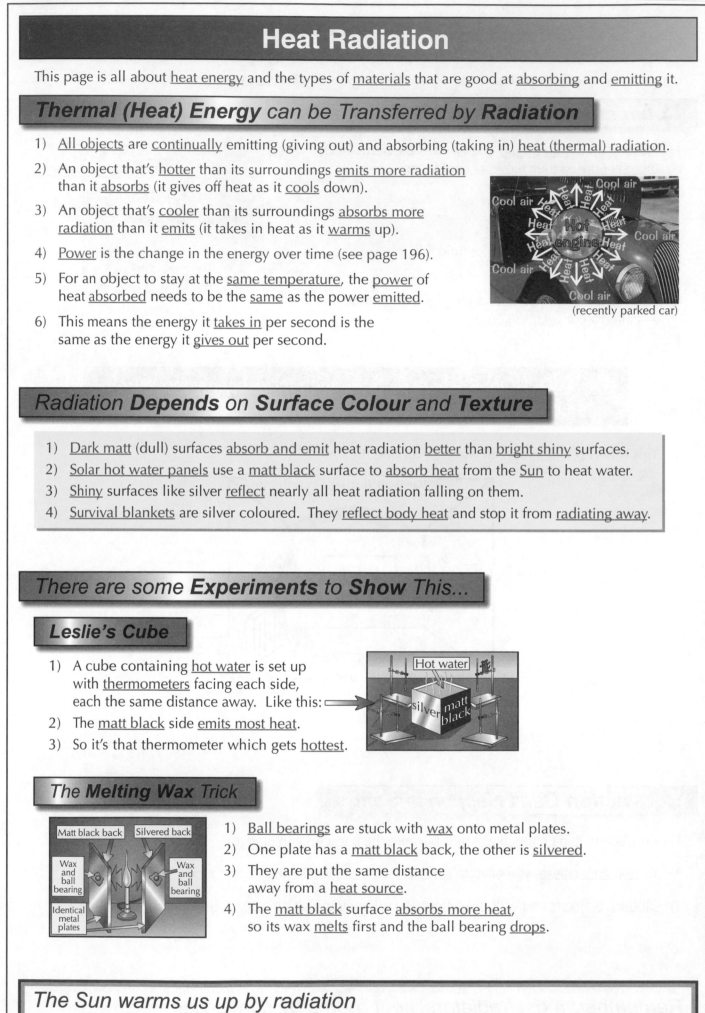

(recently parked car)

Radiation *Depends* on *Surface Colour* and *Texture*

1) <u>Dark matt</u> (dull) surfaces <u>absorb and emit</u> heat radiation <u>better</u> than <u>bright shiny</u> surfaces.

2) <u>Solar hot water panels</u> use a <u>matt black</u> surface to <u>absorb heat</u> from the <u>Sun</u> to heat water.

3) <u>Shiny</u> surfaces like silver <u>reflect</u> nearly all heat radiation falling on them.

4) <u>Survival blankets</u> are silver coloured. They <u>reflect body heat</u> and stop it from <u>radiating away</u>.

There are some *Experiments* to *Show* This...

Leslie's Cube

1) A cube containing <u>hot water</u> is set up with <u>thermometers</u> facing each side, each the same distance away. Like this:

2) The <u>matt black</u> side <u>emits most heat</u>.

3) So it's that thermometer which gets <u>hottest</u>.

The *Melting Wax* Trick

1) <u>Ball bearings</u> are stuck with <u>wax</u> onto metal plates.

2) One plate has a <u>matt black</u> back, the other is <u>silvered</u>.

3) They are put the same distance away from a <u>heat source</u>.

4) The <u>matt black</u> surface <u>absorbs more heat</u>, so its wax <u>melts</u> first and the ball bearing <u>drops</u>.

The Sun warms us up by radiation

The key idea here is that <u>heat radiation</u> is affected by the <u>colour</u> and the <u>texture</u> of surfaces.

Condensation and Evaporation

Here are some things about particles in <u>gases</u> and <u>liquids</u> you need to think about.

Condensation is When Gas Turns to Liquid

1) When a <u>gas cools</u>, the particles in the gas <u>slow down</u> and <u>lose energy</u>.

2) The attractive forces between the particles pull them <u>closer together</u>.

3) If gas particles get <u>close enough together</u> and the temperature is <u>cold enough</u>, then <u>condensation</u> happens and the gas becomes a <u>liquid</u>.

4) Water vapour in the air <u>condenses</u> when it touches a <u>cold surface</u>, e.g. drinks glasses.

condensed water vapour

Evaporation is When Liquid Turns to Gas

1) <u>Evaporation</u> is when particles <u>escape</u> from a <u>liquid</u>.

2) Particles <u>near the surface</u> of a liquid can escape and become <u>gas particles</u> if:

> • The particles are travelling in the <u>right direction</u> to escape the liquid.
> • The particles have enough <u>energy</u> to <u>break free</u> from the <u>attractive forces</u> of the <u>other particles</u> in the liquid.

not enough energy to escape the liquid

not near enough the surface to escape the liquid

this particle is able to escape the liquid and evaporates

moving in the wrong direction to escape the liquid

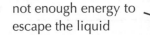

3) The <u>particles</u> with the <u>most energy</u> are <u>most likely</u> to evaporate from the liquid.

4) When the <u>particles</u> with the most energy evaporate, the <u>average energy</u> of the particles left behind <u>decreases</u>.

5) This means the <u>temperature</u> of the liquid left behind <u>falls</u> — the liquid <u>cools</u>.

Condensation and evaporation both depend on energy

If gas particles <u>lose</u> enough <u>energy</u>, the gas will <u>condense</u> into a liquid. Particles in a liquid need to have a <u>high</u> energy to be able to <u>evaporate</u>. Remember that when a particle evaporates, it takes its energy with it... So the <u>average</u> kinetic energy of the particles in the liquid <u>decreases</u>, and the liquid <u>cools</u>.

Condensation and Evaporation

The rate (speed) of <u>condensation</u> and <u>evaporation</u> depends on lots of different things.

The Speed of Condensation and Evaporation can Vary

The **Rate of Condensation** will be **Faster** if the...

1) <u>TEMPERATURE</u> of the surface the gas touches is <u>lower</u>.

2) <u>SURFACE AREA</u> of the surface the gas touches is <u>larger</u>.

The **Rate of Evaporation** will be **Faster** if the...

1) <u>TEMPERATURE</u> of the liquid is <u>higher</u>.

2) <u>DENSITY</u> of the liquid is <u>lower</u>.

3) <u>SURFACE AREA</u> of the liquid is <u>larger</u>:

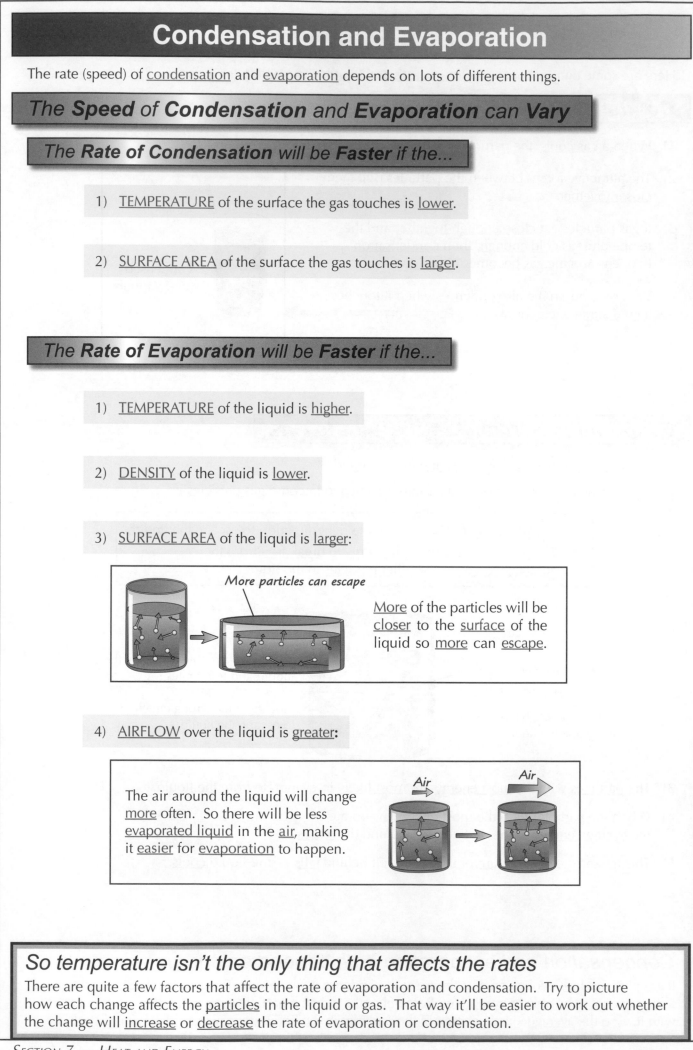

More particles can escape

<u>More</u> of the particles will be <u>closer</u> to the <u>surface</u> of the liquid so <u>more</u> can <u>escape</u>.

4) <u>AIRFLOW</u> over the liquid is <u>greater</u>:

The air around the liquid will change <u>more</u> often. So there will be less <u>evaporated liquid</u> in the <u>air</u>, making it <u>easier</u> for <u>evaporation</u> to happen.

Air   *Air*

So temperature isn't the only thing that affects the rates

There are quite a few factors that affect the rate of evaporation and condensation. Try to picture how each change affects the <u>particles</u> in the liquid or gas. That way it'll be easier to work out whether the change will <u>increase</u> or <u>decrease</u> the rate of evaporation or condensation.

Warm-Up and Exam Questions

Here are a few questions for you to try — do the warm-up ones first, then when you think you're ready, have a go at the exam questions. If there's anything you can't do, make sure you go back and check it.

Warm-Up Questions

1) Describe the particles in a gas in terms of their energy, movement and the forces between particles.
2) Describe the process of heat transfer by conduction.
3) Which of these can't happen in solids — convection or conduction?
4) Give two ways the nature of a surface could be changed so that the surface emits more infrared radiation.
5) What is meant by 'condensation'?
6) Give two ways of increasing the rate of condensation of a gas onto a cool surface.

Exam Questions

1 A student is investigating the factors that affect how quickly a drink will cool. He measures the length of time it takes for a cup of water to cool from 60 °C to 30 °C. He uses the apparatus shown on the right.

room temperature = 25 °C
thermometer
plastic cup
50 ml of water

Describe how the time taken for the same temperature change would alter if the following changes were made to the apparatus. Give a reason for each of your answers.

(a) The experiment was done in a room where the temperature was 15 °C.

(2 marks)

(b) The plastic cup was replaced with an identical metal cup.

(2 marks)

2 The diagram shows a solar heating panel which is used to heat cold water in a house.

(a) Complete the following sentences on heat transfer.

(i) Heat is transferred from the Sun to the solar heating panel

by ....

(1 mark)

(ii) Heat is transferred from the hot water in the pipe to the colder

water in the tank by ....

(1 mark)

(iii) Heat is transferred throughout the water

in the tank by ....

(1 mark)

(b) Explain why the pipes in the heating panel are painted black.

(1 mark)

Metal pipe
Glass box on roof
Pump
Hot water tank in house

Exam Questions

3   Warm air rises in the roof space of a house.

   (a)   What type of heat transfer is this? Tick the box next to the correct answer (A-C).

   A   radiation   ☐

   B   conduction   ☐

   C   convection   ☐

(1 mark)

   (b)   Explain how this heat transfer process spreads warm air around the roof space.

(3 marks)

4   Dawn has made a hot drink with boiling water. She leaves it on the windowsill while she answers the phone. When she returns, small droplets of water have appeared on the inside of the window.

   (a)   (i)   Name the process that has occurred on the window.

(1 mark)

   (ii)   Circle the correct answer to complete the following sentences to explain how this process occurred.

   Water vapour that had | evaporated |
                           | melted | cooled as it hit the window.

   The particles in the water vapour | lost |
                                       | gained | energy and turned to liquid.

(2 marks)

   (b)   The drink is still too warm, so Dawn gently blows over the top of the mug to make it cool down quicker.

   (i)   Blowing over the drink increases the rate of evaporation. Explain why.

(2 marks)

   (ii)   Why would increasing the rate of evaporation cool down the drink?

(2 marks)

5   A student is investigating the amount of heat different surfaces radiate using a Leslie's Cube, as shown on the right.
   The student records how long it takes the temperature on each thermometer to increase by 5 °C.

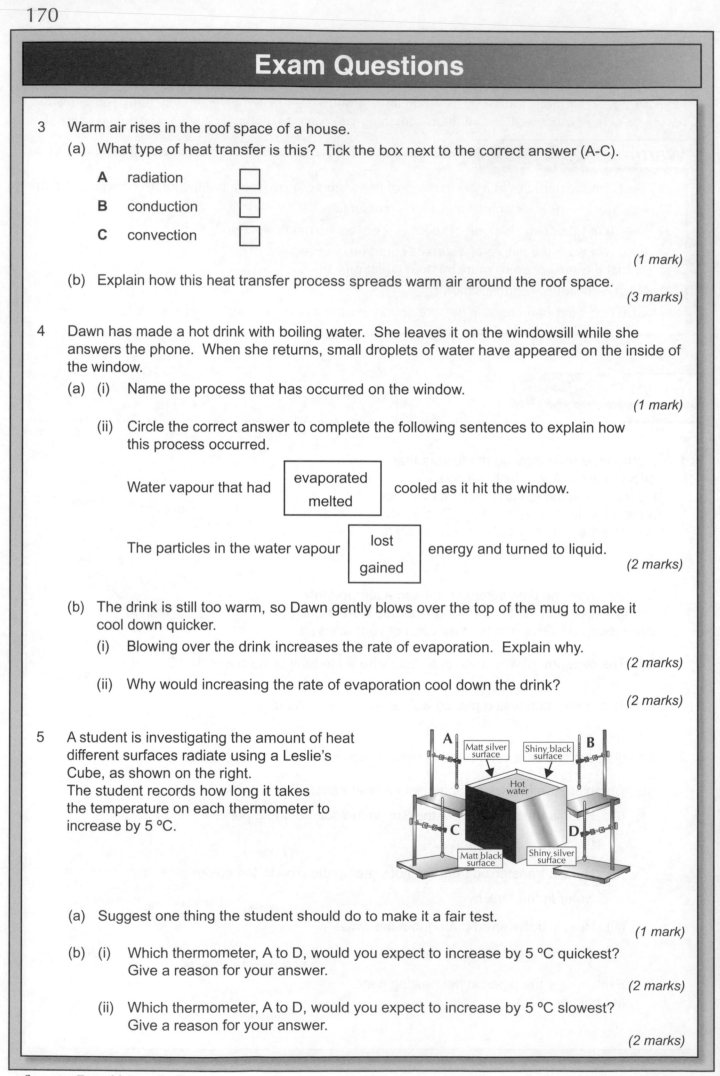

   (a)   Suggest one thing the student should do to make it a fair test.

(1 mark)

   (b)   (i)   Which thermometer, A to D, would you expect to increase by 5 °C quickest?
            Give a reason for your answer.

(2 marks)

   (ii)   Which thermometer, A to D, would you expect to increase by 5 °C slowest?
            Give a reason for your answer.

(2 marks)

Rate of Heat Transfer

There are loads of things that affect the <u>rate</u> of <u>heat transfer</u> (how <u>quickly</u> heat is transferred).

The **Rate** an Object **Transfers Heat Energy** Depends on...

Surface Area and Volume

1) <u>Heat</u> is <u>radiated</u> (sent out) from the <u>surface</u> of an object.

2) The <u>bigger</u> the <u>surface area</u>, the <u>more infrared waves</u> can be <u>emitted</u> from the surface (or <u>absorbed</u> by the surface). This means <u>heat transfer</u> is <u>quicker</u>.

- <u>Radiators</u> have <u>large surface areas</u> to <u>increase</u> the amount of heat they transfer.
- <u>Car and motorbike engines</u> often have '<u>fins</u>' to <u>increase</u> the <u>surface area</u> so heat is radiated away quicker. So the <u>engine cools quicker</u>.

3) <u>Heat sinks</u> are devices designed to transfer heat <u>away</u> from <u>objects</u> they're in <u>contact</u> with (touching), e.g. computer parts. They also have <u>fins</u> so they can <u>radiate heat</u> as quickly as possible.

4) If two objects at the <u>same temperature</u> have the <u>same surface area</u> but <u>different</u> <u>volumes</u>, the object with the <u>smaller</u> volume will cool more <u>quickly</u>.

Example

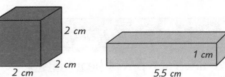

Shape A:
Surface area = 24 cm^2
Volume = 8 cm^3

Shape B:
Surface area = 24 cm^2
Volume = 5.5 cm^3

Shape A and B have the <u>same surface area</u> — but Shape B has a <u>smaller volume</u>. So, <u>Shape B</u> will lose heat <u>quicker</u> than <u>Shape A</u>.

The **Material** of the **Object** and What it's **Touching**

1) Objects made from <u>conductors</u> (see p. 164) will transfer heat more <u>quickly</u> than objects made from <u>insulators</u>.

2) Heat will be conducted away <u>much faster</u> from an object <u>in contact</u> with a <u>conductor</u> than an insulator.

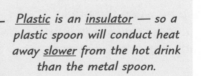

<u>Metal</u> is a <u>conductor</u> — so a metal spoon will conduct heat away <u>quickly</u> from the hot drink.

<u>Plastic</u> is an <u>insulator</u> — so a plastic spoon will conduct heat away <u>slower</u> from the hot drink than the metal spoon.

3) The <u>bigger the temperature difference</u>, the <u>faster</u> heat is transferred between the object and what it's touching.

That's why curling up in a ball helps when you're cold

By curling up in a ball, you <u>decrease</u> the <u>surface area</u> of your body that's in contact with the surroundings. Handily, this will lower your rate of heat transfer and help you keep warm.

Energy Efficiency in the Home

There are lots of things you can do to a building to <u>reduce</u> the amount of <u>heat energy that escapes</u>.

Effectiveness and Cost-effectiveness are Not the Same Thing...

1) The <u>most effective</u> methods of insulation are ones that give you the biggest <u>annual saving</u> (they save you the <u>most</u> money <u>each year</u> on your <u>heating bills</u>).

2) Eventually, the <u>money you've saved</u> on heating bills will <u>equal</u> the initial cost of putting in the insulation (the amount it cost to buy). The time it takes is called the <u>payback time</u>.

3) The <u>most cost-effective</u> methods tend to be the <u>cheapest</u>.

4) They are cost-effective because they have a <u>short payback time</u> — this means the money you save <u>covers</u> the amount you <u>paid</u> really <u>quickly</u>.

5) You can work out <u>payback time</u> using this <u>equation</u>:

$$\text{payback time} = \frac{\text{initial cost}}{\text{annual saving}}$$

EXAMPLE: It costs <u>£200</u> to install some loft insulation in a house.
If it gives an annual saving of <u>£50</u>, how long is the payback time?

ANSWER: Payback time $= \frac{200}{50} = $ <u>4 years</u>

Insulation Reduces Heat Loss from Homes

Different types of <u>insulation</u> reduce different types of <u>heat transfer</u>.

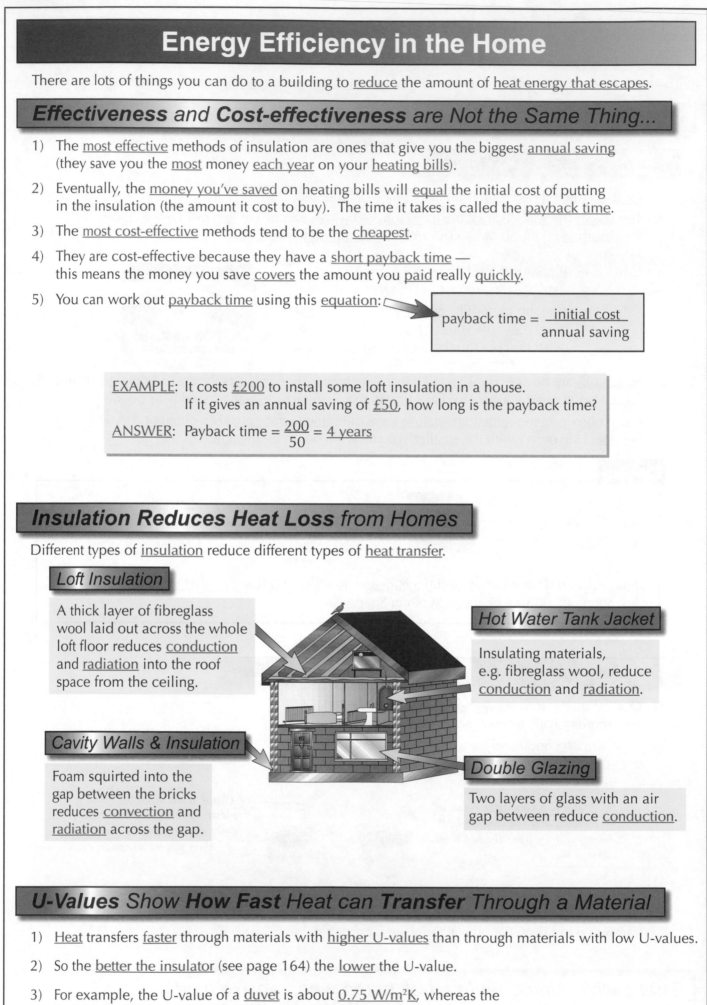

Loft Insulation
A thick layer of fibreglass wool laid out across the whole loft floor reduces <u>conduction</u> and <u>radiation</u> into the roof space from the ceiling.

Hot Water Tank Jacket
Insulating materials, e.g. fibreglass wool, reduce <u>conduction</u> and <u>radiation</u>.

Cavity Walls & Insulation
Foam squirted into the gap between the bricks reduces <u>convection</u> and <u>radiation</u> across the gap.

Double Glazing
Two layers of glass with an air gap between reduce <u>conduction</u>.

U-Values Show How Fast Heat can Transfer Through a Material

1) <u>Heat</u> transfers <u>faster</u> through materials with <u>higher U-values</u> than through materials with low U-values.

2) So the <u>better the insulator</u> (see page 164) the <u>lower</u> the U-value.

3) For example, the U-value of a <u>duvet</u> is about <u>0.75 W/m²K</u>, whereas the U-value of <u>loft insulation material</u> is around <u>0.15 W/m²K</u>.

Specific Heat Capacity

Specific heat capacity sounds a bit scary but it's actually not too bad.

Specific Heat Capacity — How Much Energy can be stored

1) It takes <u>more heat energy</u> to increase the <u>temperature</u> of some <u>materials</u> than others.

2) Materials which need to <u>gain</u> lots of energy to <u>warm up</u> also <u>release</u> loads of energy when they <u>cool down</u> again. They can 'store' a lot of heat.

3) The measure of <u>how much energy</u> a substance (material) can <u>store</u> is called its <u>specific heat capacity</u>.

> <u>Specific heat capacity</u> is the amount of <u>energy</u> needed to raise the temperature of <u>1 kg</u> of a substance by <u>1 °C</u>.

There's a Handy Formula for Specific Heat Capacity

You might have to do calculations involving <u>specific heat capacity</u>. This is the <u>formula</u>:

Energy transferred (J) $\longrightarrow$ $$E = m \times c \times \theta$$ $\longleftarrow$ Temperature change (°C)

Mass (kg)

Specific heat capacity (J/kg°C)

> <u>EXAMPLE</u>: How much energy is needed to heat 2 kg of water from 10 °C to 100 °C? (Water has a specific heat capacity of 4200 J/kg°C.)
>
> <u>ANSWER</u>: Energy needed = 2 × 4200 × (100 − 10)
> = 2 × 4200 × 90 = <u>756 000</u> J

Heaters Have High Heat Capacities to Store Lots of Energy

1) The <u>materials</u> used in <u>heaters</u> usually have <u>high</u> specific heat capacities.

2) <u>Water</u> has a <u>really high</u> specific heat capacity. It's also a <u>liquid</u>, so it can easily be <u>pumped around</u> in pipes — ideal for <u>central heating</u> systems in buildings.

3) Electric <u>storage heaters</u> store heat energy at night and then <u>release</u> it during the day. They store the heat using <u>concrete</u> or <u>bricks</u>, which have a <u>high</u> specific heat capacity.

4) Some heaters are filled with <u>oil</u>. <u>Oil</u> has a <u>lower</u> specific heat capacity than <u>water</u> — this means they're often <u>not</u> as good as <u>water</u> heating systems.

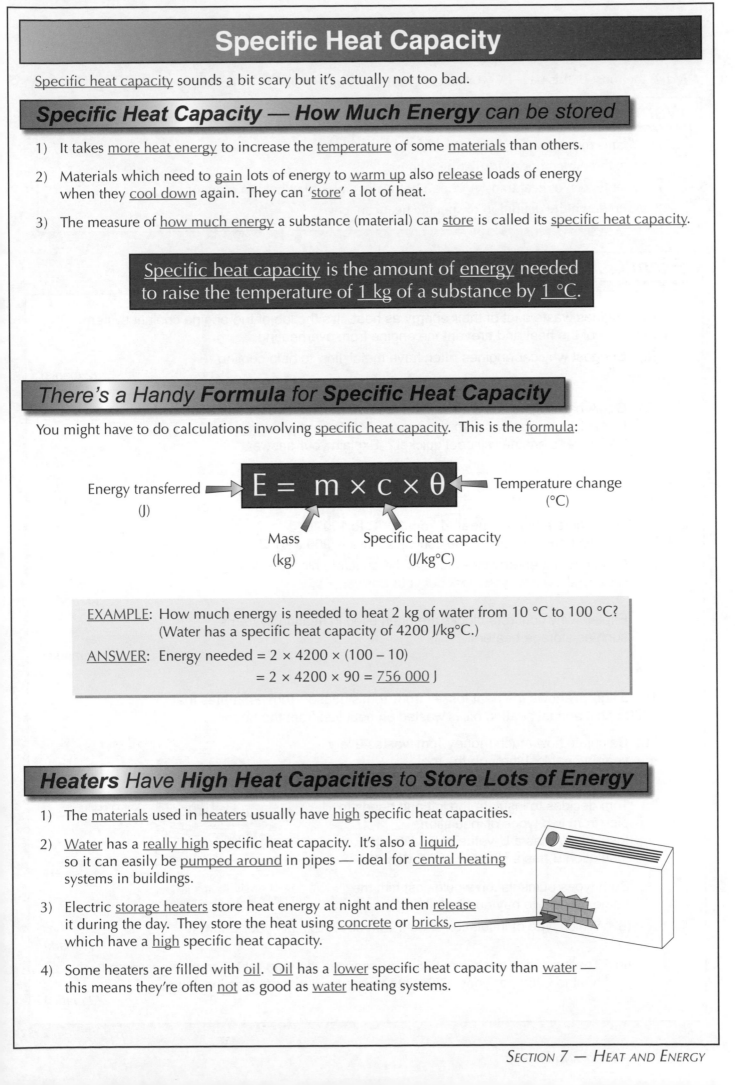

Warm-Up and Exam Questions

Make the most of this page by working through everything carefully — it's all useful stuff.

Warm-Up Questions

1) What is meant by "payback time"?
2) Give three methods of insulating a house.
3) What type(s) of heat transfer does a hot water tank jacket help to reduce?
4) Write down the definition of specific heat capacity.

Exam Questions

1 Car engines waste a lot of their energy as heat. It's the job of the engine coolant system to get rid of the heat and prevent the engine from overheating.

   (a) Suggest why car engines often have metal 'fins' to help cooling.

   (2 marks)

   (b) Car **A** has engine fins with surface area 10 m² and a volume of 3000 cm³.
        Car **B** has engine fins with surface area 10 m² and a volume of 2000 cm³.
        Which car's engine will cool quicker? Explain your answer.

   (2 marks)

2 A 0.5 kg concrete block is heated from 20 °C to 100 °C.
   The specific heat capacity of the concrete block is 900 J/kg°C.

   (a) Calculate the energy used to heat the concrete block.
        Clearly show how you work out your answer.

   (3 marks)

   (b) Explain why concrete blocks are often used in heating systems
        such as storage heaters.

   (2 marks)

3 The diagram shows the heat losses from Tom's house. Tom estimates that
   £300 of his annual heating bill is wasted on heat lost from the house.

   (a) Calculate how much money Tom wastes every
        year in heat lost through the roof.

   (1 mark)

   25% through roof

   35% through brick walls

   15% through open windows and cracks in window frames

   15% through concrete floor

   10% through glass in windows

   (b) Tom decides to insulate the loft and needs to
        pick from two types of insulation.
        Insulation A has a U-value of 0.7 W/m²K.
        Insulation B has a U-value of 0.6 W/m²K.

        Both types of insulation would cost him the
        same amount to buy and install.

        (i)   Which type of insulation should Tom buy? Explain your answer.

   (1 mark)

        (ii) The insulation costs him £350, but reduces the amount he spends on wasted
              heat to £250 per year. Calculate the payback time for the insulation.

   (3 marks)

Energy Transfer

Heat is just one type of energy, but there are lots more:

Learn These Nine Types of Energy

1) ELECTRICAL Energy...................................... — whenever a current flows.
2) LIGHT Energy... — from the Sun, light bulbs, etc.
3) SOUND Energy... — from loudspeakers or anything noisy.
4) KINETIC Energy, or MOVEMENT Energy.......... — anything that's moving has it.
5) NUCLEAR Energy.. — released only from nuclear reactions.
6) THERMAL Energy or HEAT Energy.................. — flows from hot objects to colder ones.
7) GRAVITATIONAL POTENTIAL Energy............. — stored in anything that can fall.
8) ELASTIC POTENTIAL Energy......................... — stretched springs, elastic, rubber bands, etc.
9) CHEMICAL Energy....................................... — stored in foods, fuels, batteries etc.

Potential and Chemical Energy are forms of Stored Energy

The last three above are forms of stored energy because the energy is not obviously doing anything, it's kind of waiting to happen, i.e. waiting to be turned into one of the other forms.

The Principle of the Conservation of Energy:

Energy can be transferred usefully from one form to another, stored or dissipated — but it can never be created or destroyed.

Dissipated is a fancy way of saying the energy is spread out and lost.

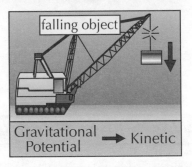

Gravitational Potential → Kinetic

Another important thing to learn is this one:

Energy is only useful when it can be converted from one form to another.

Examples of Energy Transfers

Electrical Devices, e.g. televisions: Electrical energy ➡ Light, sound and heat energy

Batteries: Chemical energy ➡ Electrical and heat energy

Electrical Generation, e.g. wind turbines: Kinetic energy ➡ Electrical and heat energy

Potential Energy, e.g. firing a bow and arrow: Elastic potential energy ➡ Kinetic and heat energy

Efficiency of Machines

Old <u>light bulbs</u> seem to be great at lighting up a room — but they also give out a lot of <u>heat</u>.
All this heat energy is '<u>wasted</u>', so old light bulbs aren't very <u>efficient</u>.

Machines Always Waste Some Energy

1) Machines <u>change energy</u> from <u>one form</u> to <u>another</u>.
For example, you put <u>chemical energy</u> into a car (petrol or diesel)
and the engine converts it into <u>kinetic (movement) energy</u>.

2) The <u>total energy out</u> is always the <u>same</u> as the <u>total energy put in</u> — energy is always <u>conserved</u>.

3) But only some of the energy that comes out is <u>useful</u>.

*Conserved means the
amount <u>stays the same</u>.*

4) The rest of the <u>energy</u> is <u>wasted</u>, often as <u>heat</u>.
In the car example, a lot of the chemical energy
is changed into wasted <u>heat and sound energy</u>.

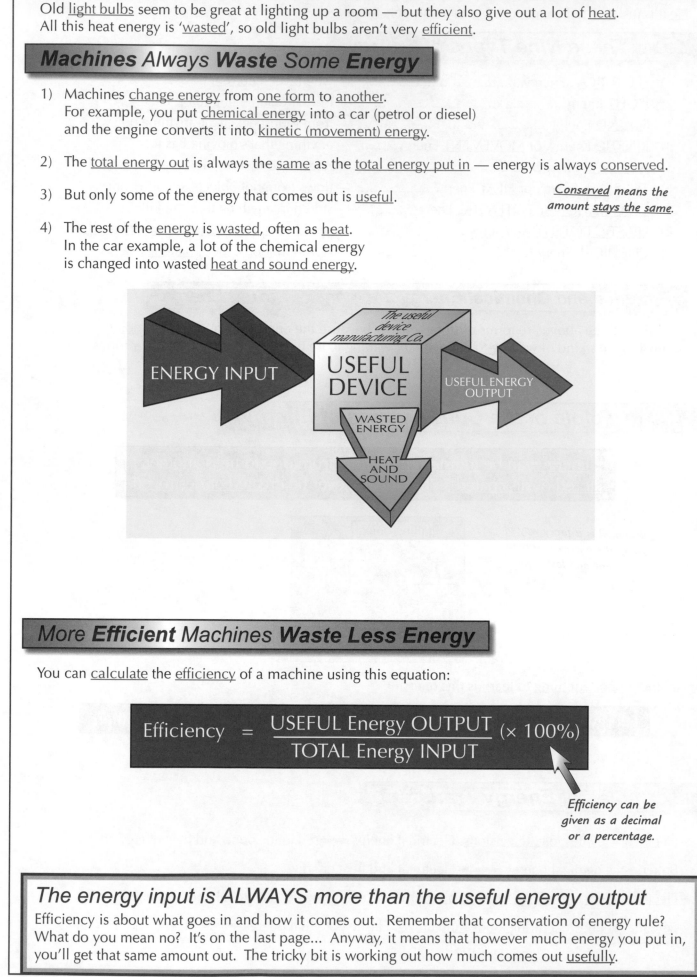

More Efficient Machines Waste Less Energy

You can <u>calculate</u> the <u>efficiency</u> of a machine using this equation:

$$\text{Efficiency} = \frac{\text{USEFUL Energy OUTPUT}}{\text{TOTAL Energy INPUT}} \; (\times 100\%)$$

*Efficiency can be
given as a decimal
or a percentage.*

The energy input is ALWAYS more than the useful energy output

Efficiency is about what goes in and how it comes out. Remember that conservation of energy rule?
What do you mean no? It's on the last page... Anyway, it means that however much energy you put in,
you'll get that same amount out. The tricky bit is working out how much comes out <u>usefully</u>.

Efficiency of Machines

And here's a handy example to show you how to use the efficiency formula from the previous page.

Efficiency = Useful ÷ Total

1) First find out the Total Energy IN.

2) Then find the Useful Energy OUT.
   The question might give you this, or it might tell you how much energy is wasted.

> Useful Energy = Total Energy – Wasted Energy.

3) Next, divide the smaller number (useful) by the bigger one (total) to get an efficiency.
   You should get an answer somewhere between 0 and 1.
   If your number is bigger than 1, you've done the division upside down.

4) You can change your answer to a percentage by multiplying it by 100.

5) You can use the formula with Sankey diagrams too — coming up on the next page.

Example:

A kettle uses 180 000 J to boil some water. 9000 J is wasted heating up the air around the kettle. What is the kettle's efficiency?

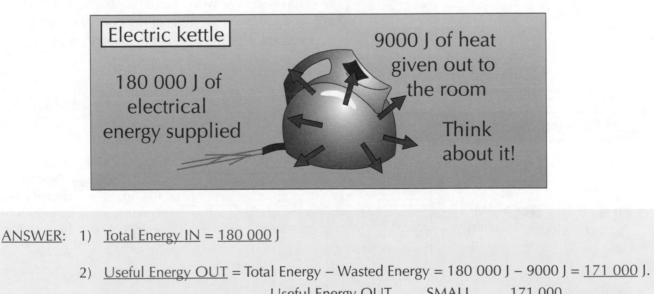

Electric kettle

180 000 J of electrical energy supplied

9000 J of heat given out to the room

Think about it!

ANSWER:

1) Total Energy IN = 180 000 J

2) Useful Energy OUT = Total Energy – Wasted Energy = 180 000 J – 9000 J = 171 000 J.

3) Efficiency of the kettle = $\dfrac{\text{Useful Energy OUT}}{\text{Total Energy IN}} = \dfrac{\text{SMALL}}{\text{BIG}} = \dfrac{171\,000}{180\,000} = 0.95$

4) Efficiency as a percentage = 0.95 × 100 = 95%.

Efficiency questions aren't too bad once you can use the equation

Some 'waste' energy can be made useful again by a heat exchanger. These clever devices use wasted heat to heat a fluid, which traps some of the energy. The heat energy in the fluid can then be converted into a useful form again. E.g. heat from an engine can be used to heat the air inside a car.

Energy Transformation Diagrams

Energy transformation diagrams (Sankey diagrams) can be a great way of showing efficiency.

The **Thickness** of the **Arrow** Represents the **Amount** of **Energy**

1) Energy transformation (Sankey) diagrams make it easy to see how much of the input energy is being used usefully and how much is being wasted.

2) The thicker the arrow, the more energy it represents.

3) You see a big thick arrow going in, then smaller arrows going off it to show the different energy transformations taking place.

4) You can have either a little sketch or a properly detailed diagram (see below).

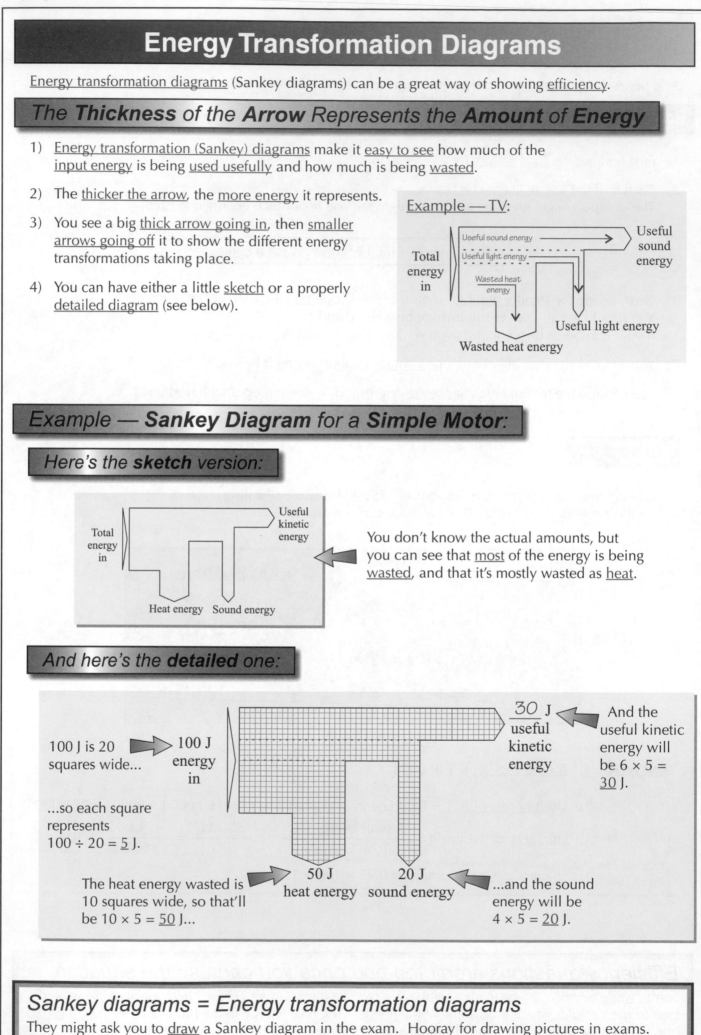

Example — TV:

Useful sound energy

Useful light energy

Wasted heat energy

Total energy in

Useful sound energy

Useful light energy

Wasted heat energy

Example — **Sankey Diagram** for a **Simple Motor**:

Here's the **sketch** version:

Total energy in

Useful kinetic energy

Heat energy   Sound energy

You don't know the actual amounts, but you can see that most of the energy is being wasted, and that it's mostly wasted as heat.

And here's the **detailed** one:

100 J is 20 squares wide...

100 J energy in

...so each square represents 100 ÷ 20 = 5 J.

The heat energy wasted is 10 squares wide, so that'll be 10 × 5 = 50 J...

50 J heat energy

20 J sound energy

30 J useful kinetic energy

And the useful kinetic energy will be 6 × 5 = 30 J.

...and the sound energy will be 4 × 5 = 20 J.

Sankey diagrams = Energy transformation diagrams

They might ask you to draw a Sankey diagram in the exam. Hooray for drawing pictures in exams.

Warm-Up and Exam Questions

You must be getting used to the routine by now — the warm-up questions get you, well, warmed up, and the exam questions give you some idea of what you'll have to cope with on the day.

Warm-Up Questions

1) What type of energy is stored in food?
2) State the principle of the conservation of energy.
3) Give an example of a device that transfers electrical energy to light energy.
4) Modern appliances tend to be more energy-efficient than older ones. What does this mean?
5) Why is the efficiency of a machine always less than 100%?

Exam Questions

1   A hairdryer is supplied with 1200 J of electrical energy each second. The hairdryer transforms this energy into 120 J of sound energy and 100 J of useful kinetic energy. The rest is transformed into useful heat energy.

   (a)   Calculate how much energy the hairdryer transforms into heat energy each second.

   (1 mark)

   (b)   Calculate the efficiency of the hairdryer.
         Write down the equation you use and clearly show how you work out your answer.

   (3 marks)

   (c)   Circle the correct answer to complete the sentence below.

         The hairdryer could be made more
         efficient by reducing the amount of energy wasted as

         | heat energy |
         | kinetic energy |
         | sound energy |

         .

   (1 mark)

2   Paul is testing the efficiency of four different light bulbs.

   (a)   Sankey diagrams for each of the bulbs are shown below.
         Which of the bulbs (**A–D**) is the most efficient? Circle the correct answer.

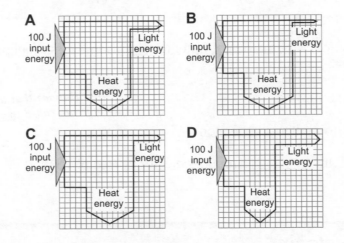

   (1 mark)

   (b)   Bulb C transfers 90 J of energy to heat energy for every 100 J put in.
         Calculate its efficiency as a percentage.

   (2 marks)

Power Stations

There are many different types of <u>energy resource</u>.
They fit into <u>two types</u>: <u>renewable</u> and <u>non-renewable</u>.

Non-Renewable Energy Resources Will Run Out One Day

The <u>non-renewables</u> are:

*Non-renewable means it
will eventually run out.*

Nuclear fuels:
* <u>uranium</u>
* and <u>plutonium</u>

Fossil fuels:
* <u>coal</u>
* <u>oil</u>
* and <u>natural gas</u>

1) They will <u>all 'run out'</u> one day.
2) They all do <u>damage</u> to the environment.
3) But they provide <u>most of our energy</u>.

Energy Sources can be Burnt to Drive Turbines in Power Stations

1) Almost <u>all</u> fossil-fuel (<u>coal</u>, <u>oil</u> and <u>gas</u>) <u>power stations</u> work in the <u>same</u> way.

2) The <u>basic features</u> of a typical power station are shown here:

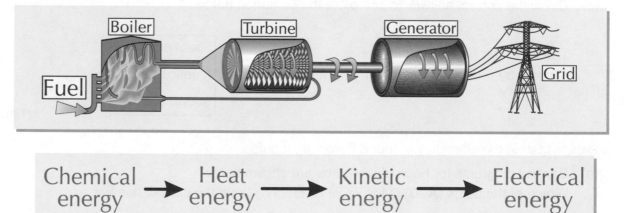

Chemical energy → Heat energy → Kinetic energy → Electrical energy

3) The <u>fuel</u> (the energy source) is <u>burnt</u> to <u>heat water</u> (or <u>air</u> in some fossil-fuel power stations) to produce <u>steam</u>.

4) The <u>steam</u> drives (turns) a <u>turbine</u>.

Power stations that use <u>steam</u> to drive a turbine are called <u>thermal power stations</u>.

5) The <u>turbine</u> is coupled (joined) to a <u>generator</u>.

6) When the turbine <u>turns</u>, the <u>generator</u> produces <u>electricity</u> (see p. 191).

It all boils down to steam...

There's a lot more info about the various energy resources over the next few pages. But <u>none</u> of them are <u>ideal</u> — they all have pros <u>and</u> cons, and the aim is to choose the least bad option overall. Unless we want to go without heating, light, transport, electricity... and so on. (I don't.)

Nuclear Energy

Before we move on, let's take a look at <u>nuclear power</u> — another non-renewable energy source.

Nuclear Reactors are Just Fancy Boilers

1) A <u>nuclear power station</u> is almost the same as the one on the previous page.

2) Instead of burning fuel, a reaction called <u>nuclear fission</u> is used to <u>heat</u> water to make <u>steam</u> to drive <u>turbines</u>, etc. This means the <u>boiler</u> has to be slightly different.

3) Nuclear power stations take the <u>longest</u> time of all the different types of power station to <u>start up</u>.

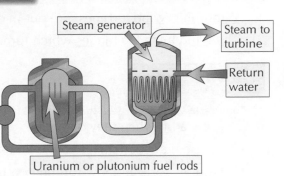

Nuclear Power Has Advantages and Disadvantages

Advantages

1) Nuclear fuel releases a <u>lot more</u> energy than <u>fossil fuels</u>.

2) Nuclear power stations <u>don't</u> produce <u>carbon dioxide</u>.

3) Nuclear <u>fuel</u> is fairly <u>cheap</u>.

Carbon dioxide (CO_2) leads to global warming (see p. 218) so not producing CO_2 is a very good thing.

Disadvantages

1) Nuclear power stations produce <u>radioactive waste</u> which is <u>dangerous</u> as it gives out <u>ionising radiation</u>.

2) The waste is also <u>hard</u> to get <u>rid</u> of as it stays radioactive for a <u>long time</u> and radioactivity is '<u>invisible</u>'.

3) <u>Exposure</u> to lots of ionising radiation (see page 213) can cause <u>damage to living cells</u>. Exposure to <u>even more</u> ionising radiation could lead to <u>cancer</u> or <u>cell death</u>.

4) Nuclear power stations take a very <u>long time</u> to start up.

5) The <u>overall cost</u> of nuclear power is <u>high</u> because it costs a lot to <u>build</u> the power stations.

6) Nuclear fuel will <u>run out</u> (it's <u>non-renewable</u>).

Many people object to nuclear energy because of the waste

Nuclear power sounds a bit scary at first, but the method of using it is just the same as for coal and oil and all that boring stuff — you give off some <u>heat</u>, which boils <u>water</u> to make <u>steam</u>. Simple.

Wind and Solar Energy

Wind and solar energy are renewable sources so they will not run out.

Wind Power — Lots of Little Wind Turbines

1) Windmills (wind turbines) are put in open spaces like on hills or at the coast.

2) The wind turns the blades which turn a turbine directly — no need for steam.

Advantages

- No pollution or carbon dioxide produced during use (only a bit when they're made).
- No permanent damage to the landscape.
- No fuel costs and low running costs.
- Wind is a renewable energy source — it won't run out.

Disadvantages

- They take up a lot of space, which can spoil the views.
- The noise can be annoying for people living near them.
- There's no power when the wind stops.
- You can't just turn up the wind and make more power whenever it's needed.
- Initial costs are quite high.

Solar Cells — Expensive But Better For The Environment

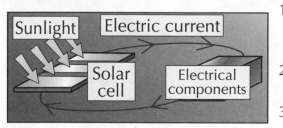

1) Radiation from the Sun is used to make electricity directly from sunlight in solar cells.

   Solar cells can also be called photocells.

2) Solar power is often used in sunny places that don't have access to other power supplies.

3) It's usually used on a small scale — to power individual homes, electric road signs and satellites.

Advantages

- No pollution or carbon dioxide when you use them.
- Work well in sunny places in the daytime.
- There are almost no running costs, so the energy is free.
- The sun is a renewable energy source — it won't run out.

Disadvantages

- Initial costs are high.
- They use quite a lot of energy to make.
- There's some pollution when you make them.
- It's not always practical or affordable to connect them to the National Grid.
- They depend on the weather, which is bad for cloudy countries like Britain.

People love the idea of wind power — just not in their backyard...

There's no perfect source of energy. Even renewable sources like wind and solar power have problems.

Wave and Tidal Energy

More renewable energy sources — <u>wave power</u> and <u>tidal power</u>.

Wave Power — Lots of Little Wave-Powered Turbines

1) <u>Wave-powered</u> turbines are put around the <u>coast</u>.
2) As waves come in they move air <u>up and down</u> which turns a turbine <u>directly</u> to make electricity.
3) Wave power doesn't work on a <u>large scale</u>, but it's <u>useful</u> on <u>small islands</u>.

Advantages

- <u>No pollution</u> or <u>carbon dioxide</u> produced.
- <u>No fuel costs</u> and <u>low running costs</u>.
- <u>Renewable</u>.

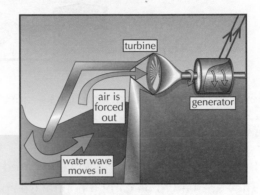

Disadvantages

- Wave turbines <u>spoil the view</u>.
- They're a <u>danger to boats</u>.
- They depend on the <u>weather</u> because waves need <u>wind</u>.
- <u>Initial costs</u> are <u>high</u>.

Tidal Barrages — Using the Sun and Moon's Gravity

1) <u>Tidal barrages</u> are <u>big dams</u> built across the mouth of a <u>river</u>, with <u>turbines</u> in them.
2) As the <u>tide comes in</u> the water rises <u>several metres</u>, turning the <u>turbines</u>.
3) The water is then allowed out through the turbines at a <u>set speed</u>, making electricity.
4) The <u>force</u> to move the water comes from the <u>gravity</u> of the <u>Sun</u> and the <u>Moon</u>.

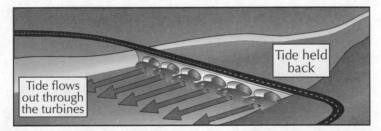

Advantages

- <u>No pollution</u> or <u>carbon dioxide</u> produced.
- Tides are <u>quite reliable</u>.
- They produce <u>lots of energy</u>.
- <u>No fuel costs</u> and <u>low running costs</u>.
- <u>Renewable</u>.

Disadvantages

- Tidal barrages <u>spoil the view</u>.
- They <u>affect boats</u> and <u>wildlife habitats</u>.
- They <u>don't work</u> when the <u>water level</u> is the <u>same</u> either side, which happens four times a day because of the tides.
- <u>Initial costs</u> are <u>quite high</u>.

Don't get wave power and tidal power confused

So now you know the <u>big big differences</u> between <u>tidal power</u> and <u>wave power</u>. They both involve salty seawater, sure — but they use it in different ways. Smile and enjoy. And <u>learn</u>.

Biofuels and Geothermal Energy

There's <u>more renewable energy</u> to be found in piles of rubbish, rocks and rainwater.

Biofuels are Made from Plants and Waste

1) Biofuels are <u>renewable energy resources</u> that come from <u>plants</u> or <u>rotting waste</u>.

2) They're <u>burnt</u> like fossil fuels in <u>thermal power stations</u> (see p. 180).

Biofuels are also called biomass.

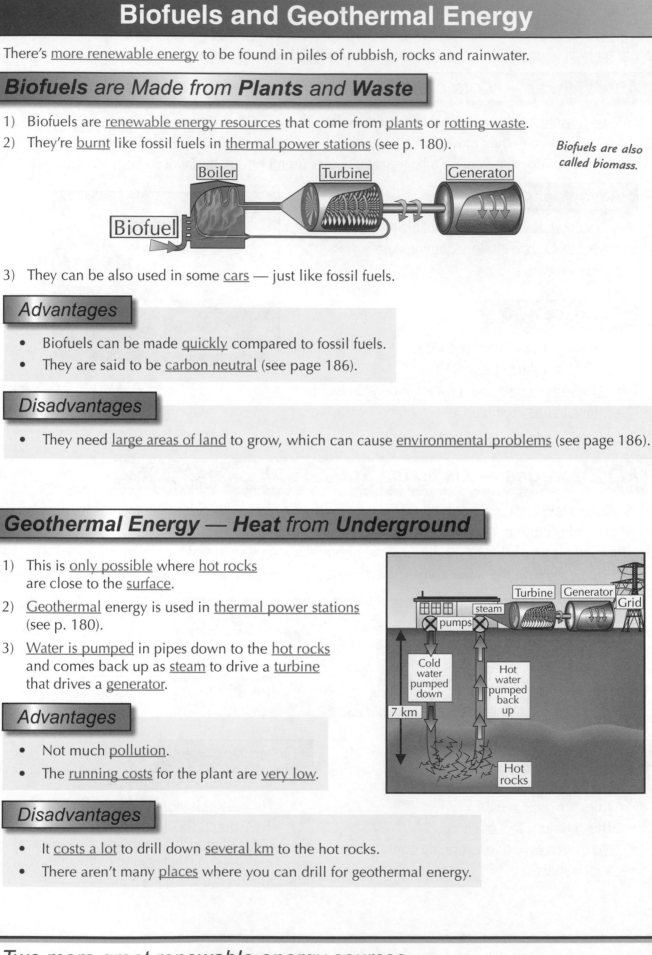

3) They can be also used in some <u>cars</u> — just like fossil fuels.

Advantages

- Biofuels can be made <u>quickly</u> compared to fossil fuels.
- They are said to be <u>carbon neutral</u> (see page 186).

Disadvantages

- They need <u>large areas of land</u> to grow, which can cause <u>environmental problems</u> (see page 186).

Geothermal Energy — Heat from Underground

1) This is <u>only possible</u> where <u>hot rocks</u> are close to the <u>surface</u>.

2) <u>Geothermal</u> energy is used in <u>thermal power stations</u> (see p. 180).

3) <u>Water is pumped</u> in pipes down to the <u>hot rocks</u> and comes back up as <u>steam</u> to drive a <u>turbine</u> that drives a <u>generator</u>.

Advantages

- Not much <u>pollution</u>.
- The <u>running costs</u> for the plant are <u>very low</u>.

Disadvantages

- It <u>costs a lot</u> to drill down <u>several km</u> to the hot rocks.
- There aren't many <u>places</u> where you can drill for geothermal energy.

Two more great renewable energy sources

Biofuels aren't the nicest of things — dead plants and poo — my favourite. But burning biofuels could be a good way of sorting out our energy problems as there's a lot of the stuff about already.

Hydroelectricity

One final type of <u>renewable energy</u> to learn about — <u>hydroelectric energy</u>.

Hydroelectricity uses Dams

1) <u>Valleys</u> are <u>flooded</u> by building a <u>big dam</u>.

2) The dam catches and stores <u>rainwater</u>.

3) The water is allowed out <u>through turbines</u>, driving them <u>directly</u>.

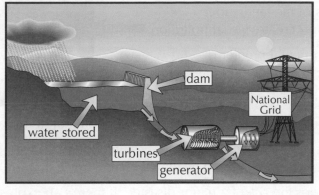

4) Here's a <u>block diagram</u>:

| 1) Water stored in a <u>reservoir</u> above the <u>turbines</u> using a <u>dam</u>. | → | 2) <u>Gravity</u> causes the water to rush through the <u>turbines</u>. | → | 3) A <u>generator</u> makes <u>electricity</u> from the movement of the turbines. |

Advantages

1) <u>No pollution</u> or <u>carbon dioxide</u> released when they're running.

2) Electricity can be made whenever it's <u>needed</u>.

3) It's fairly <u>reliable</u> (except during <u>droughts</u>).

4) <u>No fuel costs</u> and <u>low running costs</u>.

Disadvantages

1) <u>Initial costs</u> are <u>high</u>.

2) <u>Rotting plants</u> in the <u>flooded valley</u> give off CO_2.

3) Wildlife can <u>lose</u> their <u>habitat</u>.

4) Reservoirs behind the dams can look <u>ugly</u> when they <u>dry up</u>.

Ugly and damaging to habitats, but relatively clean

In Britain only a pretty <u>small percentage</u> of our electricity comes from <u>hydroelectric power</u> at the moment, but in some other parts of the world they rely much more heavily on it. For example, in the last few years, <u>99%</u> of <u>Norway</u>'s energy came from hydroelectric power. 99% — that's huge!

Energy Sources and the Environment

They might produce lots of energy, but using <u>non-renewable energy sources</u> and <u>biofuels</u> to generate electricity can have <u>damaging effects</u> on the <u>environment</u>. Read on...

Non-Renewables are Linked to Environmental Problems

1) All <u>fossil fuels</u> release <u>carbon dioxide</u> (CO_2) into the atmosphere when they're burned. All this CO_2 adds to the <u>greenhouse effect</u>, and contributes to <u>global warming</u> (see p. 218-219).

2) Burning coal and oil releases <u>sulfur dioxide</u>, which causes <u>acid rain</u> (which can <u>harm</u> plants and wildlife).

3) <u>Coal mining</u> makes a <u>mess</u> of the <u>landscape</u>, destroys <u>wildlife habitats</u> and creates <u>visual pollution</u>.

4) <u>Oil spillages</u> cause <u>environmental problems</u>, affecting creatures that live in and around the sea.

5) <u>Nuclear power</u> doesn't produce any harmful gases.

6) But the <u>nuclear waste</u> it produces is very <u>dangerous</u>. It's very difficult to <u>make safe</u> and <u>get rid of</u>.

7) The <u>overall cost</u> of nuclear power is <u>high</u>. The cost of setting up the <u>power plant</u> and final <u>decommissioning</u> (taking the <u>plant apart</u> and <u>dealing</u> with any <u>nuclear waste</u>) are both huge.

8) <u>Nuclear power</u> always carries the risk of a <u>major disaster</u>. If there's an explosion at the power plant, a lot of dangerous material could be released into the atmosphere.

Biofuels Have Their Disadvantages Too

1) The <u>plants</u> that grow to produce biofuels (or to feed the animals that produce the dung) <u>take in</u> CO_2 from the atmosphere as they grow.

2) When the biofuels are <u>burnt</u>, this CO_2 is <u>re-released</u> into the atmosphere.

3) So the overall amount of CO_2 in the atmosphere <u>stays the same</u> — this is why biofuels are said to be <u>carbon neutral</u>.

4) In some regions, large areas of <u>forest</u> have been <u>cleared</u> to make room to grow <u>biofuels</u>, which causes lots of species to lose their <u>natural habitats</u>.

Huge areas of land are needed to produce biofuels on a large scale.

5) The <u>rotting</u> and <u>burning</u> of the plants from these forests also releases <u>CO_2</u> and <u>methane</u> gases.

Carbon Capture can Reduce the Impact of Carbon Dioxide

1) <u>Carbon capture and storage</u> (CCS) is used to <u>reduce</u> the amount of CO_2 released into the atmosphere and help <u>reduce</u> the strength of the <u>greenhouse effect</u> (see page 217).

2) CCS works by <u>collecting</u> the CO_2 from power stations <u>before</u> it is released into the atmosphere.

3) The captured CO_2 can then be <u>pumped</u> into empty <u>gas fields</u> and <u>oil fields</u> like those under the <u>North Sea</u>. It can be safely <u>stored</u> there without it adding to the greenhouse effect.

4) CCS is a <u>new technology</u> that's <u>developing quickly</u>. There might be loads of new and exciting ways to trap CO_2 just around the corner.

Empty oil and gas fields are just the empty holes underground left over when all the fuel has been removed.

Comparison of Energy Resources

Here's a nice summary of the good and bad points of all the different energy sources.

Set-Up/Decommissioning (Shut down) Time

1) These are both affected by the size of the power station and how complicated it is to design and build.

2) Planning issues can also add to the time it takes to set up a power station. E.g. talks over whether a nuclear power station should be built on a stretch of beautiful coastline can last years.

3) Gas power stations are the quickest of the fossil-fuel power stations to set up.

4) Nuclear power stations take by far the longest (and cost the most) to decommission (shut down).

Set-Up Costs

1) Renewable resources often need bigger power stations than non-renewables to produce the same amount of electricity

2) The bigger the power station, the more expensive it is to build.

3) Nuclear reactors and hydroelectric dams are huge and complicated to build. This means they're usually the most expensive.

Can we Rely on Them?

1) All the non-renewables are reliable energy sources (until they run out).

2) Many of the renewable sources depend on the weather. This means they're pretty unreliable here in the UK.

3) Tidal power, geothermal power and biofuels are all reliable (they don't depend on the weather).

Running/Fuel Costs

Renewables usually have the lowest running costs, because there's no actual fuel used.

Location Issues

A power station has to be near to the stuff it runs on.

Solar — pretty much anywhere, though the sunnier the better

Gas — pretty much anywhere there's piped gas (most of the UK)

Hydroelectric — hilly, rainy places with floodable valleys, e.g. the Lake District, Scottish Highlands

Wind — exposed, windy places like coasts or out at sea

Oil — near the coast (oil transported by sea)

Waves — on or near the coast

Coal — near coal mines, e.g. Yorkshire, Wales

Nuclear — away from people (in case of disaster), near water (for cooling)

Tidal — big river estuaries where a dam can be built

Geothermal — only in volcanic places

Environmental Issues

1) If there's a fuel involved, there will be waste pollution.

2) If it relies on the weather, it's often ugly and noisy.

Atmospheric Pollution	Using Up Resources
Coal, Oil, Gas, (+ others, though less so).	Coal, Oil, Gas, Nuclear.

Visual Pollution	Noise Pollution
Coal, Oil, Gas, Nuclear, Tidal, Waves, Wind, Hydroelectric.	Coal, Oil, Gas, Nuclear, Wind.

Other Problems	Damages
Nuclear (dangerous waste, explosions), Hydroelectric (dams bursting).	Wildlife Habitats Hydroelectric, Tidal, Biofuels.

No energy source is perfect...

Every type of energy resource has advantages and disadvantages — and they're all here for you to learn. Things aren't all bad though, because it's nearly the end of the section — just the questions to go.

Warm-Up and Exam Questions

Hopefully the last few pages have stuck, but there's only one way to check — and that's with some questions. Warm-up questions to get you started, and exam questions to really get your teeth into.

Warm-Up Questions

1) List the non-renewable energy sources.
2) Describe the major problems with using nuclear power.
3) Give two disadvantages of using solar cells.
4) Describe the difference between wave and tidal power.
5) Explain what is meant by biofuels.
6) Give two ways in which using coal as an energy source causes environmental problems.
7) What does CCS stand for?

Exam Questions

1 An old coal-fired power station has an output of 2 MW (2 million watts). The electricity company plans to replace it with wind turbines which have a maximum output of 4000 W each.

    (a) Calculate the minimum number of wind turbines required to replace the old power station.

(1 mark)

    (b) Suggest why more wind turbines than this might be needed in reality.

(1 mark)

    (c) Give **two** reasons why some people might oppose the wind farm development.

(2 marks)

2 The diagram below shows a block diagram which explains how a thermal power station works. Complete the sentences on the block diagram.

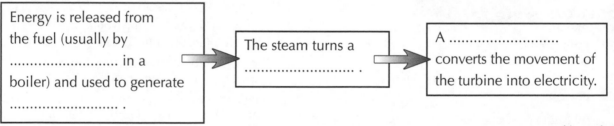

    Energy is released from the fuel (usually by .... in a boiler) and used to generate ....

    The steam turns a ....

    A .... converts the movement of the turbine into electricity.

(4 marks)

3 The inhabitants of a remote island do not have access to fossil fuels or nuclear energy. They are considering using wind, solar and hydroelectric power to generate electricity.

    (a) Suggest **two** other renewable energy resources they could use.

(2 marks)

    (b) The islanders decide that both solar and hydroelectric power could reliably generate enough electricity for all their needs. Suggest **two** other factors they should consider when deciding which method of electricity generation to use.

(2 marks)

    (c) *In this question you will be assessed on the quality of your English, the organisation of your ideas and your use of appropriate specialist vocabulary.*

        Don't panic — this isn't as scary as it looks. All it means is that you need to write in full sentences and use proper spelling and punctuation. You'll also need to use scientific words that relate to the question.

        Discuss the advantages and disadvantages of using solar energy compared to hydroelectric energy to generate electricity.

(6 marks)

Exam Questions

4   Geothermal energy can be described as a renewable energy source.

(a) Describe what is meant by geothermal energy.

(1 mark)

(b) Explain what 'renewable energy' means.

(1 mark)

(c) Give **two** disadvantages of using geothermal energy to generate electricity.

(2 marks)

(d) In geothermal energy power plants, steam is used to drive turbines.
Which of the energy sources listed below drive turbines directly, rather than making
steam to drive a turbine? Tick the boxes next to the **two** correct answers.

A   Nuclear   ☐

B   Gas   ☐

C   Wind   ☐

D   Tidal   ☐

(2 marks)

5   Strattington Council are discussing plans to build a new power station along their coastline.

(a) Draw straight lines to link **one** advantage and **one** disadvantage to each of the
energy sources listed below.

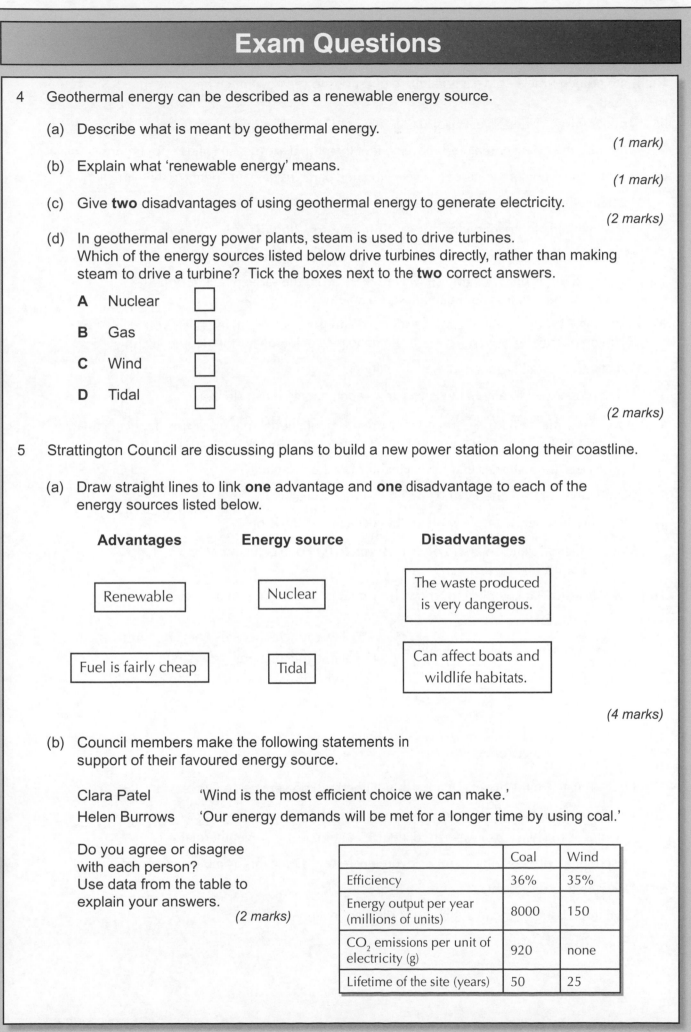

Advantages	Energy source	Disadvantages
Renewable	Nuclear	The waste produced is very dangerous.
Fuel is fairly cheap	Tidal	Can affect boats and wildlife habitats.

(4 marks)

(b) Council members make the following statements in
support of their favoured energy source.

Clara Patel   'Wind is the most efficient choice we can make.'

Helen Burrows   'Our energy demands will be met for a longer time by using coal.'

Do you agree or disagree
with each person?
Use data from the table to
explain your answers.

(2 marks)

	Coal	Wind
Efficiency	36%	35%
Energy output per year (millions of units)	8000	150
CO_2 emissions per unit of electricity (g)	920	none
Lifetime of the site (years)	50	25

Revision Summary for Section 7

Right, it's crunch time — have a go at these questions to see how much has gone in...

1) True or false? A hot object cools faster in a cold room than in a warm room.

2) Describe the arrangement and movement of the particles in: a) solids,   b) liquids,   c) gases.

3) What is the name of the process where vibrating particles pass on energy to the particles next to them?

4) Explain why survival blankets are silver.

5) What happens to the particles of a gas as it turns to a liquid?

6) What is the name given to the process where a gas turns to a liquid?

7) The two designs of car engine shown are made from the same material. Which engine will transfer heat quicker? Explain why.

Engine A   Engine B

8)* If it costs £4000 to double glaze your house and the double glazing saves you £100 on energy bills every year, calculate the payback time for the double glazing.

9) What can you tell from a material's U-value?

10) What property of a material tells you how much energy it can store?

11)* A toy has a mass of 0.5 kg. The toy is made from a material that has a specific heat capacity of 1000 J/kg°C. How much energy does it take to heat the toy from 20 °C to 200 °C?

12) Do heaters use materials that have a high or low heat capacity?

13) Name nine types of energy and give an example of each.

14) Describe the energy transformations that occur in a television.

15)* What is the efficiency of a motor that converts 100 J of electrical energy into 70 J of useful kinetic energy?

16)* The following Sankey diagram shows how energy is converted in a catapult.

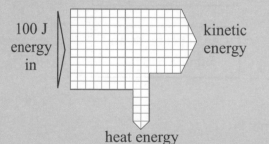

100 J energy in

kinetic energy

heat energy

a) How much energy is converted into kinetic energy?
b) How much energy is wasted?
c) What is the efficiency of the catapult?

17) Draw a diagram to show how a fossil-fuel (thermal) power station works.

18) Give one advantage and one disadvantage for using the following types of power:
     a) wind,   b) solar,   c) wave,   d) tidal,   e) biofuels,   f) geothermal.

19) Describe the process of generating hydroelectricity. Draw this as a block diagram.

20) Describe two disadvantages of using hydroelectricity.

21) Give three issues that affect the use of different energy resources.

* Answers on p. 245

Generating Electricity

Generators make electricity using coils and magnets. It's a bit weird, but don't get bogged down.

Moving a *Magnet* in a *Coil* of Wire Induces a *Current*

1) You can create a current in a coil of wire by moving a magnet in or near it.

2) This is called electromagnetic induction (or the dynamo effect).

3) As you move the magnet, the magnetic field through the coil changes. This change induces (creates) a voltage which creates a current if the coil is part of a complete circuit.

4) If you change the direction of the magnet moving in the coil of wire, it changes the direction of the current.

5) Putting the magnet through the coil of wire the other way round (south end first rather than north) will produce a current in the opposite direction.

6) You can also induce a current in a wire by moving a coil of wire in a magnetic field (see below).

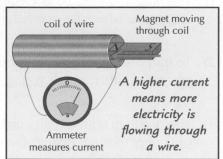

coil of wire   Magnet moving through coil

Ammeter measures current

A higher current means more electricity is flowing through a wire.

A higher voltage means the electric current has more energy.

Four Factors Affect the Size of the Induced Current

1) If you want a bigger current you have to increase at least one of these four things:

> 1) The STRENGTH of the MAGNET
> 2) The AREA of the COIL
> 3) The number of TURNS on the COIL
> 4) The SPEED of movement

2) To reduce the current, you would reduce one of those factors.

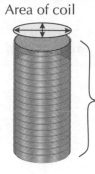

Area of coil

Number of turns (number of loops)

This is How All Generators Work

1) Generators generate currents by electromagnetic induction.

2) They do this by rotating (turning) a magnet or by rotating a coil of wire and keeping the magnet fixed.

3) They generate an alternating current (AC).

4) All generators just need something to do the turning. That could be anything from a steam-driven turbine (like in a power station, see p. 180) to a water wheel.

5) Dynamos are small-scale generators. They're used to power low-power devices, e.g. on bikes to power the lights.

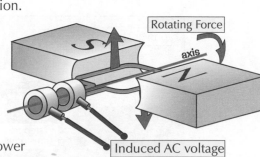

Rotating Force

axis

Induced AC voltage

So THAT's how they make electricity — I always wondered...

The National Grid (p.192) is fed by hundreds of generators — mostly powered by burning things to make steam, which turns a turbine, which turns the coil in a magnetic field. And that's how you get electricity. Great and also slightly weird at the same time. Isn't physics fun...

Electricity and the National Grid

The National Grid is the network of pylons and cables that covers the whole of Britain, getting electricity to homes everywhere. Whoever you pay for your electricity, it's the National Grid that gets it to you.

Electricity is Distributed via the National Grid...

1) The National Grid takes electrical energy from power stations to where it's needed in homes and industry.

2) To transmit the huge amount of power needed, you need either a high voltage or a high current.

3) The problem with a high current is that you lose loads of energy through heat in the cables.

4) It's much cheaper to boost the voltage up really high (to 400 000 V) and keep the current very low.

'Distributed' is just a fancy way of saying the electricity is spread out and taken to where it's needed.

...With a Little Help from Pylons and Transformers

1) To get the voltage to 400 000 V to transmit power requires transformers as well as big pylons.

2) The step-up transformers are used to increase the voltage up to 400 000 V at one end.

3) It's then reduced again ('stepped down') to safe usable levels using a step-down transformer.

power station

step-up transformer

step-down transformer

consumers

Transformers can increase or decrease the voltage

Don't worry about the details — just remember that transformers can increase and decrease the voltage to minimise energy losses in the National Grid. Because of this they save energy and money.

Electricity and the National Grid

There are **Different Ways** to Transmit Electricity

1) Electrical energy can be moved around by cables <u>buried in the ground</u>, as well as in <u>overhead</u> power lines.

2) Each different option has its <u>pros and cons</u>:

	Set-up cost	Amount of looking after needed	Easy to get to if there's a problem?	How it looks	Affected by weather	Reliability	How easy to set up
Overhead Cables	lower	lots needed	yes	ugly	yes	less reliable	easy
Underground Cables	higher	not much	no	hidden	no	more reliable	hard

Supply and *Demand*

1) Our energy demands keep on <u>increasing</u>.

2) There are <u>two ways</u> these demands can be met in the future:

The <u>energy supplied</u> to the National Grid will need to <u>increase</u>, e.g. by building more power stations.

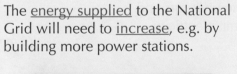

OR

The <u>energy demands</u> of consumers (people who use electricity — us) will need to <u>decrease</u>, e.g. by washing clothes at lower temperatures.

Energy demands are ever-increasing

The National Grid has been working ever since 1935. It's gone through loads of changes and updates since then to meet our ever-increasing energy demands. We all need to try and cut down the amount of energy we use and waste every day, to <u>reduce</u> the country's energy demands.

Warm-Up and Exam Questions

Have you been reading the last three pages carefully? Only one way to tell really — have a go at these warm-up and exam questions. If you get any wrong, go back and read those bits again.

Warm-Up Questions

1) What kind of current do generators produce — AC or DC?
2) What is a dynamo?
3) What is the National Grid?
4) Are our energy demands increasing or decreasing?

Exam Questions

1 The National Grid transmits electricity from power stations to homes and businesses all over the country.

(a) Circle the correct answers to complete the sentence below.

Electricity is transmitted over long distances in the

National Grid at [high / low] voltage and [high / low] current.

(2 marks)

(b) Explain why the National Grid uses step-up transformers.

(2 marks)

(c) *In this question you will be assessed on the quality of your English, the organisation of your ideas and your use of appropriate specialist vocabulary.*

The residents of a remote part of Scotland are planning to be connected to the National Grid using underground cables.

Discuss the advantages and disadvantages of using underground cables compared to overhead power lines to transmit electricity.

(6 marks)

2 The diagram shows a coil of wire connected to an ammeter. Tim moves a bar magnet into the coil as shown. The pointer on the ammeter moves to the left.

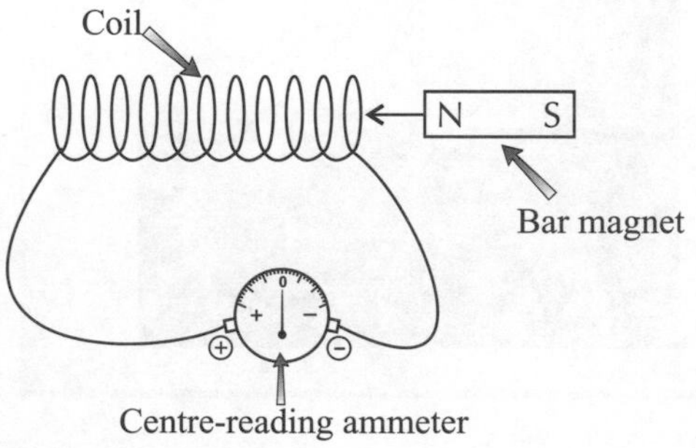

Coil

N S

Bar magnet

Centre-reading ammeter

(a) Explain why the pointer moves.

(1 mark)

(b) What could Tim do to get the ammeter's pointer to move to the right?

(1 mark)

(c) How could Tim get a larger reading on the ammeter?

(1 mark)

(d) What reading will the ammeter show if Tim holds the magnet still inside the coil?

(1 mark)

Power and the Cost of Electricity

Electrical power is the <u>amount of electrical energy used per second</u>.

Running Costs Depend on an Appliance's Power Rating

1) Power is measured in <u>watts</u> (W) or <u>kilowatts</u> (kW).

2) <u>1 kW = 1000 W</u>.

Things that need electrical energy to work are usually called components, devices or appliances.

3) An appliance with a <u>high</u> power rating uses <u>more</u> energy <u>per second</u> than something with a lower power rating.

4) So <u>high-power</u> appliances <u>cost more</u> to use because they use <u>more energy</u>.

5) The <u>power rating</u> of an appliance can be found using this equation:

$$\text{Power (in W)} = \text{Voltage (in V)} \times \text{Current (in A)}$$

EXAMPLE: Find the power rating of a light bulb, in W and kW, if the voltage is 230 V and the current is 0.5 A.

ANSWER: Power = Voltage × Current = 230 × 0.5 = <u>115 W</u>
115 W ÷ 1000 = <u>0.115 kW</u>

Kilowatt-hours (kWh) are "UNITS" of Energy

1) Your electricity meter records how much <u>energy</u> you use in units of <u>kilowatt-hours</u>, or <u>kWh</u>.

A kilowatt-hour is the amount of electrical energy used by a 1 kW appliance left on for 1 hour.

2) The <u>cost</u> of using an appliance depends on its <u>power rating</u> and <u>how long it's on for</u>.

3) The <u>higher</u> its power rating and the <u>longer</u> it's on, the <u>more</u> it costs.

Watt's the answer — well, part of it...

Get a bit of practice using the power equation by trying this question:
A kettle uses a current of 12 A from the 230 V mains supply. Calculate its power rating in kilowatts.*

*Answers on p.246

Power and the Cost of Electricity

There are couple of handy equations you can use to calculate the energy used by an appliance, and the cost of running it.

The **Energy Transferred** by an Appliance depends on its **Power**

You can calculate the amount of energy an appliance uses in kWh using this equation:

$$\text{ENERGY} = \text{POWER} \times \text{TIME}$$
$$\text{(in kWh)} \quad \text{(in kW)} \quad \text{(in hours)}$$

Cost depends on the **Amount** of **Energy Transferred**

1) You can calculate the cost of using an appliance with this equation:

$$\text{COST} = \text{NUMBER OF kWh} \times \text{PRICE PER kWh}$$

2) To work out the cost of electricity, you might have to work out first how many kilowatt-hours have been used, then multiply this number by the price per unit (the price per kWh).

Example

Find the cost of leaving a 60 W light bulb on for 30 minutes if 1 kWh costs 10p.

ANSWER:

1) First change 60 W into kW: 60 W = 60 ÷ 1000 kW = 0.06 kW

2) Then change minutes into hours: 30 mins ÷ 60 mins = 0.5 h

3) Energy = Power × Time = 0.06 kW × 0.5 h = 0.03 kWh

4) Cost = number of kWh × price per kWh = 0.03 × 10p = 0.3p

Another couple of equations to add to your physics tool belt...

How about another lovely question? Go on, you know you want to...
How many kWh of energy would a 2.7 kW kettle use if you ran it for 3 minutes?*

Choosing Electrical Appliances

Sadly, this isn't about what <u>colour</u> MP3 player to get. Sorry.

Sometimes You Have a *Choice* of *Electrical Equipment*

1) Before you decide which one to use, you need to look at the <u>advantages</u> <u>and disadvantages</u> (good and bad points) of each.

> - How <u>cheap/expensive</u> is it to buy?
> - How much <u>energy</u> will it <u>use/waste</u>?
> - Will it be <u>cheap to run</u>?
> - <u>Size</u> and <u>shape</u> — will it fit where you want it to? Can it be easily carried?
> - Can it be used when there <u>isn't</u> an <u>electricity supply</u>, e.g. when camping?
> - How <u>well</u> will it do the job?

2) From that you can work out which one is <u>most suitable</u> (the best) to use.

Example: Mains Fans and Hand-held Fans

	Mains-powered fan	Hand-held battery-powered fan
Cost to buy	£10-£300	£1-£15
Cost to run	Fairly cheap	Quite expensive
Size	A range of sizes — can be very large.	small
Can it be used in places without electricity?	No	Yes
Can it be used to cool large areas?	Yes	No

1) If you were picking a fan to cool a work place — a <u>mains-powered fan</u> would be best. They can be <u>very large</u> and <u>fairly cheap</u> to run, and can be used to <u>cool entire rooms</u>.

2) Also, workers might need to use their <u>hands</u> to do their job, so <u>hand-held</u> fans wouldn't be very useful.

3) If you wanted a fan to cool you while <u>travelling</u>, a <u>hand-held fan</u> would be the best choice.

4) You might <u>not</u> be near an <u>electricity supply</u> while travelling, and carrying around a <u>huge fan</u> would be annoying.

5) In the exam, you might be asked to use data to <u>compare two appliances</u>. For example, you might need to calculate the <u>efficiency</u> (p. 176) and <u>cost</u> of running devices — then you can pick the best one.

Decisions, decisions...

When choosing appliances just use your common sense. Don't panic — pick out the good and bad points of each of the appliances before you make a decision about which one is best.

Access to Electricity

Having an electricity supply isn't only great for watching telly. From keeping <u>food fresh</u> to <u>hospital care</u>, having <u>access to electricity</u> really helps improve people's lives.

People's Lives are Affected by Access to Electricity

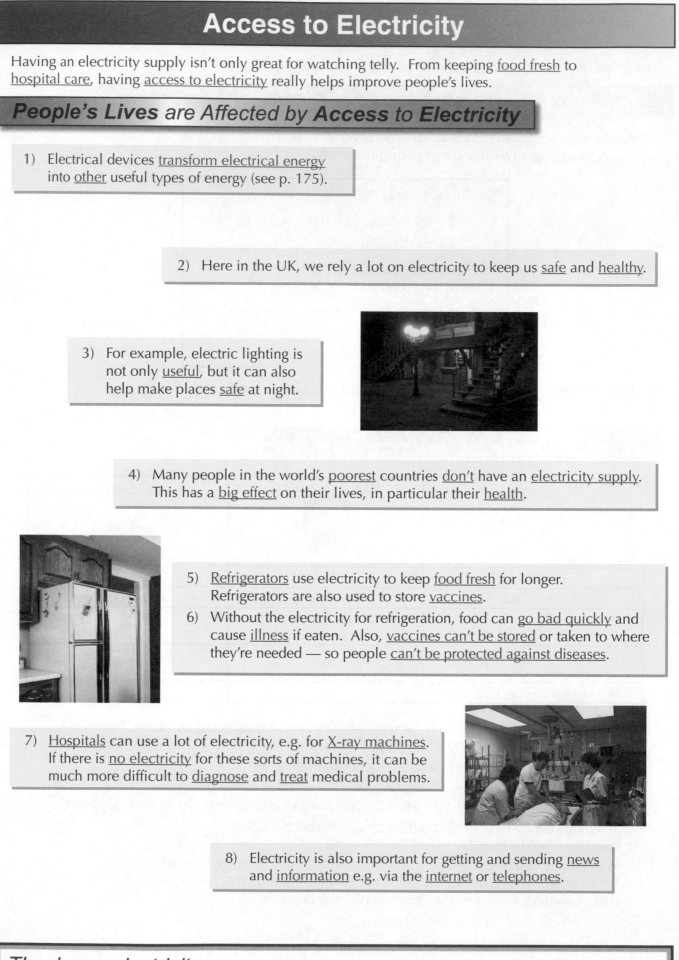

1) Electrical devices <u>transform electrical energy</u> into <u>other</u> useful types of energy (see p. 175).

2) Here in the UK, we rely a lot on electricity to keep us <u>safe</u> and <u>healthy</u>.

3) For example, electric lighting is not only <u>useful</u>, but it can also help make places <u>safe</u> at night.

4) Many people in the world's <u>poorest</u> countries <u>don't</u> have an <u>electricity supply</u>. This has a <u>big effect</u> on their lives, in particular their <u>health</u>.

5) <u>Refrigerators</u> use electricity to keep <u>food fresh</u> for longer. Refrigerators are also used to store <u>vaccines</u>.

6) Without the electricity for refrigeration, food can <u>go bad quickly</u> and cause <u>illness</u> if eaten. Also, <u>vaccines can't be stored</u> or taken to where they're needed — so people <u>can't be protected against diseases</u>.

7) <u>Hospitals</u> can use a lot of electricity, e.g. for <u>X-ray machines</u>. If there is <u>no electricity</u> for these sorts of machines, it can be much more difficult to <u>diagnose</u> and <u>treat</u> medical problems.

8) Electricity is also important for getting and sending <u>news</u> and <u>information</u> e.g. via the <u>internet</u> or <u>telephones</u>.

Thank you electricity...

Can you imagine trying to get by without using electricity? It doesn't sound fun. Make sure you know the different ways having <u>reliable access</u> to electricity improves people's standard of living.

Warm-Up and Exam Questions

I know that you can't wait to get into the exam questions, but these warm-up questions are great for getting the basics straight first.

Warm-Up Questions

1) What are the units of power?
2) Which would cost more to run for 10 minutes — a 10 kW or a 100 kW appliance?
3) Give the formula for calculating the cost of using an appliance.
4) Suggest one thing you need to consider when choosing an electrical appliance.

Exam Questions

1 John goes travelling for twelve weeks, but leaves some appliances (such as his freezer) switched on whilst he's away. He takes meter readings before his trip and on his return. The meter readings are shown below.

(a) Calculate the total energy used during this time.

(1 mark)

(b) His electricity supplier charges him 14p per kilowatt-hour (kWh).

   (i) What is a kilowatt-hour?

(1 mark)

   (ii) How much should his supplier charge him for the twelve weeks he was away? Show how you work out your answer.

(2 marks)

(c) John puts his holiday clothes on to wash. His washing machine draws 2.5 A of current when used with the 230 V mains electricity supply. Calculate the power rating of the washing machine. Circle the correct answer below.

   A 575 W

   B 575 kW

   C 92 W

   D 92 kW

(1 mark)

2 People in some countries don't have access to a reliable electricity supply like the National Grid. Describe **three** ways in which not having access to electricity can have a negative impact on people's standard of living.

(3 marks)

Wave Basics

Now it's time for the exciting science behind the <u>wave machine</u> at the swimming pool.

Waves Have Amplitude, Wavelength, Frequency and Speed

1) All waves are <u>disturbances</u> that are caused by a <u>vibrating source</u>.
2) They <u>transfer energy</u> in the direction that the <u>wave travels</u>, but <u>do not transfer matter</u>.
3) The <u>amplitude</u> is the distance from the <u>rest position</u> to a <u>crest</u> or <u>trough</u> — see picture below.

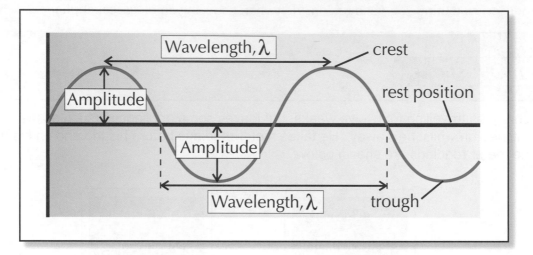

4) Waves with a <u>greater amplitude</u> have <u>more energy</u>.
5) The <u>wavelength</u> is the length of a <u>full cycle</u> of the wave, e.g. from <u>crest to crest</u>.
6) <u>Frequency</u> is the <u>number of complete waves</u> passing a certain point <u>per second</u>.
   OR the <u>number of waves</u> produced by a source <u>each second</u>.
7) Frequency is measured in <u>hertz (Hz)</u>. 1 Hz is <u>1 wave per second</u>.
8) The <u>speed</u> is how <u>fast</u> it goes.
9) You can work out the <u>distance</u> a wave has travelled by using the formula:

$$\text{distance} = \text{speed} \times \text{time}$$
$$\text{(m)} \qquad \text{(m/s)} \qquad \text{(s)}$$

Waves Can Be Transverse

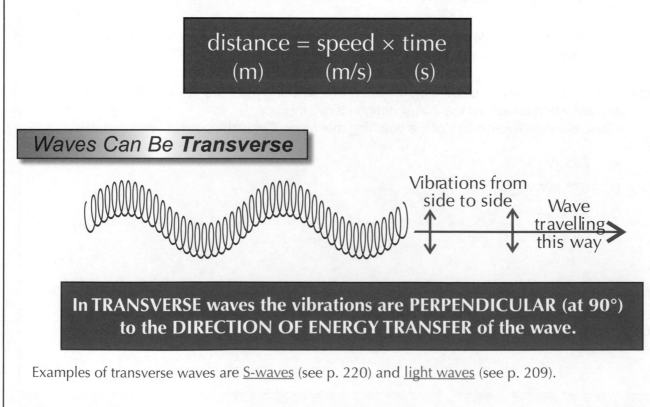

**In TRANSVERSE waves the vibrations are PERPENDICULAR (at 90°)
to the DIRECTION OF ENERGY TRANSFER of the wave.**

Examples of transverse waves are <u>S-waves</u> (see p. 220) and <u>light waves</u> (see p. 209).

Wave Basics

Longitudinal Waves have vibrations *Along the Same Line*

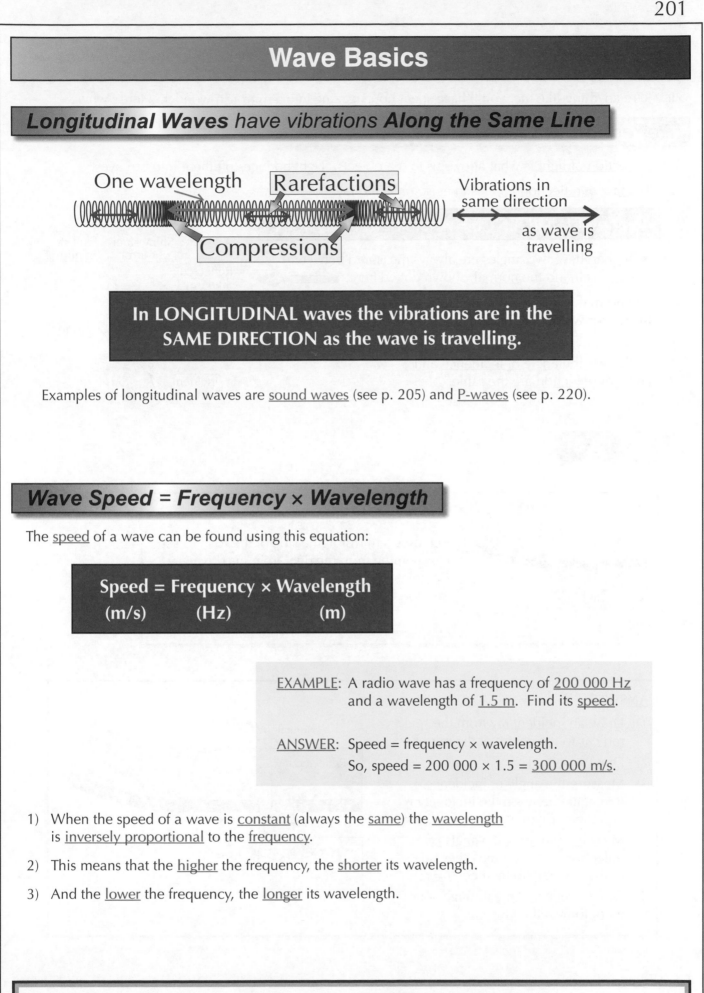

One wavelength   Rarefactions   Vibrations in same direction as wave is travelling

Compressions

In LONGITUDINAL waves the vibrations are in the SAME DIRECTION as the wave is travelling.

Examples of longitudinal waves are <u>sound waves</u> (see p. 205) and <u>P-waves</u> (see p. 220).

Wave Speed = Frequency × Wavelength

The <u>speed</u> of a wave can be found using this equation:

Speed = Frequency × Wavelength
(m/s)   (Hz)   (m)

<u>EXAMPLE</u>: A radio wave has a frequency of <u>200 000 Hz</u> and a wavelength of <u>1.5 m</u>. Find its <u>speed</u>.

<u>ANSWER</u>: Speed = frequency × wavelength.
So, speed = 200 000 × 1.5 = <u>300 000 m/s</u>.

1) When the speed of a wave is <u>constant</u> (always the <u>same</u>) the <u>wavelength</u> is <u>inversely proportional</u> to the <u>frequency</u>.

2) This means that the <u>higher</u> the frequency, the <u>shorter</u> its wavelength.

3) And the <u>lower</u> the frequency, the <u>longer</u> its wavelength.

Compressions and rarefactions — must be longitudinal

Get to grips with the wave speed equation above by having a go at this question: A sound wave travelling in a solid has a frequency of <u>19 000 Hz</u> and a wavelength of <u>0.125 m</u>. Find its speed.*

Reflection

If you're anything like me, you'll have spent hours gazing into a <u>mirror</u> in wonder. Here's why...

Reflection of Light Lets Us See Things

1) <u>Reflection of light</u> is what allows us to see objects. Light bounces off them into our eyes.

2) The <u>law of reflection</u> applies to every reflected ray:

Angle of INCIDENCE = Angle of REFLECTION

3) Note that these two angles are always measured between the <u>ray</u> itself and the <u>normal</u>, shown dotted here.

4) The normal is just a <u>line at right angles</u> to the mirror where the <u>incident ray</u> hits it.

5) Whenever you're <u>drawing</u> reflections you need to make sure the <u>angle of incidence</u> and <u>angle of reflection</u> are the same.

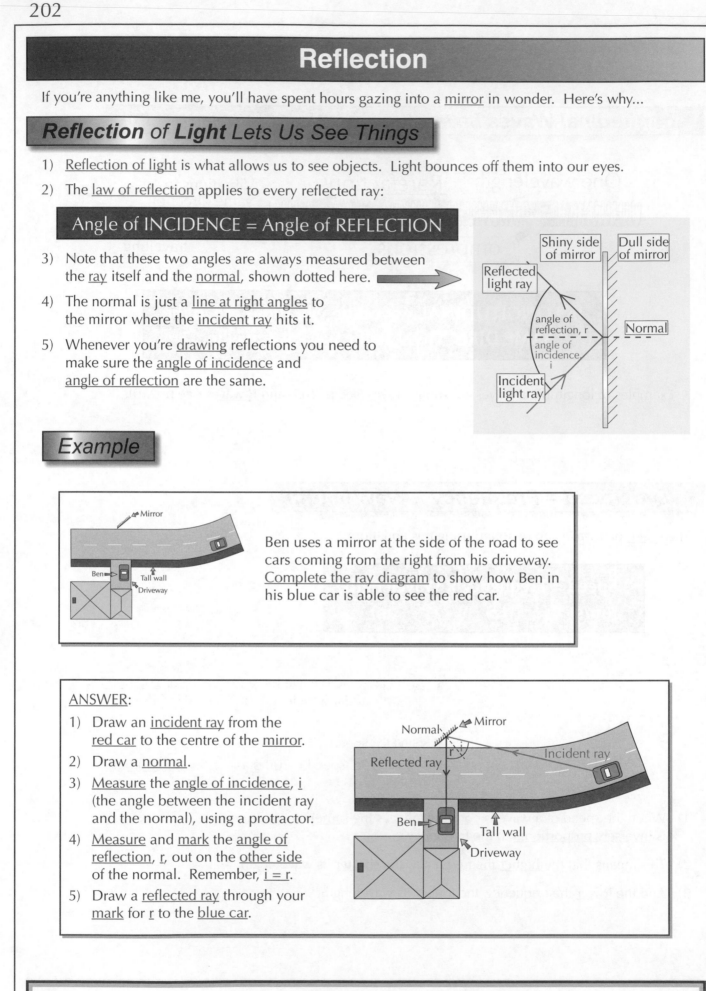

Example

Ben uses a mirror at the side of the road to see cars coming from the right from his driveway. <u>Complete the ray diagram</u> to show how Ben in his blue car is able to see the red car.

<u>ANSWER:</u>

1) Draw an <u>incident ray</u> from the <u>red car</u> to the centre of the <u>mirror</u>.

2) Draw a <u>normal</u>.

3) <u>Measure</u> the <u>angle of incidence</u>, <u>i</u> (the angle between the incident ray and the normal), using a protractor.

4) <u>Measure</u> and <u>mark</u> the <u>angle of reflection</u>, <u>r</u>, out on the <u>other side</u> of the normal. Remember, <u>i = r</u>.

5) Draw a <u>reflected ray</u> through your <u>mark</u> for <u>r</u> to the <u>blue car</u>.

The world would be a boring place without reflection

Mirrors are so great they get their own law — the law of reflection: the angle of incidence = the angle of reflection. Practise drawing nice, clear ray diagrams so that you can show how it works.

Reflection and Diffraction

If you liked reflection, you'll love <u>diffraction</u>. But there's a little bit more on reflection up first...

An *Image* Formed in a *Plane Mirror* is *Virtual* and *Upright*

Here are four important points for how an image is formed in a <u>plane mirror</u> (a mirror with a flat surface):

1) The image is the <u>same size</u> as the object.

2) It is <u>as far behind</u> the mirror as the object is in front.

3) The image is <u>virtual</u> (it appears to be coming from a completely different place) and <u>upright</u>.

4) The image is <u>laterally inverted</u> — the <u>right side</u> of the object appears to be <u>left side</u> of the image. Likewise, the left side of the object appears to be the right side of the image.

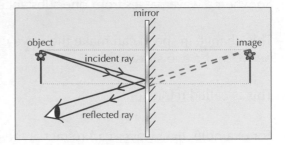

Diffraction — *Waves Spreading Out*

1) All waves <u>spread out</u> at the edges when they pass through a <u>gap</u> or <u>pass an object</u>.

> For example, you can <u>hear</u> someone through an open door even if you can't see them. The sound waves <u>diffract</u> as they go through the door and fill the room.

2) This is called <u>diffraction</u>.

3) Changing the <u>size of the gap</u> affects how much it diffracts (spreads out).

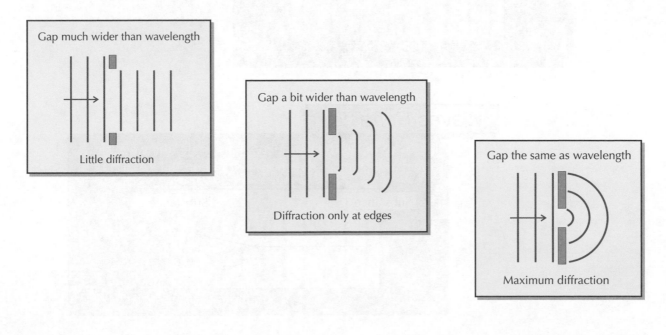

Diffraction = Spreading out...

And if gap size = wavelength you get loads of diffraction. <u>All</u> waves (light, sound, water waves...) can be <u>reflected</u> and <u>diffracted</u>. They can also be <u>refracted</u> — see the next page for more juicy details...

Refraction

Ah, and now for the most exciting wave property of all... refraction.

Refraction — Waves Changing Speed and Direction

1) Waves travel at different speeds in different substances.

2) So when a wave passes from one substance to another it changes speed.

3) This change in speed can make the wave change direction at the boundary between the two substances.

4) This is called refraction.

5) For example, light waves can refract at the boundary as they pass from air into a glass block.

6) Waves are only refracted if they meet the boundary at an angle.

7) If they're travelling at right angles to the boundary they will change speed, but NOT direction.

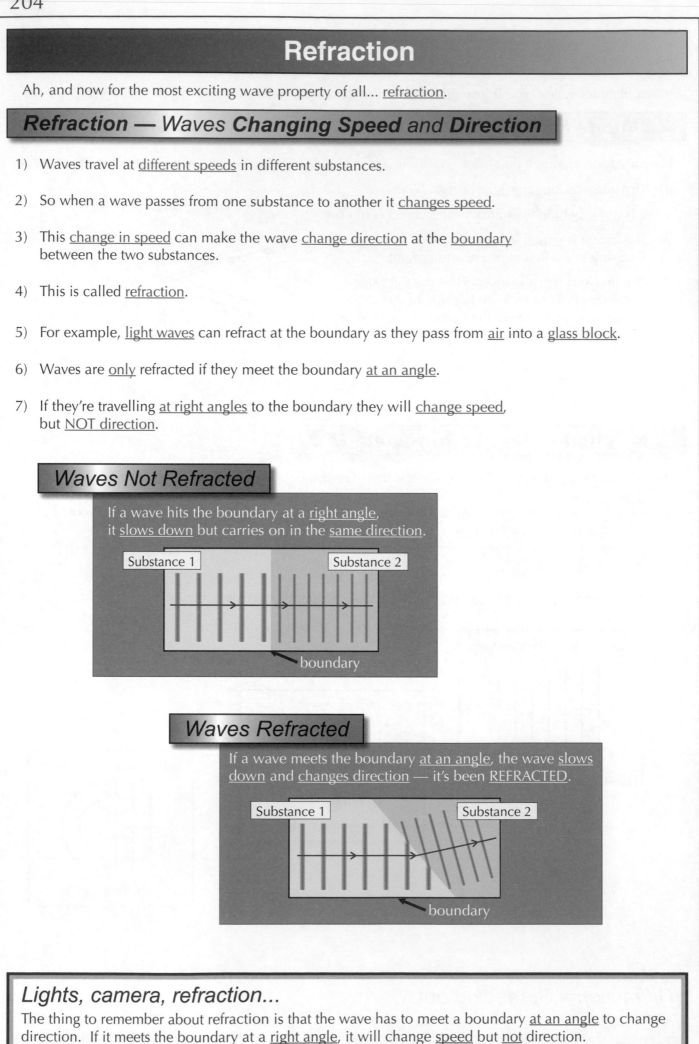

Waves Not Refracted

If a wave hits the boundary at a right angle, it slows down but carries on in the same direction.

Substance 1   Substance 2

boundary

Waves Refracted

If a wave meets the boundary at an angle, the wave slows down and changes direction — it's been REFRACTED.

Substance 1   Substance 2

boundary

Lights, camera, refraction...

The thing to remember about refraction is that the wave has to meet a boundary at an angle to change direction. If it meets the boundary at a right angle, it will change speed but not direction.

Sound Waves

We hear sounds after <u>vibrations</u> reach our <u>eardrums</u>.

Sound Travels as a *Wave*

1) <u>Sound waves</u> are caused by <u>vibrating objects</u>.

2) These vibrations are passed through the surrounding medium (substance, e.g. air) as a series of <u>compressions</u> (squashed up bits).

3) Sound waves are a type of <u>longitudinal wave</u> (see page 201).

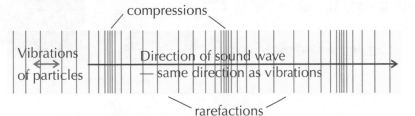

4) Sometimes the sound will eventually travel into someone's <u>ear</u>, at which point the person might <u>hear it</u>.

5) Sound can't travel in <u>space</u>, because it's mostly a <u>vacuum</u> (there are no particles).

Sound Waves Can **Reflect, Refract and Diffract**

1) Sound waves will be <u>reflected</u> by <u>hard flat surfaces</u>.

2) <u>Echoes</u> are just <u>reflected</u> sound waves.

3) You hear a <u>delay</u> between the <u>original</u> sound and the <u>echo</u> because the echoed sound waves have to <u>travel further</u>, and so take <u>longer</u> to reach your ears.

4) Sound waves will also <u>diffract</u> and <u>refract</u> (see p. 203 and p. 204).

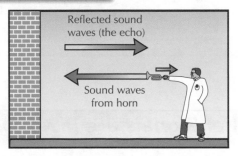

The **Higher** the **Frequency**, the Higher the **Pitch**

1) <u>High frequency</u> sound waves sound <u>high pitched</u> like a <u>squeaking mouse</u>.

2) <u>Low frequency</u> sound waves sound <u>low pitched</u> like a <u>mooing cow</u>.

3) <u>High frequency</u> (or high pitch) also means <u>shorter wavelength</u> (see page 201).

4) The <u>loudness</u> of a sound depends on the <u>amplitude</u> of the sound wave.

5) A <u>higher amplitude</u> means a <u>louder sound</u>.

Frequency is the number of complete vibrations each second (see p. 200).

1) Sound waves with frequencies <u>above 20 000 Hz</u> are called <u>ultrasound</u>.

2) Ultrasound is too <u>high pitched</u> for humans to hear.

3) Sound that has a frequency <u>below 20 Hz</u> is called <u>infrasound</u>.

4) Infrasound is too <u>low pitched</u> for humans to hear.

Analogue and Digital Signals

Sound and images can be sent as analogue or digital signals, but digital technology is taking over.

Information is Converted into Signals

1) Information is converted (changed) into electrical signals before it's transmitted (sent out).

2) It's then sent long distances down telephone lines or superimposed (mixed) onto EM waves (see p. 209).

3) It's sent out as either analogue or digital signals.

Information means things like your voice on a phone or the pictures of a TV programme.

Analogue Signals Vary

Analogue

1) An analogue signal can vary continuously.

2) This means it can take any value in a particular range.

Digital Signals are Either On or Off

1) Digital signals can only take one of a small number of values (usually two). For example, 0 or 1.

2) Digital signals are created by switching the wave on or off.

3) This creates pulses — short bursts of waves.

4) 0 = off (no pulse) and 1 = on (pulse).

5) A digital receiver will decode these pulses to get a copy of the original signal.

6) For example, the digital code in this picture is 01001101001010.

Digital

Remember: digital is just 0 or 1

The main thing is that analogue varies continuously but digital is just 0 or 1. Make sure you study the page, and the pictures, hard. Then you won't struggle continuously if it comes up in the exam.

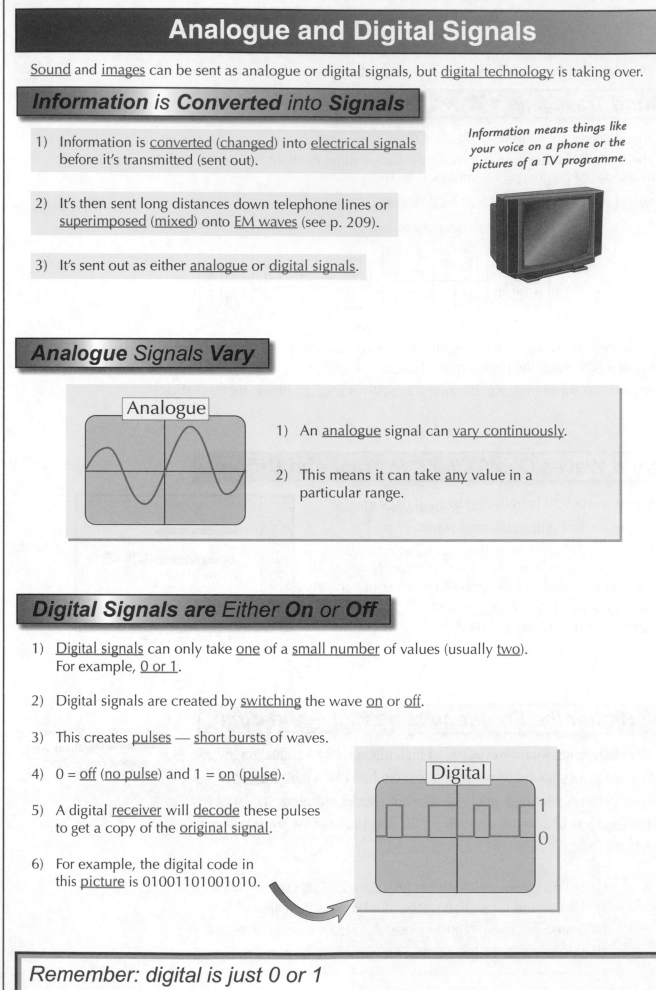

Analogue and Digital Signals

And here's why we're using <u>digital signals</u> more and more nowadays...

Digital Signals are Better Quality

1) <u>Signals</u> pick up <u>noise</u> as they travel.

2) Noise can make it <u>hard</u> to figure out what the <u>original</u> signal and information were like.

3) Noise is less of a problem with <u>digital</u> signals than with analogue.

4) So digital signals are <u>higher quality</u> because the information received is the <u>same</u> as the original.

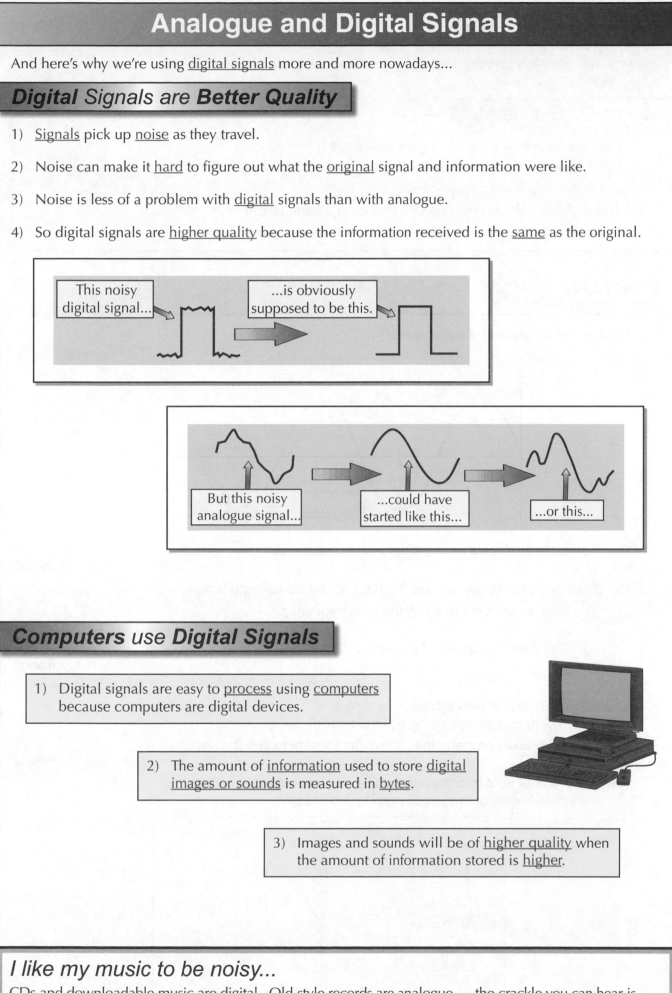

Computers use Digital Signals

1) Digital signals are easy to <u>process</u> using <u>computers</u> because computers are digital devices.

2) The amount of <u>information</u> used to store <u>digital images or sounds</u> is measured in <u>bytes</u>.

3) Images and sounds will be of <u>higher quality</u> when the amount of information stored is <u>higher</u>.

I like my music to be noisy...

CDs and downloadable music are digital. Old-style records are analogue — the crackle you can hear is noise. Digital TV signals are great, unless you live in a part of the country which has poor reception.

Warm-Up and Exam Questions

Practice, practice and more practice is the only real way to get on in life.
So practice you shall have...

Warm-Up Questions

1) Give the formula for calculating the distance a wave has travelled.
2) What type of wave are S-waves — transverse or longitudinal?
3) What happens when a wave passes through a gap?
4) True or false? Waves only refract if they meet a boundary at an angle.
5) Which is affected more by noise — an analogue or a digital signal?

Exam Questions

1 Look at this diagram of a water wave.

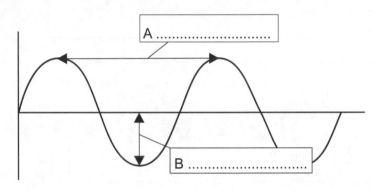

(a) Complete the labels on the diagram.

(2 marks)

(b) The frequency of the wave is 0.5 Hz, and the wavelength is 5 m.

(i) Explain what is meant by the term frequency.

(1 mark)

(ii) Calculate the speed of the wave. Show how you work out your answer.

(2 marks)

2 The diagram below shows a student looking at a
pencil from behind a screen using a plane mirror.

(a) Name the wave property that allows the student to see the pencil.

(1 mark)

(b) Draw rays of light to complete the ray diagram below, and show
the virtual image of the pencil seen by the student.

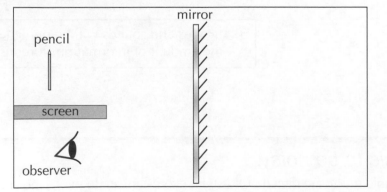

(3 marks)

EM Waves and Communication

Types of <u>electromagnetic</u> (EM) wave have a lot in common with one another, but their <u>differences</u> make them useful to us in different ways.

There are **Seven Types** of **EM Wave**

1) EM waves with <u>different wavelengths</u> (or frequencies) have different properties.

2) We group them into <u>seven basic types</u> of EM wave.

3) They form a <u>continuous spectrum</u> (this means there are <u>no gaps</u> between each type of EM wave).

4) They're shown below increasing in <u>frequency</u> and <u>energy</u> (decreasing wavelength) from left to right.

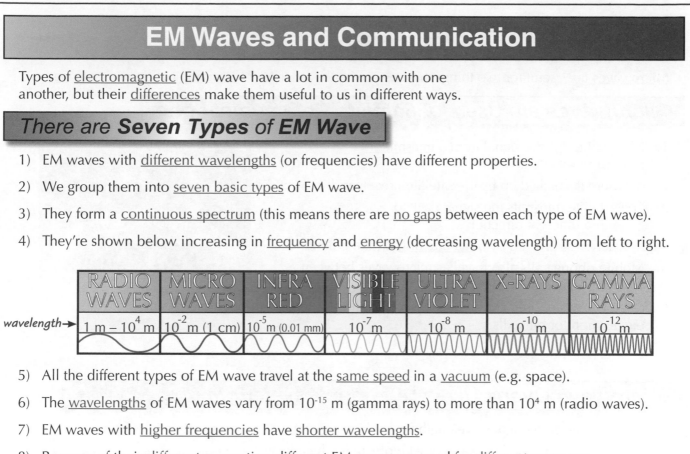

RADIO WAVES	MICRO WAVES	INFRA RED	VISIBLE LIGHT	ULTRA VIOLET	X-RAYS	GAMMA RAYS
$1\text{ m} - 10^{4}\text{ m}$	10^{-2} m (1 cm)	$10^{-5}\text{ m (0.01 mm)}$	10^{-7} m	10^{-8} m	10^{-10} m	10^{-12} m

wavelength→

5) All the different types of EM wave travel at the <u>same speed</u> in a <u>vacuum</u> (e.g. space).

6) The <u>wavelengths</u> of EM waves vary from 10^{-15} m (gamma rays) to more than 10^{4} m (radio waves).

7) EM waves with <u>higher frequencies</u> have <u>shorter wavelengths</u>.

8) Because of their <u>different properties</u>, different EM waves are used for <u>different purposes</u>.

Radio Waves are Used Mainly for Communication

Microwaves, infrared and visible light are also used for communication.

1) <u>Long-wave radio</u> can be sent and received halfway round the world.

2) That's because long wavelengths <u>diffract</u> (<u>bend</u> or <u>spread out</u>, see p.203) around the curved surface of the Earth. They also get around <u>hills</u> and into <u>tunnels</u>.

3) This <u>diffraction effect</u> makes it possible for radio signals to be <u>received</u> even if the receiver <u>isn't</u> in the <u>line of sight</u> of the <u>transmitter</u>.

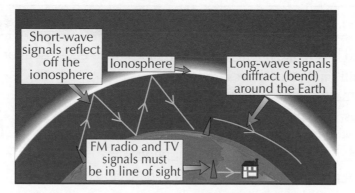

Short-wave signals reflect off the ionosphere

Ionosphere

Long-wave signals diffract (bend) around the Earth

FM radio and TV signals must be in line of sight

4) The radio waves used for <u>TV and FM radio</u> transmissions have <u>very short</u> wavelengths.

5) To receive TV and FM signals, there must be nothing between the <u>aerial</u> and the <u>transmitter</u> — the signal doesn't bend around hills or travel far <u>through</u> buildings.

6) <u>Short-wave radio</u> signals can, like long-wave, be received at <u>long distances</u> from the transmitter.

7) That's because they are <u>reflected</u> by the Earth's upper atmosphere (see diagram above).

Microwaves

Microwaves are useful for two things that begin with the letter 'c' — communication and cooking.

Microwaves are Used for Satellite Communications

1) For satellite TV, the signal from a transmitter is transmitted into space...

2) ... where it's picked up by the satellite's receiver dish.

3) The satellite transmits the signal back to Earth in a different direction...

4) ... where it's received by a satellite dish on the ground.

5) Mobile phone calls also travel as microwaves between your phone and the nearest transmitter.

6) Microwaves are used by remote-sensing satellites — to 'see' through the clouds, e.g. to monitor oil spills.

Microwave Ovens Use a Different Wavelength from Mobiles

1) Microwaves of the right wavelength for cooking penetrate a few centimetres into food.

2) Then they're absorbed by water or fat molecules which heats them up.

3) The heat energy is then conducted or convected (see pages 164-165) to other parts of the food to cook it right through.

Penetrate means to pass into or through something.

4) Microwaves can pass through glass and plastics.

5) So food will still cook if it's in a glass or plastic container.

6) BUT microwaves can be reflected by shiny metal.

7) So don't wrap your food in foil if you're microwaving it.

8) If microwaves from the oven are absorbed by your body tissue, the cells may be burned or killed.

9) Microwave ovens have to be carefully sealed so you aren't burned by the microwaves.

Mobile Phone Microwaves May be Damaging to Health

1) The microwaves used by mobile phones are different from the ones used for cooking.

2) BUT some people still think microwaves from mobile phones and masts might damage your health.

3) IF they are dangerous, then people who use mobile phones or live near masts would be at risk.

4) You'd also be more at risk the more you use your phone.

5) There's no conclusive proof that mobile phones are dangerous though.

6) Different studies have found conflicting (opposite) results so scientists can't agree with each other.

No conclusive proof means there's not enough proof to say for sure.

7) The results of studies are published so they can be checked by other scientists until everyone agrees.

Some microwaves can be dangerous if they're absorbed

So different types of microwave are used for different things. Some are definitely dangerous — they'd cook you as quickly as they cook chicken — but people aren't so sure about the ones used by mobiles.

Infrared and Visible Light

You use <u>visible</u> and <u>infrared</u> light every day, for seeing, for taking <u>pictures</u> and for <u>controlling your telly</u>.

Visible Light is Useful for Photography

1) Cameras use a <u>lens</u> to focus <u>visible light</u> onto a light-sensitive <u>film</u> or electronic <u>sensor</u>.

2) The lens <u>aperture</u> (opening) controls <u>how much light</u> enters the camera.

3) The <u>shutter speed</u> allows you to control how <u>long</u> the film or sensor is <u>open</u> to the light.

4) The <u>longer</u> the film or sensor is open to the light — the <u>more light</u> will enter the camera and react with the film.

light-sensitive film or sensor
lens
aperture
subject

Infrared Has Many Uses Around the Home

1) <u>Infrared radiation</u> (IR) can be used to send information between <u>mobile phones</u> or <u>computers</u> — but only over <u>short distances</u>.

2) <u>Automatic doors</u> use it too.

3) IR sensors can detect <u>body heat</u> so they're used in <u>security systems</u> like burglar alarms and security lights.

4) When a person <u>walks in front</u> of the sensor, it detects their body heat and <u>turns on</u> an alarm or a light.

5) <u>Thermal imaging cameras</u> work in a similar way — they detect heat and use it to <u>create</u> a <u>picture</u>.

Remote Controls also use Infrared

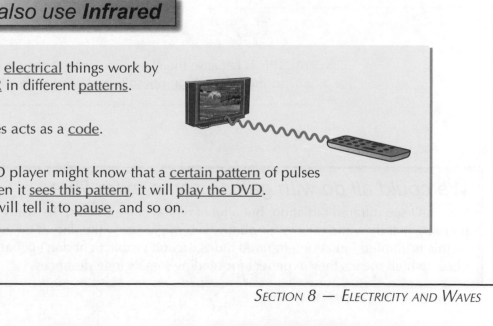

1) <u>Remote controls</u> for <u>electrical</u> things work by <u>flashing pulses of IR</u> in different <u>patterns</u>.

2) The pattern of pulses acts as a <u>code</u>.

3) For example, a DVD player might know that a <u>certain pattern</u> of pulses means <u>play</u>. So when it <u>sees this pattern</u>, it will <u>play the DVD</u>. A <u>different</u> pattern will tell it to <u>pause</u>, and so on.

Infrared and Visible Light

Optical fibres are great for sending lots of information from one place to another.

Infrared and Light are Used in Optical Fibres

1) Optical fibres are cables with a glass core.

2) They're used to send information as infrared or light waves.

3) Optical fibres work by bouncing waves off the sides of the glass core.

4) The wave enters one end of the fibre and is reflected repeatedly until it comes out at the other end.

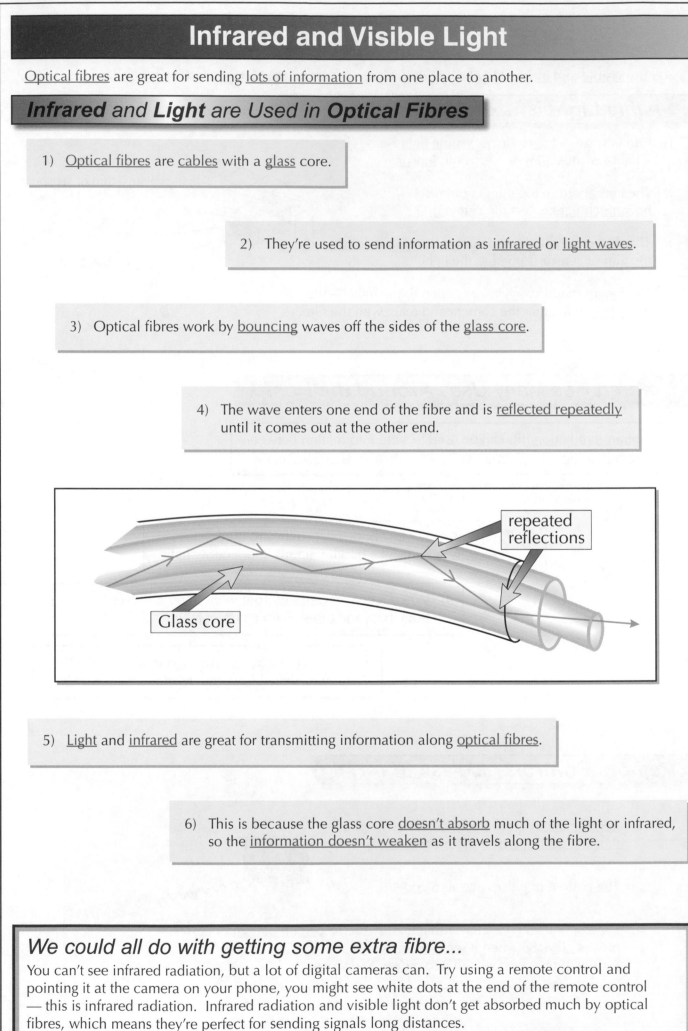

repeated reflections

Glass core

5) Light and infrared are great for transmitting information along optical fibres.

6) This is because the glass core doesn't absorb much of the light or infrared, so the information doesn't weaken as it travels along the fibre.

We could all do with getting some extra fibre...

You can't see infrared radiation, but a lot of digital cameras can. Try using a remote control and pointing it at the camera on your phone, you might see white dots at the end of the remote control — this is infrared radiation. Infrared radiation and visible light don't get absorbed much by optical fibres, which means they're perfect for sending signals long distances.

Ionising Radiation

High-energy EM radiation is <u>more harmful</u> than low-energy radiation.

Some EM Radiation Causes *Ionisation*

1) Everything is made of <u>atoms</u> and <u>molecules</u>.

2) When radiation hits an atom or molecule, it sometimes has <u>enough energy</u> to <u>remove an electron</u> and <u>change</u> the atom or molecule.

3) This process is called <u>ionisation</u>:

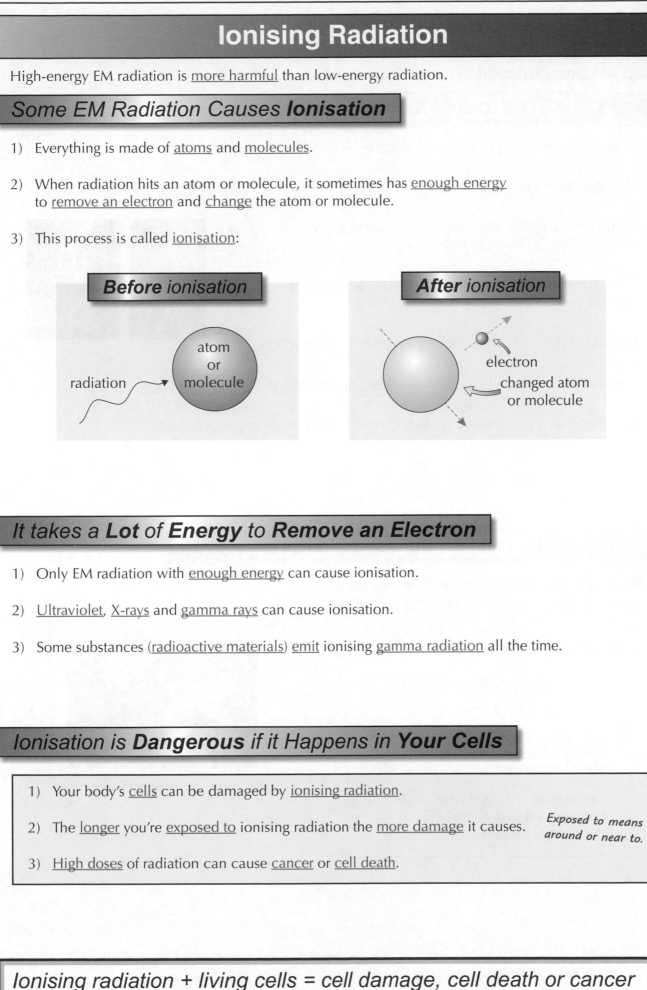

It takes a **Lot** of **Energy** to **Remove an Electron**

1) Only EM radiation with <u>enough energy</u> can cause ionisation.

2) <u>Ultraviolet</u>, <u>X-rays</u> and <u>gamma rays</u> can cause ionisation.

3) Some substances (<u>radioactive materials</u>) <u>emit</u> ionising <u>gamma radiation</u> all the time.

Ionisation is **Dangerous** if it Happens in **Your Cells**

1) Your body's <u>cells</u> can be damaged by <u>ionising radiation</u>.

2) The <u>longer</u> you're <u>exposed to</u> ionising radiation the <u>more damage</u> it causes.   *Exposed to means around or near to.*

3) <u>High doses</u> of radiation can cause <u>cancer</u> or <u>cell death</u>.

Ionising radiation + living cells = cell damage, cell death or cancer

Ionising radiation can be <u>harmful</u>, but X-rays and gamma rays can be really <u>useful</u> too. Some uses of these electromagnetic waves are coming up next so stay tuned. It's only a page away...

X-Rays and Gamma Rays

X-rays and gamma rays are both types of ionising radiation.

X-rays are Used to See Inside People

1) X-rays are ionising, so can cause damage to your cells (see previous page).

2) Hospitals take X-ray pictures of people to see if they have broken bones.

3) X-rays pass easily through flesh but are absorbed by denser materials like bone and metal.

4) If you have an X-ray taken, you might have lead shields put over parts of your body that aren't injured.

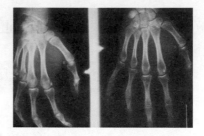

5) Lead absorbs X-rays so it protects your body from ionisation.

6) Hospital staff wear lead aprons or stand behind concrete to protect themselves.

7) X-ray imaging is also used in airports to check what's inside passengers' bags.

Gamma Radiation can be Used to Treat Cancers

1) Gamma rays are directed carefully so they kill the cancer cells without killing too many normal cells.

2) They can also be used to diagnose cancer:

- A radioactive isotope is injected into the patient.

- A camera that 'sees' gamma rays is then used to spot where the radioactive isotope travels in the body.

- This creates an image which can then be used to detect where there might be cancer.

Don't lie to an X-ray — they can see right through you...

Don't worry too much about the dangers of radiation. It's worth having an X-ray to find out if you've broken a bone or are ill. It takes a lot more radiation than you get from an X-ray to do much damage.

UV Radiation and Ozone

Ultraviolet radiation can also cause <u>ionisation</u> — but the <u>ozone layer</u> protects us from a lot of it.

Ultraviolet Radiation Causes Skin Cancer

1) If you spend a lot of time in the <u>Sun</u>, you can expect to get a <u>tan</u> and maybe <u>sunburn</u>.

2) But the <u>more time</u> you spend in the Sun, the <u>more chance</u> you also have of getting: <u>skin cancer</u>, <u>cataracts</u> (an <u>eye</u> condition), and <u>premature skin aging</u>.

3) This is because the Sun's rays include <u>ultraviolet radiation</u> (UV) which damages cells.

4) <u>Darker skin</u> gives some <u>protection</u> against UV rays because it <u>absorbs</u> more UV radiation.

5) This means <u>less UV</u> reaches cells <u>deeper inside</u> the body, so it causes less damage.

6) <u>Sunscreens</u> (sun block or sun cream) also <u>protect</u> us from the Sun.

7) They all have a <u>Sun Protection Factor</u> (SPF).

8) The <u>higher</u> the factor, the <u>less damage</u> done.

9) This means the higher the factor, the <u>longer</u> you can stay in the Sun without burning. For example, an <u>SPF</u> of <u>15</u> means you can spend <u>15 times longer</u> in the Sun <u>without burning</u>.

> <u>EXAMPLE</u>: Ruvani normally burns after 40 minutes in the Sun.
> Before going to the beach, she applies sunscreen with SPF 8.
> For how long can she sunbathe before she will start to burn?
> <u>ANSWER</u>: Time = 40 mins × 8 = 320 minutes = <u>5 hours and 20 minutes</u>.

You must keep re-applying the suncream throughout the day to be protected though and especially after swimming.

We Know the Risks

1) Scientists and the government <u>tell us</u> about the risks of UV through the <u>news</u> and <u>advertising</u>.

2) They tell us this so we know how to <u>keep safe</u>, which helps <u>improve everyone's health</u>.

3) We're also warned of the risks of using <u>sunbeds</u> too much, because this can cause the <u>same damage</u> as <u>too much Sun</u>.

There's a Hole in the Ozone Layer over Antarctica

1) The <u>ozone layer</u> is a layer of gas around the Earth that absorbs some of the <u>UV rays</u> from the <u>Sun</u>.

2) It <u>reduces</u> the amount of UV reaching Earth, so it <u>protects</u> us from <u>harm</u>.

3) Scientists have found that the <u>amount of ozone</u> over <u>Antarctica</u> is <u>dropping</u> unexpectedly.

4) The <u>low level</u> of ozone looks like a 'hole'.

5) To make sure the results are <u>accurate</u> (spot on), scientists have done <u>many different studies</u> using <u>lots of equipment</u> to look at the ozone layer.

6) This helps them <u>make sure</u> that their ideas about what's happening are <u>correct</u>.

Make sure you protect yourself when you're out in the Sun

<u>Too much</u> time in the Sun can cause skin cancer, but <u>a bit</u> of Sun can be a <u>good thing</u> (it helps your body's production of <u>vitamin D</u>). So don't avoid it altogether. Just be careful when you're sunbathing.

Warm-Up and Exam Questions

Another load of pages learnt, another load of practice questions to do.
Will the questions ever end? Well, no — it's the best way to learn, so tough.

Warm-Up Questions

1) Which type of wave is reflected by the Earth's upper atmosphere (the ionosphere)?
2) Explain how microwaves heat food.
3) Give one example of a use of infrared radiation.
4) What are optical fibres used for?
5) Why is ionising radiation dangerous?
6) What does SPF stand for?
7) Which type of radiation does the ozone layer absorb?

Exam Questions

1   The diagram shows a light ray entering an optical fibre.

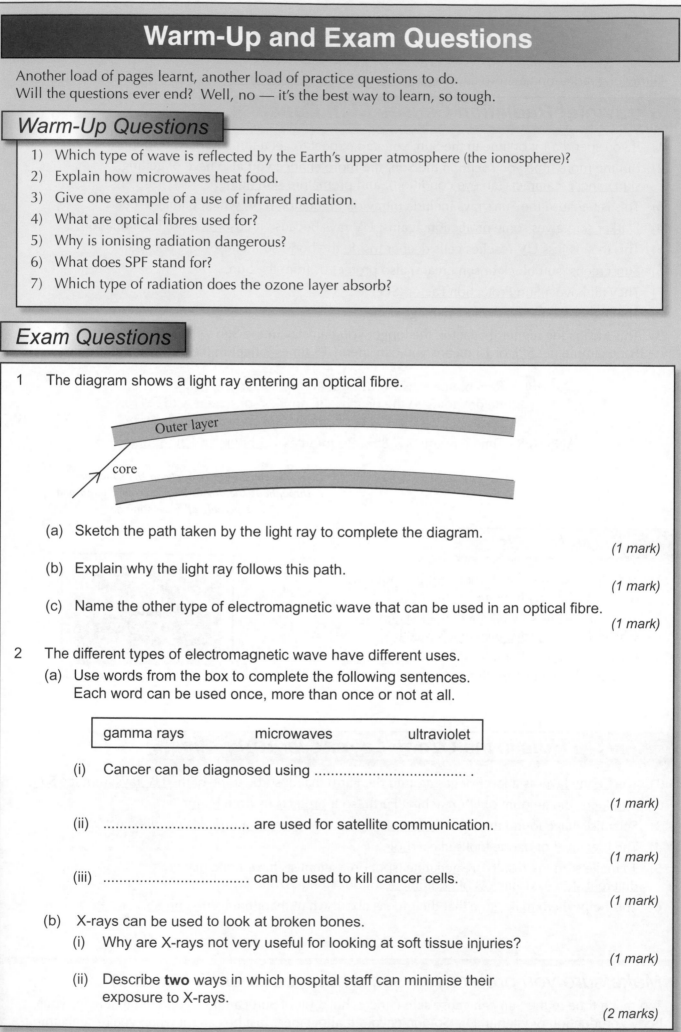

Outer layer

core

(a)   Sketch the path taken by the light ray to complete the diagram.

(1 mark)

(b)   Explain why the light ray follows this path.

(1 mark)

(c)   Name the other type of electromagnetic wave that can be used in an optical fibre.

(1 mark)

2   The different types of electromagnetic wave have different uses.

(a)   Use words from the box to complete the following sentences.
Each word can be used once, more than once or not at all.

gamma rays	microwaves	ultraviolet

(i)   Cancer can be diagnosed using ....

(1 mark)

(ii)   .... are used for satellite communication.

(1 mark)

(iii)   .... can be used to kill cancer cells.

(1 mark)

(b)   X-rays can be used to look at broken bones.
(i)   Why are X-rays not very useful for looking at soft tissue injuries?

(1 mark)

(ii)   Describe **two** ways in which hospital staff can minimise their
exposure to X-rays.

(2 marks)

The Greenhouse Effect

The atmosphere <u>keeps us warm</u> by <u>trapping heat</u>.

Infrared Radiation *is* Absorbed *by the* Atmosphere

1) The Earth is surrounded by an <u>atmosphere</u> made up of different <u>gases</u> — the <u>air</u>.

2) <u>Most wavelengths</u> of electromagnetic radiation <u>pass through</u> the atmosphere <u>easily</u>.

3) But the greenhouse gases in the atmosphere <u>absorb</u> some wavelengths like <u>infrared</u>.

The Greenhouse Effect *Helps* Regulate *Earth's Temperature*

1) The Earth <u>absorbs radiation</u> from the <u>Sun</u>, which warms the Earth's surface up.

2) The Earth then <u>gives off</u> some of this heat, which tends to <u>cool</u> it down.

3) Some of the <u>heat</u> (<u>infrared</u> radiation) given off by the Earth
   is <u>absorbed</u> by <u>greenhouse gases</u> in the Earth's atmosphere.

4) These gases <u>stop</u> the heat from radiating back into <u>space</u>.

5) So the atmosphere acts as an <u>insulating</u> layer,
   stopping the Earth losing all its heat at night.

6) This is known as the <u>greenhouse effect</u>.

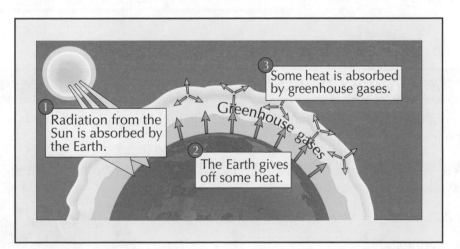

1. Radiation from the Sun is absorbed by the Earth.

2. The Earth gives off some heat.

3. Some heat is absorbed by greenhouse gases.

Greenhouse gases

The greenhouse effect is a pretty big deal

You'll have been hearing all about the greenhouse effect for a while now. It's an upset in this effect that most scientists think is causing global warming — and that's causing lots of problems for the whole planet. So make sure you understand how the greenhouse effect works before moving on.

Global Warming and Climate Change

Having too many greenhouse gases floating about in the atmosphere has led to global warming.

There are **Different Sources** of **Greenhouse Gases**

1) Carbon dioxide, methane and water vapour are all greenhouse gases.

2) They come from natural and man-made sources.

Carbon Dioxide

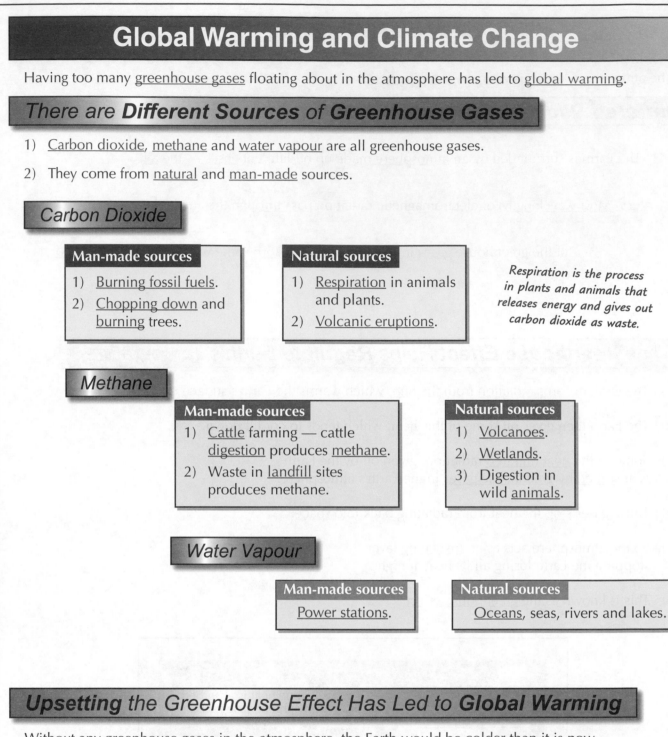

Man-made sources

1) Burning fossil fuels.
2) Chopping down and burning trees.

Natural sources

1) Respiration in animals and plants.
2) Volcanic eruptions.

Respiration is the process in plants and animals that releases energy and gives out carbon dioxide as waste.

Methane

Man-made sources

1) Cattle farming — cattle digestion produces methane.
2) Waste in landfill sites produces methane.

Natural sources

1) Volcanoes.
2) Wetlands.
3) Digestion in wild animals.

Water Vapour

Man-made sources

Power stations.

Natural sources

Oceans, seas, rivers and lakes.

Upsetting the Greenhouse Effect Has Led to **Global Warming**

Without any greenhouse gases in the atmosphere, the Earth would be colder than it is now. So we need greenhouse gasses — just not too much of them.

1) Burning fossil fuels (coal, oil, gas) has increased the amount of carbon dioxide (CO_2) in the atmosphere.

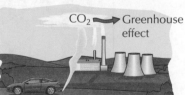

$CO_2 \rightarrow$ Greenhouse effect

2) The global temperature has also risen during this time.

3) This is global warming.

4) A lot of evidence has been collected that shows the rise in carbon dioxide is causing global warming by upsetting the greenhouse effect.

5) So there's now a scientific consensus (general agreement) that humans are causing global warming.

6) Global warming is a type of climate change and it also causes other types. For example, global warming can also cause changes to the weather (see next page).

Global Warming and Climate Change

<u>Climate change</u> is going on all around us, so you really should learn something about it...

The **Effects** of **Global Warming** Could be Pretty **Serious**

Rising **Sea Level**

1) As the sea gets warmer it <u>expands</u>, so sea level <u>rises</u>.

2) Sea level <u>has risen</u> a little bit over the last 100 years.

3) If it keeps rising <u>low-lying</u> places could be <u>flooded</u>.
For example, places like the <u>Netherlands</u>, the <u>Maldives</u> and <u>places in the UK</u> (like East Anglia) could end up <u>under water</u>.

4) Higher temperatures also make <u>ice melt</u>.

5) Water that's currently <u>trapped</u> on land as ice runs into the <u>sea</u>, causing sea level to rise <u>even more</u>.

More **Extreme Weather**

1) Global warming has <u>changed weather patterns</u> in many parts of the world.

2) Many regions will suffer <u>more extreme weather</u> because of global warming.

Weather patterns means things like dry summers or wet winters.

3) There may be <u>longer</u>, <u>hotter droughts</u> or <u>more hurricanes</u>.

4) Hurricanes form over <u>warm water</u>, so if the oceans get warmer there'll be <u>more</u> hurricanes.

Food **Crop Failure**

1) <u>Changing weather patterns</u> also affect <u>food production</u>.

2) Some places are now <u>too dry</u> to grow food and some are <u>too wet</u>.

3) This will <u>get worse</u> as <u>temperature increases</u> and weather patterns change more.

Some countries may disappear altogether...

Global warming might sound like a good thing because it could make your next holiday <u>warmer</u>, but it won't be much fun if there's a drought, or you can't even go somewhere because it's <u>under water</u>.

Seismic Waves

Earthquakes cause seismic waves, which pass through the Earth.
Scientists use these waves to find out about the Earth's inner structure.

Earthquakes Cause Different Types of Waves

1) Earthquakes produce seismic (shock) waves that travel on the surface and inside the Earth.

2) Scientists record these seismic waves using instruments on the Earth's surface.

3) They record the time it takes for them to reach different parts of the Earth.

4) Scientists also note which parts of the Earth don't get any waves at all.

5) There are two different types of wave that travel through the Earth — P-waves and S-waves.

P and S Waves Help to Tell Us What's Down There

P-Waves travel through Liquids and Solids

1) About halfway through the Earth, P-waves change direction.

2) So there must be a sudden change in properties as you go from the mantle to the core.

3) P-waves can pass through the core.

4) P-waves are longitudinal waves (see p. 201).

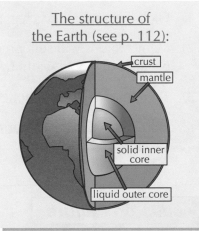

The structure of
the Earth (see p. 112):

crust
mantle
solid inner core
liquid outer core

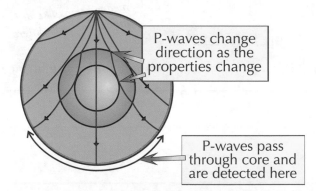

P-waves change direction as the properties change

P-waves pass through core and are detected here

S-Waves only travel through Solids

1) S-waves are not detected on the other side of the core.

2) S-waves can't travel through liquids.

3) So this tells us that part of the core is liquid.

4) S-waves do travel through the mantle, which tells us that it's solid.

5) S-waves are transverse waves (see p. 200).

6) S-waves travel slower than P-waves.

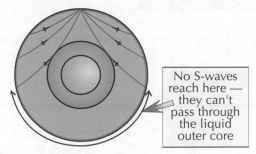

No S-waves reach here — they can't pass through the liquid outer core

Warm-Up and Exam Questions

Here's the final page of warm-up and exam questions of this section. There's still the revision summary to go after these though, but that'll be easy after all the hard work you've put in so far.

Warm-Up Questions

1) Name one greenhouse gas.
2) Give one natural source of methane.
3) Describe one possible effect of global warming.
4) Name the two types of seismic wave.
5) Why do seismic waves change direction as they travel through the Earth?

Exam Questions

1   The graph on the right shows how atmospheric carbon dioxide (CO_2) concentration and global temperature have varied over the last 250 000 years.

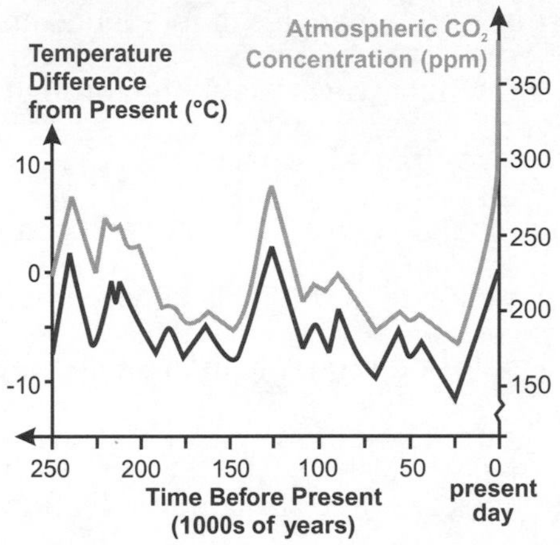

(a) Describe what the graph shows.
     Tick the boxes next to the **two** correct answers (A-D).

   A CO_2 concentration and temperature have varied a lot over the last 250 000 years.   ☐

   B CO_2 concentration and temperature show no correlation.   ☐

   C CO_2 concentration and temperature show a positive correlation.   ☐

   D   A change in CO_2 concentration causes a change in temperature.   ☐

(2 marks)

(b) Mark with an X on the graph the time when the temperature was most different from its present value.

(1 mark)

(c) Suggest **one man-made** and **one natural source** of CO_2.

(2 marks)

2   P-waves and S-waves both travel through the Earth.
     Complete the following sentences about P-waves and S-waves.

(a) .... travel the fastest.

(1 mark)

(b) .... can't travel through liquids.

(1 mark)

(c) .... are transverse waves.

(1 mark)

Revision Summary for Section 8

It's question time — again. Do as many of the questions as you can. Any harder ones — go back and have another read of the pages, then try them again.

1) Briefly explain how generators produce electricity.

2) What does a step-down transformer do?

3) What units of electrical energy does an electricity meter record?

4)* Calculate how many kWh of electrical energy are used by a 0.5 kW heater used for 15 minutes.

5) Describe two ways that electricity is used in hospitals.

6) Which type of wave has vibrations that are perpendicular to the direction of energy transfer
    — transverse or longitudinal?

7)* Find the speed of a wave with frequency 50 000 Hz and wavelength 0.03 m.

Wave speed = Frequency × Wavelength

8) a) Sketch a diagram of a ray of light being reflected in a mirror.

    b) Label the normal and the angles of incidence and reflection.

9) Draw a diagram showing a wave diffracting through a gap.

10) Why can't sound waves travel in space?

11) Are high frequency sound waves high pitched or low pitched?

12) Draw diagrams of analogue and digital signals and briefly explain the differences between them.

13) Why are digital signals better quality than analogue signals?

14) List the types of electromagnetic waves — start with the ones with the lowest frequencies.

15) Describe how satellites are used for communication.

16) What type of wave do television remote controls usually use?

17) Briefly describe ionisation.

18) Explain how X-rays can be useful in hospitals.

19) What are the effects of being exposed to too much UV radiation?

20) What gas in the atmosphere protects us from UV radiation from the Sun?

21) Briefly describe what is meant by the 'greenhouse effect'.

22) What is global warming?

23) Give one example of extreme weather.

24) What causes seismic waves?

* Answers on p. 247

Galileo and Copernicus

Our models of the size and shape of the Solar System and the Universe have changed over time.

Ptolemaic Model — Earth at the Centre

1) The Ptolemaic model says that the Sun, Moon, planets and stars all orbit the Earth in perfect circles.

2) The Ptolemaic model is a geocentric model — it has the Earth at the centre.

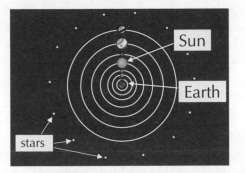

A model is a bit like a theory — it's an idea that explains something.

3) It was the accepted model (the one people believed) until the 1500s, when it began to be replaced (see below).

Copernican Model — Sun at the Centre

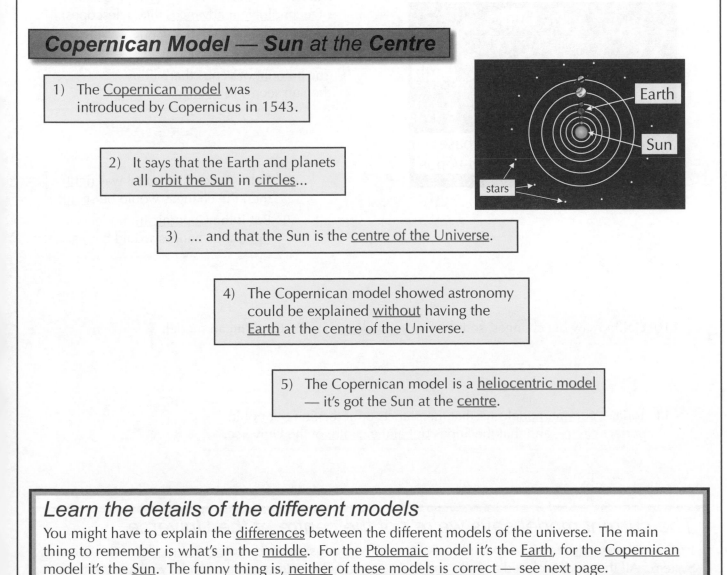

1) The Copernican model was introduced by Copernicus in 1543.

2) It says that the Earth and planets all orbit the Sun in circles...

3) ... and that the Sun is the centre of the Universe.

4) The Copernican model showed astronomy could be explained without having the Earth at the centre of the Universe.

5) The Copernican model is a heliocentric model — it's got the Sun at the centre.

Learn the details of the different models

You might have to explain the differences between the different models of the universe. The main thing to remember is what's in the middle. For the Ptolemaic model it's the Earth, for the Copernican model it's the Sun. The funny thing is, neither of these models is correct — see next page.

Galileo and Copernicus

People believed in the Ptolemaic model for a <u>very long time</u>. But 400 years ago, in a town in Italy, a man called <u>Galileo</u> found real evidence that this model <u>wasn't true</u>. Read on to find out more...

Galileo Found Evidence for the Copernican Model

1) <u>Galileo</u> was one of the first astronomers to use a <u>telescope</u>.

2) He used his telescope to find evidence to <u>support</u> the Copernican model.

3) Galileo saw <u>moons orbiting Jupiter</u>.

4) This showed <u>not everything</u> was in orbit around the Earth — so the Ptolemaic model was <u>wrong</u>.

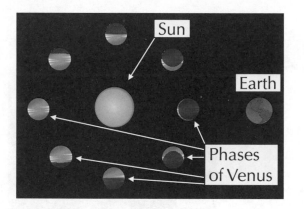

5) Models and theories often <u>change</u> because of <u>technological advances</u> (like telescopes).

6) Galileo also noticed that <u>Venus</u> has <u>phases</u> (like the Moon).

7) The <u>amount</u> of Venus that's <u>lit</u> by the Sun seems to <u>change</u>.

8) If the <u>Ptolemaic</u> model was <u>right</u> then the changes would be <u>small</u>.

9) But if the <u>Copernican</u> model was <u>right</u>, the changes would be <u>big</u>.

10) Galileo <u>saw</u> big changes, so it was <u>more evidence</u> for the Copernican model.

11) Today's <u>current model</u> says that the planets orbit the Sun but <u>not</u> in perfect <u>circles</u>, and that the Sun is <u>not at the centre</u> of the Universe.

The current model says we're not the centre of the Universe

It's taken <u>thousands</u> of years and lots of new technology for us to reach our <u>current model</u> of the Solar System. All the models played a <u>really important part</u> in helping us reach the model we have today.

The Solar System

Everything in the Solar System goes around and around the Sun.

Planets Orbit the Sun

1) The Solar System consists of a star (the Sun) and lots of stuff orbiting (going around) it.

   - The planets orbit the Sun.
   - Moons orbit some planets.
   - The Moon orbits the Earth.
   - The asteroid belt orbits the Sun (see below).

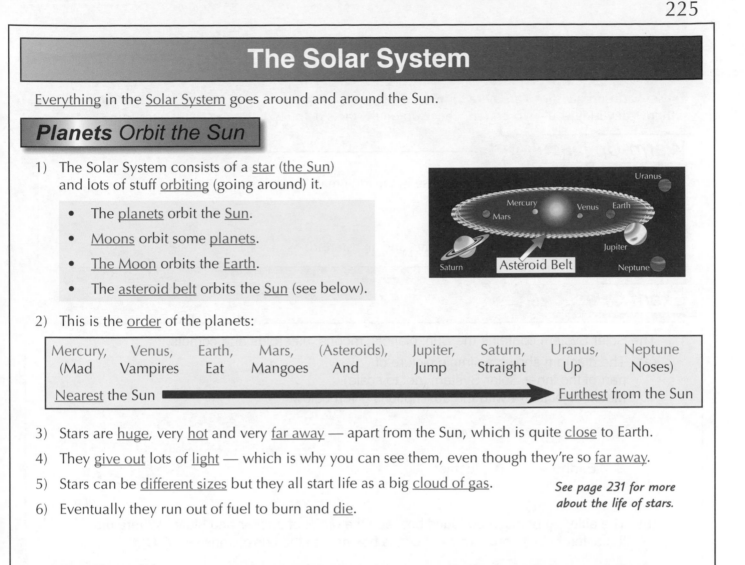

2) This is the order of the planets:

Mercury,	Venus,	Earth,	Mars,	(Asteroids),	Jupiter,	Saturn,	Uranus,	Neptune
(Mad	Vampires	Eat	Mangoes	And	Jump	Straight	Up	Noses)

Nearest the Sun ➤ Furthest from the Sun

3) Stars are huge, very hot and very far away — apart from the Sun, which is quite close to Earth.

4) They give out lots of light — which is why you can see them, even though they're so far away.

5) Stars can be different sizes but they all start life as a big cloud of gas.

6) Eventually they run out of fuel to burn and die.

See page 231 for more about the life of stars.

There's a **Belt** of **Asteroids** Orbiting Between **Mars** and **Jupiter**

1) When the Solar System was forming, the rocks between Mars and Jupiter didn't form a planet.

2) This left millions of asteroids — bits of rubble and rock.

3) They orbit the Sun between Jupiter and Mars (see above).

Comets Orbit the Sun in Very **Elliptical Orbits**

Comet

1) Comets are balls of dust and ice.

2) They orbit the Sun in very elongated ellipses (squashed circles).

3) Comets come from objects orbiting the Sun far beyond the planets.

4) Heat from the Sun melts the comet's ice, leaving a bright tail of debris.

5) This tail is what we see from the Earth.

6) Comets speed up as they get nearer to stars (like the Sun).

Comet in an elliptical orbit (red line).

Pluto — the ninth planet

It used to be that you had to learn nine planets, but in 2006 scientists decided that Pluto, the ninth planet, was too small to be called a planet really. So, for now at least, there are only eight.

Warm-Up and Exam Questions

These warm-up questions are here to make sure you know the basics.
If there's anything you've forgotten, check up on the facts before you try the exam questions.

Warm-Up Questions

1) What is in the centre of the Universe in the Ptolemaic model?
2) Which planet is nearest the Sun?
3) What are comets made of?
4) Give one difference between a comet and an asteroid.

Exam Questions

1   The Solar System contains the Sun, planets, moons, asteroids and comets.

(a)   The diagram shows a simple picture of
part of the inner Solar System (not to scale).
Match objects **1-4** with the descriptions given below.

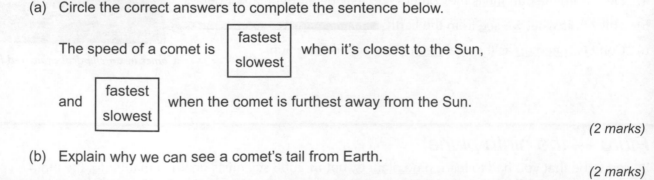

A	Venus	**C**	Mars
B	Earth	**D**	comet

(4 marks)

(b)   The asteroid belt can be found between the orbits of Jupiter and Mars. Where did
the asteroid belt come from? Tick the box next to the correct answer (A-C).

A   Small bits of rubble and rock that didn't form planets.   ☐

B   Balls of dust and ice from beyond the Solar System.   ☐

C   Rocks broken off from Mars long after the Solar System formed.   ☐

(1 mark)

2   The Ptolemaic model was the accepted model of the Universe until
Galileo found evidence to support the Copernican model.

(a)   Suggest **one** piece of technology that helped Galileo to do this.

(1 mark)

(b)   *In this question you will be assessed on the quality of your English, the
organisation of your ideas and your use of appropriate specialist vocabulary.*

Discuss the differences and similarities between the Ptolemaic,
Copernican and current model of the Solar System.

(6 marks)

3   The speed of a comet changes during its orbit around the Sun.

(a)   Circle the correct answers to complete the sentence below.

The speed of a comet is | fastest |
                           | slowest | when it's closest to the Sun,

and | fastest |
       | slowest | when the comet is furthest away from the Sun.

(2 marks)

(b)   Explain why we can see a comet's tail from Earth.

(2 marks)

Beyond the Solar System

The <u>Universe</u> is <u>big</u> — huge in fact.

We're in the **Milky Way Galaxy**

1) Our <u>Sun</u> is one of <u>thousands of millions</u> of <u>stars</u> which form the <u>Milky Way galaxy</u>.

2) The Milky Way is just <u>one galaxy</u>.

3) There are <u>thousands of millions</u> of galaxies in the <u>Universe</u>.

You are here

You Can **Measure the Distance** to **Stars** Using **Light**

1) You can get an idea of how far away a star is by <u>measuring</u> the <u>light</u> radiation coming from it (its <u>brightness</u>).

Light is a type of EM radiation (see p. 209).

2) A star that <u>looks</u> very bright on Earth could be either:
   a) quite <u>close</u> to Earth but <u>not</u> very <u>bright</u>, OR
   b) a <u>long way away</u> and <u>very bright</u>.

3) But astronomers know <u>how much radiation</u> certain types of star <u>actually</u> emit.

4) So by seeing how bright they look <u>from Earth</u>, they can tell <u>how far away</u> those stars must be.

5) You can also use <u>parallax</u> to measure the distance to nearby stars.

6) Parallax is when something <u>appears to move</u> when you look at it from different <u>places</u>.

7) <u>Pictures</u> of the sky are taken six months apart.

8) The <u>movement</u> of a star between the two photos lets you work out <u>how far away</u> it is.

> Hold your finger at <u>arm's length</u> and look at it first through your <u>left eye</u>, then your <u>right</u> — it seems to <u>move</u>. This is an example of <u>parallax</u>.

9) Stars that are <u>further away</u> appear to move <u>less</u>.

First picture

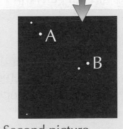

Second picture —
taken six months later

1) A and B are <u>stars</u>.
2) <u>A</u> has moved <u>more</u> than <u>B</u> in the <u>second picture</u>.
3) B must be <u>further away</u> from Earth because it has <u>moved less</u>.

Long ago, in a galaxy far away...

Measuring the distance to a star is <u>very hard</u> (especially ones that are really far away) — so if someone says that they know how far away a star in a distant galaxy is to the nearest kilometre, they're lying.

Looking into Space

Looking at <u>different frequencies</u> of EM radiation from space can help us find out what's going on 'out there'.

Space Telescopes Have a Clearer View Than Those on Earth

1) <u>Telescopes</u> help you to see distant objects clearly. But there can be problems...

2) The Earth's <u>atmosphere</u> absorbs a lot of electromagnetic radiation from space before it can reach us.

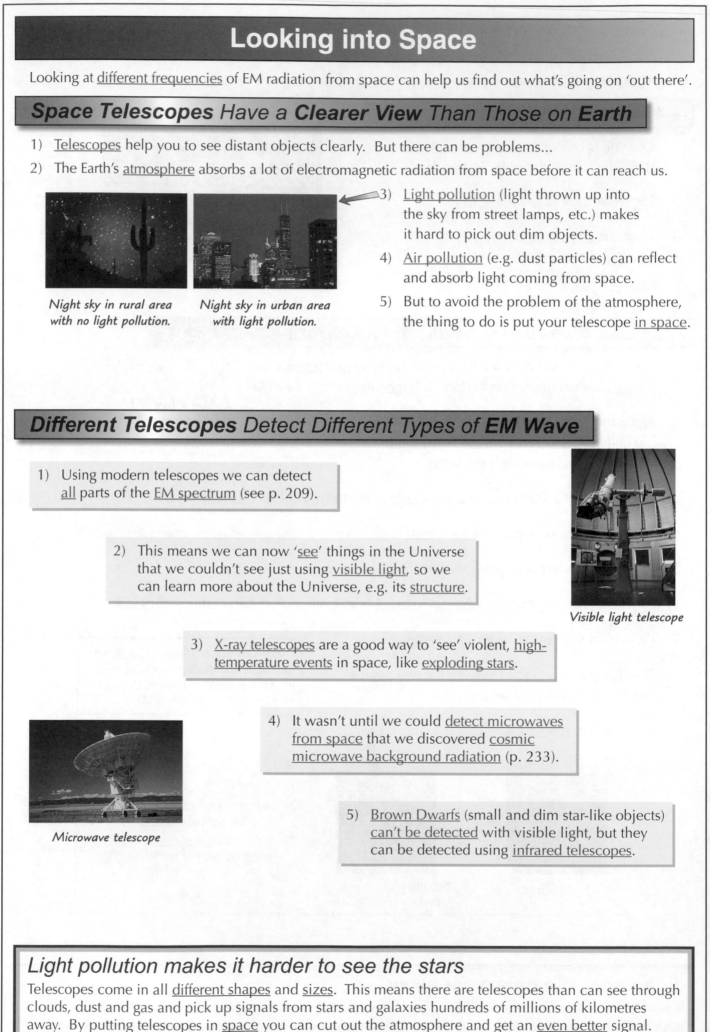

Night sky in rural area with no light pollution.

Night sky in urban area with light pollution.

3) <u>Light pollution</u> (light thrown up into the sky from street lamps, etc.) makes it hard to pick out dim objects.

4) <u>Air pollution</u> (e.g. dust particles) can reflect and absorb light coming from space.

5) But to avoid the problem of the atmosphere, the thing to do is put your telescope <u>in space</u>.

Different Telescopes Detect Different Types of EM Wave

1) Using modern telescopes we can detect <u>all</u> parts of the <u>EM spectrum</u> (see p. 209).

2) This means we can now '<u>see</u>' things in the Universe that we couldn't see just using <u>visible light</u>, so we can learn more about the Universe, e.g. its <u>structure</u>.

Visible light telescope

3) <u>X-ray telescopes</u> are a good way to 'see' violent, <u>high-temperature events</u> in space, like <u>exploding stars</u>.

4) It wasn't until we could <u>detect microwaves from space</u> that we discovered <u>cosmic microwave background radiation</u> (p. 233).

Microwave telescope

5) <u>Brown Dwarfs</u> (small and dim star-like objects) <u>can't be detected</u> with visible light, but they can be detected using <u>infrared telescopes</u>.

Light pollution makes it harder to see the stars

Telescopes come in all <u>different shapes</u> and <u>sizes</u>. This means there are telescopes than can see through clouds, dust and gas and pick up signals from stars and galaxies hundreds of millions of kilometres away. By putting telescopes in <u>space</u> you can cut out the atmosphere and get an <u>even better</u> signal.

Looking into Space

We've come a long way since the first telescopes were invented some <u>400 years ago</u>. Now they not only let us see <u>stars</u> and <u>galaxies</u>, but also events from the <u>early Universe</u>.

As *Telescopes* Get Better — We Can Learn More About the Universe

1) Some telescopes are now a lot bigger, and so can <u>gather more light</u>.

2) This means we can now see things we couldn't see before as they were <u>too faint</u>.

3) Improved <u>magnification</u> (making things appear bigger) means we can now look <u>further</u> into space — more and more galaxies are being <u>discovered</u>.

4) Modern telescopes often work alongside <u>computers</u>.

5) Computers help create <u>clearer</u> and <u>sharper</u> images and make it easy to <u>take</u> pictures to analyse later.

6) They also make it possible to collect and store <u>huge amounts</u> of data, 24 hours a day, without having to rely on <u>humans</u>.

7) They also make it easier and quicker to <u>analyse</u> all this data.

8) Discovering <u>more</u> galaxies and objects in space is important to help scientists <u>learn more</u> about the Universe, e.g. how galaxies are <u>formed</u>.

Distances in **Space** Can Be Measured Using **Light Years**

1) The <u>distances</u> in space are so <u>big</u> we use <u>light years</u> to measure them instead of kilometres.

2) A light year is the <u>distance</u> that <u>light travels</u> in one <u>year</u>.

3) Light travels <u>really fast</u> — 300 000 km/s in a <u>vacuum</u> (like space).

4) Just remember — a light year is a measure of <u>DISTANCE</u> (<u>not</u> time).

A vacuum is a place with nothing in it, not even air.

We See Stars and Galaxies as They Were **In The Past**

1) Light travels <u>really fast</u> but space is <u>very big</u> so it still takes a <u>long time</u> for the light to reach us.

2) When we look at anything in space, we see it as it was when the <u>light first left it</u>.

It takes light 8 minutes to travel from the Sun to the Earth.

3) This means we see things in space how they were in the <u>past</u>.

4) It takes <u>8 minutes</u> for light from the <u>Sun</u> to reach Earth, so we see the Sun as it was <u>8 minutes ago</u>.

Not just looking back into space, but also back in time

<u>Modern telescopes</u> have helped us find out lots of things about the Universe. It's all very clever really...

Warm-Up and Exam Questions

Three more pages down — another page of questions to answer.

Warm-Up Questions

1) What is a galaxy?
2) Name the method used to measure distances to nearby stars.
3) Why might brighter street lights make it harder to see the stars?
4) What unit do we use to measure distances in space?
5) What is the speed of light in a vacuum (like space)?

Exam Questions

1   Optical space telescopes are put into space to observe objects in our galaxy and other, distant galaxies.

  (a)   What is the name of our galaxy?

(1 mark)

  (b)   Approximately how many stars are there in our galaxy?

(1 mark)

  (c)   How many galaxies are there in the Universe?
        Circle the correct answer.

        hundreds   millions

                  hundreds of thousands   thousands of millions

(1 mark)

  (d)   Give **two** advantages of having an optical
        telescope in space rather than on Earth.

(2 marks)

  (e)   It's important to use telescopes that detect other types of electromagnetic
        waves, as well as visible light. Suggest **one** event or object in space that
        could not be detected using just visible light.

(1 mark)

2   Astronomers can measure the distance to nearby stars using parallax.

  (a)   Describe the parallax method for measuring distances to nearby stars.

(3 marks)

  (b)   These two photographs, taken
        six months apart, show the same
        part of the night sky. Which star,
        X or Y, is the furthest from the Earth?
        Give a reason for your answer.

(2 marks)

The Life Cycle of Stars

Stars go through lots of <u>stages</u> in their lives — here's the life cycle of a star with a <u>similar mass</u> to the <u>Sun</u>. Enjoy...

Nebula

1) At first, stars <u>form</u> from <u>clouds of dust and gas</u> called <u>NEBULAS</u>.

2) a) The <u>force of gravity</u> makes the gas and dust <u>spiral in together</u>.
   b) <u>Gravitational energy</u> has been changed into <u>heat energy</u>, so the <u>temperature rises</u>.

Main Sequence Star

3) a) When the <u>temperature</u> is <u>high enough</u>, <u>hydrogen nuclei fuse</u> (join) together to make <u>helium nuclei</u>.
   b) When they fuse they give out huge amounts of <u>energy</u> — a star is born.
   c) The star then enters a <u>long stable period</u> (it doesn't change for ages).
   d) The <u>pressure</u> from the <u>heat</u> pushing <u>outwards</u> is <u>balanced</u> by the <u>force of gravity</u> pulling everything <u>inwards</u>.
   e) In this stable period it's called a <u>MAIN SEQUENCE STAR</u> and it can last for <u>several billion years</u>.

4) a) Eventually the <u>hydrogen</u> in the core begins to <u>run out</u>.
   b) The star then <u>swells</u> into a <u>RED GIANT</u>.

Red Giant

5) a) The star then becomes <u>unstable</u>.
   b) It <u>ejects</u> (throws out) its <u>outer layer</u> of <u>dust and gas</u> as a <u>planetary nebula</u>.

planetary nebula.... and a White Dwarf

6) This leaves behind a <u>hot</u>, <u>dense</u> solid core — a <u>WHITE DWARF</u>, which just <u>cools down</u> and eventually <u>fades</u>.

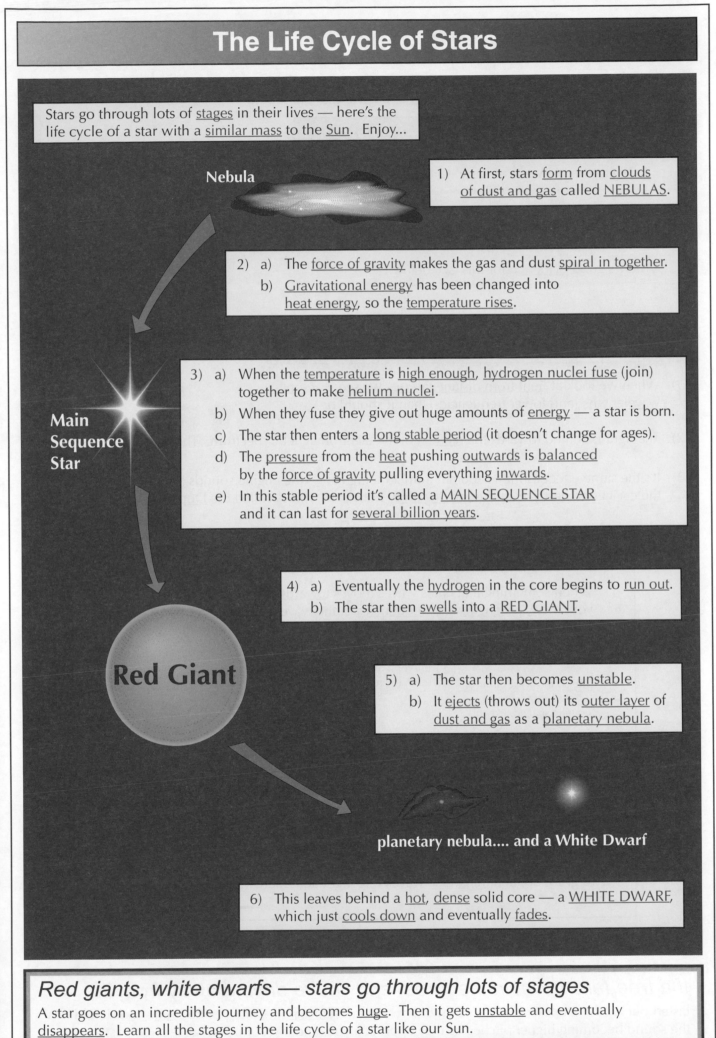

Red giants, white dwarfs — stars go through lots of stages

A star goes on an incredible journey and becomes <u>huge</u>. Then it gets <u>unstable</u> and eventually <u>disappears</u>. Learn all the stages in the life cycle of a star like our Sun.

The Life of the Universe

OK. Let's not kid ourselves — this is a pretty <u>scary</u> topic. How the Universe <u>started</u> is a <u>BIG</u> question. But <u>looking</u> at <u>stars</u> and <u>galaxies</u> might <u>help</u> us answer that question...

The **Universe** Seems to be **Expanding**

1) As big as the Universe already is, it looks like it's getting <u>even bigger</u>.

2) <u>Galaxies</u> seem to be moving away from each other.

3) There's good <u>evidence</u> for this (see below).

Light from **Other Galaxies** is **Red-shifted**

1) When we look at <u>light from distant galaxies</u> we see it at <u>longer wavelengths</u> (and lower frequencies) than it should be.

2) The light is shifted towards the <u>red end</u> of the electromagnetic spectrum. This is called <u>red-shift</u>.

3) It's the same effect as the vrrroomm from a racing car — the engine sounds <u>lower-pitched</u> when the car's gone past you and is <u>moving away</u> from you. This is called the <u>Doppler effect</u>.

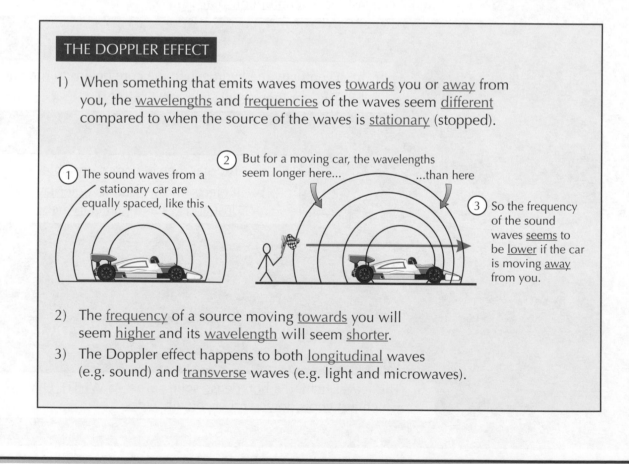

THE DOPPLER EFFECT

1) When something that emits waves moves <u>towards</u> you or <u>away</u> from you, the <u>wavelengths</u> and <u>frequencies</u> of the waves seem <u>different</u> compared to when the source of the waves is <u>stationary</u> (stopped).

1. The sound waves from a stationary car are equally spaced, like this

2. But for a moving car, the wavelengths seem longer here... ...than here

3. So the frequency of the sound waves <u>seems</u> to be <u>lower</u> if the car is moving <u>away</u> from you.

2) The <u>frequency</u> of a source moving <u>towards</u> you will seem <u>higher</u> and its <u>wavelength</u> will seem <u>shorter</u>.

3) The Doppler effect happens to both <u>longitudinal</u> waves (e.g. sound) and <u>transverse</u> waves (e.g. light and microwaves).

If a tree falls down in the forest and you're driving away from it...

Listen out for the Doppler effect next time you hear a fast <u>motorbike</u> or a police <u>siren</u>. You should hear the sound becoming higher pitched as they approach you, and lower pitched as they go past.

The Life of the Universe

Once upon a time there was a really <u>Big Bang</u> — that's the <u>best theory</u> we've got.

The **Further Away** a Galaxy is, the **Greater** the **Red-shift**

1) <u>Measurements</u> of the red-shift suggest that <u>all the galaxies</u>
(apart from a few close ones) are <u>moving away from us</u> very quickly...

2) ... and it's the <u>same result</u> whichever direction you look in.

3) <u>More distant</u> galaxies have <u>greater</u> red-shifts than nearer ones.

4) This means that more distant galaxies are
<u>moving away</u> from us <u>faster</u> than nearer ones.

5) This is evidence that the whole Universe is <u>expanding</u>.

It All **Started Off** with a Very **Big Bang** (Probably)

1) If distant galaxies are moving <u>away</u> from us
then something must have <u>got them going</u>.

2) That 'something' was probably a <u>big explosion</u>
— so they called it the <u>Big Bang</u>...

3) According to the Big Bang theory, all the
matter and energy in the Universe must have
been packed into a <u>very small space</u>.

4) Then it <u>exploded</u> from that single
point and started expanding.

5) The <u>expansion</u> is still going on.

There's **Microwave Radiation** Coming from All **Directions**

1) Scientists have detected <u>low frequency electromagnetic radiation</u>
coming from <u>all parts</u> of the Universe.

2) This radiation is largely in the <u>microwave</u> part of the electromagnetic spectrum.

3) It's known as the <u>cosmic microwave background radiation</u> (CMBR).

4) The <u>Big Bang theory</u> is the <u>only</u> theory that can explain the CMBR.

5) The CMBR comes from radiation that was around shortly after the <u>beginning</u> of the Universe.

There are microwaves in space from the Big Bang

Most scientists accept the idea of the Big Bang — red-shift and cosmic microwave background
radiation are <u>strong evidence</u> for it. But the theory does have some <u>limitations</u>. What limitations?
Well that's all covered on the next page.

The Life of the Universe

And finally, here's what you've been waiting for... the end of the section (apart from lots of questions).

The **Big Bang Theory** Has Its **Limitations**

1) The Big Bang theory <u>isn't perfect</u> — there are some observations that the theory can't yet explain.

2) For example, the Big Bang theory predicts that the Universe's expansion should be <u>slowing down</u> — but as far as we can tell it's actually <u>speeding up</u>.

3) It also doesn't explain what actually <u>caused</u> the explosion in the first place. Or what things were like <u>before</u> the explosion (or if there was a 'before').

4) But even though the Big Bang theory <u>doesn't</u> answer all our questions, it won't just be <u>dumped</u>.

5) It's more likely that scientists will <u>make changes</u> to the theory so that it works better. As it's the <u>best</u> theory that we've got to explain how the Universe began.

We **Don't Know How** (or **If**) the Universe Will **End**

1) How and when the Universe will end depends on <u>how fast</u> it's <u>expanding</u>.

2) This is <u>hard to measure</u> because it's tricky to measure <u>distances</u> in space <u>accurately</u>.

3) You also need to <u>observe</u> (look at) the <u>motion of objects</u> to see how fast the Universe is expanding.

Measuring something accurately means getting the measurement spot on.

4) This means looking at things like how galaxies <u>move</u>.

5) This is <u>difficult</u> because they're <u>far away</u> and <u>pollution</u> gets in the way (p.228).

Not everyone agrees, but the Big Bang theory fits the evidence best

<u>Proving</u> a scientific theory is impossible. If enough evidence points a certain way, then a theory can look pretty <u>believable</u>. But that doesn't <u>prove</u> it's a <u>fact</u> — <u>new evidence</u> may change people's minds.

Warm-Up and Exam Questions

You can only escape this section if you can answer the following questions — good luck.

Warm-Up Questions

1) At the end of its main sequence stage, what does a star become?
2) What will a star the same size as the Sun become at the end of its life?
3) Briefly describe the Big Bang theory.
4) What is 'cosmic microwave background radiation'?
5) Give one limitation of the Big Bang theory.

Exam Questions

1   Stars go through many stages in their lives.

(a) Describe how stars form.

(3 marks)

(b) Explain why a main sequence star does not collapse or explode.

(2 marks)

(c) When main sequence stars begin to run out of hydrogen in their core,
they swell and become Red Giants. Complete the sentences below
to describe what happens next:

The star becomes unstable and ejects its outer layer as a ....

This leaves behind a .... which will eventually fade.

(2 marks)

2   (a) Circle the correct answers to complete the sentence below.

When we view light from distant galaxies, it appears to be | blue-shifted
red-shifted |

due to the | Doppler
Galileo | effect.

(2 marks)

(b) What does the evidence in part (a) tell us about the movement of distant galaxies?

(1 mark)

(c) Suggest why this evidence supports the Big Bang theory.

(2 marks)

(d) Name **one** other piece of evidence for the Big Bang theory.

(1 mark)

Revision Summary for Section 9

Now a reward for getting through loads of pages of pretty tough science — a page of lovely questions. Okay, I know it seems a bit scary, but it's really important to check that you've learnt all the right stuff.

1) Describe the Copernican model of the Solar System.

2) Explain how Galileo's observations of Jupiter supported the Copernican model.

3) List the eight planets found in the Solar System in order — start with the planet nearest to the Sun.

4) Why do comets have bright tails?

5) Explain how the brightness of a star can tell you how far away it is.

6) Explain why air pollution makes it difficult to see stars.

7) Explain why we need telescopes for other parts of the electromagnetic spectrum, as well as visible light.

8) What kind of events in space can X-ray telescopes be used to observe?

9) What is a light year?

10) Explain why we see stars and galaxies as they were in the past.

11) What force makes gas and dust come together to make a star?

12) What is a 'main sequence' star?

13) How long does the stable period of a star last?

14) What are the final two stages of a star's life?

15) If a car is moving towards you, will the engine sound higher or lower-pitched than if it were standing still?

16) How can we tell that the Universe is expanding?

17) Why don't we know how (or if) the Universe will end?

Page 18

Warm-Up Questions

1) eyes, ears, nose, tongue, skin

2) a synapse

3) glands

4) E.g. nerves act faster than hormones. / Nerves act for a short time but hormones act for a long time. / Nerves act on a very precise area but hormones act in a more general way.

5) Day 1 is when the bleeding starts.

Exam Questions

1 (a) A reflex/reflex action *(1 mark)*

(b) (i) B *(1 mark)*

(ii) D *(1 mark)*

(c) When the electrical impulse reaches the end of the neurone, it is taken across the synapse by chemicals *(1 mark)*. The chemicals set off a new electrical impulse in the next neurone *(1 mark)*.

2 (a) It inhibits it *(1 mark)*.

(b) FSH *(1 mark)*

(c) day 14 *(1 mark)*

3 How to grade your answer:

0 marks: No advantages or disadvantages of using the pill given.

1-2 marks: Brief discussion of one advantage and one disadvantage of using the pill.

3-4 marks: Discussion of several advantages and disadvantages of using the pill. The answer has a logical structure and spelling, punctuation and grammar are mostly correct.

5-6 marks: A clear, detailed and full discussion of multiple advantages and disadvantages of using the pill. The answer has a logical structure and uses correct spelling, grammar and punctuation.

Here are some points your answer may include:

Advantages: the pill's very effective at preventing pregnancy. / It reduces some types of cancer.

Disadvantages: there's still a very slight chance of getting pregnant. / It can cause side effects like headaches. / It doesn't protect against STDs.

Page 22

Warm-Up Questions

1) The growth response of a plant to light.

2) auxins

3) shoots

4) A cutting from a plant can be put in soil and given rooting powder which contains a plant growth hormone. It will produce roots rapidly and start growing as a new plant. The new plant is a clone.

Exam Questions

1 (a) hormones *(1 mark)*

(b) weeds *(1 mark)*

(c) crops *(1 mark)*

2 (a)

Direction of Stem Growth	Stem
Upwards	B
To the right	A
No growth	C

(1 mark for one or two letters placed correctly, 2 marks for all three letters placed correctly)

(b) Plant growth is caused by auxins *(1 mark)*. Auxins are only made in the tips of shoots and roots *(1 mark)*. So without the tip the stem won't grow *(1 mark)*.

Pages 27-28

Warm-Up Questions

1) Because your cells need the right conditions to function properly.

2) nervous communication systems, hormonal communication systems

3) A receptor detects a change in the environment, an effector produces a response to the change.

4) The enzymes in the body work best at this temperature.

5) So that more heat can be lost to your surroundings.

6) In type 1 diabetes the pancreas can't produce insulin.
In type 2 diabetes a person can't respond to insulin properly.

Exam Questions

1 (a) C (Insulin) *(1 mark)*

(b) (i) eating foods containing carbohydrates *(1 mark)*

(ii) respiration *(1 mark)*

(c) So that your cells get a constant supply of energy *(1 mark)*.

2 (a) it will rise *(1 mark)*

(b) in sweat *(1 mark)*, in urine *(1 mark)*

(c) kidney *(1 mark)*

3 (a) Katie. She will lose more water through her skin than Colin because she will be sweating more *(1 mark)*.

(b) Katie. She will have more concentrated urine than Colin because she will be losing more water through sweating (and breathing) *(1 mark)*.

(c) maintaining a constant internal environment *(1 mark)*

4 How to grade your answer:

0 marks: No mention of how the body maintains core temperature.

1-2 marks: Brief description of how the body maintains core temperature.

3-4 marks: Some explanation of how the body maintains core temperature. The answer has a logical structure and spelling, punctuation and grammar are mostly correct.

5-6 marks: A clear, detailed and full explanation of how the body maintains core temperature. The answer has a logical structure and uses correct spelling, grammar and punctuation.

Here are some points your answer may include:

Very little sweat is produced. This means less heat is transferred from the skin to the environment through evaporation. / Less blood flows near the surface of the skin, so less heat is lost to the surroundings. / Shivering produces heat through respiration. / Exercising produces heat through respiration. / Adding extra clothes helps keep the body warm.

5 Water is lost from the body as sweat, in breath, as urine. Water is taken into the body in food, in drink. *(1-2 correct, 1 mark. 3-4 correct, 2 marks. 5 correct, 3 marks)*

Page 29

Revision Summary for Section 1

5) a) Response A

b) Response B

Page 35

Warm-Up Questions

1) E.g. because they are a good source of energy.

2) increase

3) E.g. it can lead to a person being underweight. / It can cause deficiency diseases.

4) It increases your risk of heart disease.

5) E.g. is the report a scientific study, published in a well-known journal? / Was it written by a qualified person who doesn't work for the people selling the product? / Did the study ask a large enough group of people to give reliable results? / Have there been other studies which found similar results?

Exam Questions

1   Not eating enough vitamin C can cause scurvy *(1 mark)*.
Not eating enough protein can cause Kwashiorkor *(1 mark)*.
Eating too much carbohydrate or fat can cause obesity *(1 mark)*.

2 (a) $(40 \div 100) \times 512 = 204.8$ kcal OR $(512 \div 100) \times 40 = 204.8$ kcal
(2 marks for correct answer, otherwise 1 mark for correct working)

  (b) Food B is healthier *(1 mark)*. It contains much less energy/carbohydrate/fat, so it is less likely to cause obesity *(1 mark)*. It also contains more protein, which is important for building and repairing cells *(1 mark)*.

3 (a) Dave *(1 mark)*, energy *(1 mark)*

  (b) Exercise increases the amount of energy used by the body and decreases the amount stored as fat *(1 mark)*. It also builds muscle so it helps to boost your metabolic rate *(1 mark)*. The more energy you use (and the less fat you store), the less likely you are to become obese *(1 mark)*.

  (c) Any one of, e.g. his diet may be too high in carbohydrate/fat. / He may have been born with a low metabolic rate, so his cells use less energy than normal. *(1 mark)*.

Page 41

Warm-Up Questions

1) To bring the nutrients and oxygen needed to keep the heart beating all the time.

2) To help keep the blood flowing in the right direction.

3) One cell thick.

4) Because individuals are different.

5) E.g. to see if there are any genetic similarities between people who are affected by heart disease.

Exam Questions

1   A — 4 *(1 mark)*

   B — 1 *(1 mark)*

   C — 3 *(1 mark)*

   D — 2 *(1 mark)*

2 (a) nicotine *(1 mark)*

  (b) Drinking too much alcohol increases blood pressure *(1 mark)*, which can increase the risk of developing heart disease *(1 mark)*.

  (c) People in richer countries can usually afford to eat more high-fat foods than people in poorer countries *(1 mark)* and often don't need to do as much exercise *(1 mark)*.

3 How to grade your answer:

   0 marks: No description or explanation given.

   1-2 marks: Brief description of the effect of high blood pressure on arteries.

   3-4 marks: Detailed description with some explanation for how high blood pressure can damage arteries and lead to a heart attack. The answer has a logical structure and spelling, punctuation and grammar are mostly correct.

   5-6 marks: A clear, detailed and full explanation of how high blood pressure can damage the arteries and lead to a heart attack. The answer has a logical structure and uses correct spelling, grammar and punctuation.

Here are some points your answer may include:

High blood pressure can damage the inside of an artery. / Fatty deposits can sometimes build up in damaged areas of arteries. / These deposits restrict blood flow and cause the blood pressure in arteries to increase. / Damage caused by fatty deposits can eventually cause an artery to be blocked completely. / If an artery supplying the heart becomes completely blocked, an area of the heart muscle will be totally cut off from its blood supply. / This causes a heart attack.

Page 45

Warm-Up Questions

1) To lower their risk of heart and circulatory disease.

2) A placebo is a substance that's like the real drug but doesn't do anything. Using a placebo allows the doctor to see the actual difference the drug makes.

3) Any two of, e.g. ecstasy / cannabis / heroin.

4) Any one of, e.g. alcohol / nicotine.

Exam Questions

1 (a) stimulants *(1 mark)*, steroids *(1 mark)*

  (b) E.g. taking steroids increases muscle size *(1 mark)* so taking them can improve an athlete's performance *(1 mark)*.

2 (a) A driver might not react to a problem quickly enough to stop an accident happening *(1 mark)*.

  (b) If a person stops drinking alcohol they will suffer physical withdrawal symptoms *(1 mark)*.

  (c) Any two of, e.g. increased crime/violence / costs to the NHS / costs to economy through people being too ill to work. *(1 mark for each, up to 2 marks)*

3 (a) E.g. it caused fetuses to be born with very short arms and legs *(1 mark)*.

  (b) E.g. leprosy *(1 mark)*

4 To check that they work *(1 mark)*. To find out their toxicity *(1 mark)*. To find the best dosage *(1 mark)*.

Pages 51-52

Warm-Up Questions

1) A microorganism that enters the body and causes disease.

2) Viruses invade your cells and make copies of themselves. The cell will then burst, releasing all the new viruses. This cell damage is what makes you feel ill.

3) Unique molecules on the surface of cells/pathogens.

4) kill bacteria

5) So that harmful pathogens won't grow.

6) A big outbreak of disease.

Exam Questions

1 White blood cells engulf and digest pathogens *(1 mark)*, produce antibodies that kill pathogens *(1 mark)* and produce antitoxins that stop toxins produced by the invading pathogens *(1 mark)*.

2 (a) The inactive bacteria carry antigens *(1 mark)*, which cause the white blood cells to produce antibodies to attack them *(1 mark)*. Some of these white blood cells become memory cells and stay in the blood *(1 mark)*. If live typhoid bacteria infect the body after this, memory cells can rapidly mass produce antibodies to kill off the bacteria *(1 mark)*.

(b) The people who aren't vaccinated are unlikely to catch the disease because there are fewer people able to pass it on *(1 mark)*.

(c) E.g. Vaccines don't always work — sometimes they don't give you immunity *(1 mark)*. You can sometimes have a bad reaction to a vaccine *(1 mark)*.

3 (a) Antibiotic C is the most effective at killing the bacteria *(1 mark)* as the clear zone around the disc, where the bacteria have been killed, is larger than in the case of the other two antibiotics *(1 mark)*.

This is a simple matter of looking carefully at the experimental results and interpreting them — it's common sense more than anything else.

(b) He could repeat the experiment to check that his results were the same. *(1 mark)*

Questions about reliability are very common in exams — the most obvious ways of making an experiment reliable are by having as big a sample size as possible (e.g. by doing an experiment lots of times), and by keeping all variables constant, except for the one you're investigating.

(c) To kill unwanted microorganisms *(1 mark)*.

(d) E.g. antibiotics cannot be used to kill viruses *(1 mark)*.

4 (a) (i)   mutations *(1 mark)*

(ii) natural *(1 mark)*

(iii) E.g. MRSA *(1 mark)*

(b) E.g. by not over-using antibiotics *(1 mark)*

Page 53

Revision Summary for Section 2

2)   A professional runner

11) a) Dave because he has a more stressful job than Tricia / he smokes / he does less exercise than Tricia / he has a diet higher in saturated fats and salt than Tricia.

b)   Improve your diet, e.g. eat less fatty foods and salt / be less stressed / stop smoking / don't use drugs like ecstasy and cannabis / reduce the amount of alcohol you consume / do regular moderate exercise.

Pages 58-59

Warm-Up Questions

1) the nucleus

2) A short length of a chromosome that controls the development of different characteristics.

3) Different versions of the same gene.

4) E.g. breathing problems, lung infections, fertility problems

5) Y chromosome

Exam Questions

1 (a) (i)   XX *(1 mark)*

(ii) XY *(1 mark)*

(b) 1 in 2 / 50% *(1 mark)*. The chances of the child being a boy are the same (50%) at each pregnancy *(1 mark)*.

2 (a)

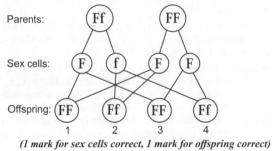

(1 mark)

(b) **A** 25% *(1 mark)*

3 (a) RR or Rr *(1 mark)*

(b) No *(1 mark)*. The baby will inherit a dominant allele from Nate, so it will be able to roll its tongue *(1 mark)*.

4 (a)

Parents: Ff   FF

Sex cells: F   f   F   F

Offspring: FF   Ff   FF   Ff
            1   2   3   4

(1 mark for sex cells correct, 1 mark for offspring correct)

(b) They will all be unaffected *(1 mark)*.

(c) 2 and 4 *(1 mark)*

Page 64

Warm-Up Questions

1) In sexual reproduction there are two parents; in asexual reproduction there is only one. / Sexual reproduction involves the fusion of male and female gametes; in asexual reproduction there is no fusion of gametes. / Sexual reproduction produces variation; asexual reproduction does not. / The offspring of sexual reproduction are different to the parents; the offspring of asexual reproduction are clones of the parent.

2) By tissue culture, by taking cuttings.

3) Advantages: e.g. cloning quickly gets you lots of "ideal" offspring. / Studying clones could also help us understand some diseases.

Disadvantages: e.g. cloned organisms all have the same genes, so if a disease appears they could all be wiped out. / It's possible that cloned animals might not be as healthy as normal ones.

Exam Questions

1 (a) E.g. to cut the gene out of the donor organism's DNA *(1 mark)*. To cut the DNA of the recipient organism *(1 mark)*.

(b) E.g. to give resistance to viruses/insects/herbicides *(1 mark)*.

(c) Any two of, e.g. they could affect the numbers of other plants around the crop / they might not be safe to eat *(1 mark each, up to 2 marks)*.

2 Remove the genetic material/nucleus from an unfertilised egg cell *(1 mark)*. Insert a complete set of chromosomes from an adult body cell into the empty egg cell *(1 mark)*. Stimulate the egg cell with an electric shock to make it divide *(1 mark)*. When the embryo is a ball of cells, implant it into a surrogate mother/an adult female to develop *(1 mark)*.

3 A human gamete contains half the normal number of chromosomes *(1 mark)*. Two gametes fuse together to form a zygote during fertilisation *(1 mark)*. The zygote inherits half of its chromosomes from its father *(1 mark)*.

4 (a) specialised. *(1 mark)*

(b) implanted into *(1 mark)*

(c) same *(1 mark)*

Page 73

Warm-Up Questions

1) E.g. not all organisms interbreed. Some hybrids are fertile.

2) It reduces heat loss.

3) E.g. bright warning colours to scare predators away.

4) a) eye colour

   b) scar

   c) weight

Exam Questions

1 (a) Species C *(1 mark)*

   (b) Yes, you would expect Species D to look more similar to Species E than Species F *(1 mark)*. Species D and E share a more recent common ancestor, so they are more closely related/have more similar genes *(1 mark)*.

2 (a) Any three from, e.g. they're autotrophs (they make their own food) / they have chlorophyll / they're multicellular / they have cell walls *(1 mark each, up to 3 marks)*.

   (b) E.g. has spines instead of leaves to reduce water loss / storing water in its stem / roots spread out over a large area to absorb water quickly *(1 mark each, up to 3 marks)*.

3 (a) Living things show genetic variation — they're not all the same *(1 mark)*. Some individuals of a particular species will have features that give them a better chance of surviving than others *(1 mark)*. Those individuals will then have a better chance of reproducing and passing on their genes *(1 mark)*. This means that more individuals in the next generation will have the features that help the organisms to survive *(1 mark)*.

   Remember, individuals in a species are naturally selected for but individuals cannot evolve — only a species as a whole can evolve.

   (b) E.g. his ideas went against common religious beliefs that life on Earth was made by a "Creator" (God). / He could not explain how new characteristics appeared or were passed on to offspring. / There wasn't enough evidence to convince many scientists *(1 mark each, up to 3 marks)*.

   (c) (i) He thought that if a characteristic was used a lot by an organism then it would become more developed during its lifetime *(1 mark)*. He believed that these developed characteristics would then be passed on to the next generation *(1 mark)*.

       (ii) Lamarck's hypothesis was rejected because experiments didn't support it *(1 mark)*. The discovery of genetics supported Darwin's idea because it provided an explanation of how organisms born with helpful characteristics can pass them on *(1 mark)*.

Pages 82-83

Warm-Up Questions

1) Plants: any three from light, space, water, nutrients from the soil
   Animals: space (territory), food, mates

2) The mass of living material in a food chain.

3) So much energy is lost at each stage that there's not enough left to support more organisms after four or five stages.

4) burning/combustion

5) nitrates

Exam Questions

1 (a) 30 beetles × 12.5 g = 375 g *(1 mark)*

   (b) C. The mass of the organisms decreases at each level as shown by this pyramid *(1 mark)*.

   (c) Their energy initially comes from the Sun *(1 mark)*.

   (d) mass lost between the first level and the second level
   = mass of cabbages − mass of beetles
   925 g − 375 g = 550 g
   (1 mark for correct working. 1 mark for final answer. Award full marks if error carried forward from part (a), but working is correct.)

2 (a) E.g. Peter could use sludgeworms/phytoplankton as living indicators *(1 mark)* — high numbers of these could indicate a high level of pollution *(1 mark)*.

   OR Peter could use mayfly larvae as a living indicator *(1 mark)* — high numbers of these would indicate that the water is clean *(1 mark)*.

   (b) E.g. Peter could use a dissolved oxygen meter to measure how much oxygen is in the water *(1 mark)* — not much oxygen in the water means it's polluted *(1 mark)*.

3 (a) Materials in living organisms are returned to the environment either in waste materials *(1 mark)* or when they die and decay *(1 mark)*. Microorganisms break down the materials, returning them to the environment *(1 mark)*.

   (b) Any two of, e.g. warm / good oxygen supply / lots of decomposers *(1 mark each, up to 2 marks)*.

4 (a) proteins *(1 mark)*

   (b) feeding *(1 mark)*

   (c) fungi *(1 mark)*

5 (a) (i) A = decay / respiration *(1 mark)*.

       (ii) B = eating / feeding *(1 mark)*.

       (iii) C = respiration *(1 mark)*.

   (b) E.g. there would be less photosynthesis and so more carbon dioxide in the atmosphere/less carbon dioxide removed from the atmosphere *(1 mark)*.

   (c) photosynthesis *(1 mark)*

Page 84

Revision Summary for Section 3

3)

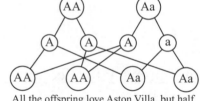

| parents' phenotypes: | Loves Aston Villa | Loves Aston Villa |

parents' genotypes: AA, Aa

sex cells' genotypes: A, A, A, a

possible genotypes of offspring: AA, AA, Aa, Aa

phenotypes: All the offspring love Aston Villa, but half of them carry the allele for being normal.

Pages 93-94

Warm-Up Questions

1) An element is a substance that consists of only one type of atom. There are about 100 elements.

2) a) 2
   b) 8

3) 2, 8, 3

4) molecules

5) $C_6H_{12}O_6 + 6O_2 \rightarrow 6CO_2 + 6H_2O$

Exam Questions

1 (a) 7 *(1 mark)*

   (b) N *(1 mark)*

   (c) non-metal *(1 mark)*

   (d) Any one of: e.g. phosphorus / arsenic / antimony / bismuth *(1 mark)*. It's in the same group as nitrogen so it will have the same number of electrons in its outer shell *(1 mark)* which gives it similar chemical properties *(1 mark)*.

2 (a) Nothing/it stays the same *(1 mark)*.

(b) 17 − 4 = 13 g *(1 mark)*

(c) Ionic *(1 mark)*

3 (a) 11 *(1 mark)*

(b) Any one of: lithium / potassium / rubidium / caesium / francium *(1 mark)*

(c) 1 *(1 mark)*

4 (a) sulfuric acid + ammonia → ammonium sulfate *(1 mark)*

(b) $H_2SO_4 + 2NH_3 \rightarrow (NH_4)_2SO_4$ *(1 mark for correct products and reactants, 1 mark for correctly balancing the equation)*

(c) 15 *(1 mark)*

There are eight atoms of hydrogen, one atom of sulfur, four atoms of oxygen, and two atoms of nitrogen.

(d) C *(1 mark)*

5 (a) positive *(1 mark)*, negative *(1 mark)*, opposite *(1 mark)*

(b) In a non-metal compound each atom shares an electron with another atom *(1 mark)*. This is called covalent bonding *(1 mark)*.

Pages 100-101

Warm-Up Questions

1) In the centre block.

2) Any three of: e.g. strong/hard to break / can be bent or hammered into different shapes / conduct heat / conduct electricity.

3) It is brittle/easy to break.

4) A mixture of metals, or a mixture of a metal and a non-metal.

5) alloys

Exam Questions

1 (a) A material's strength is how good it is at resisting a force *(1 mark)*.

(b) Tensile strength is how much a material can resist a pulling force *(1 mark)*, compressive strength is how much a material can resist a pushing force *(1 mark)*.

(c) hard/stiff/strong *(1 mark)*, density *(1 mark)*, moulded *(1 mark)*

2 (a) Aluminium and copper are both more expensive and less strong than steel *(1 mark)*. Tungsten is stronger than steel but even more expensive than brass *(1 mark)*. Cast iron is cheaper than steel but it is a lot less strong *(1 mark)*.

(b) (i) It can be turned into an alloy by mixing it with other metals *(1 mark)*.

(ii) E.g. it's corrosion-resistant *(1 mark)*, it has a low density (light) *(1 mark)*

3 (a) E.g. it doesn't corrode / it's strong / it has a low density *(1 mark each, up to 3 marks)*.

(b) Any one of: e.g. it conducts electricity / it conducts heat *(1 mark)*.

4 (a) low carbon steel — easily shaped *(1 mark)*
high carbon steel — very hard, inflexible *(1 mark)*
stainless steel — corrosion resistant *(1 mark)*

(b) High carbon steel — e.g. blades for cutting tools / bridges *(1 mark)*
Low carbon steel — e.g. car bodies *(1 mark)*
Stainless steel — e.g. cutlery / containers for corrosive substances *(1 mark)*

(c) Scientists understand the properties of metals so alloys can be designed for specific uses *(1 mark)*.

5 (a) He repeats the experiment to make sure that his results are reliable *(1 mark)*.

(b) To make the experiment a fair test *(1 mark)*. He needs to control all the other variables that might affect his results, so he can be sure that only the variable he is changing is affecting his results *(1 mark)*.

(c) Wire 5 would be best *(1 mark)*. The wire needs to have a high tensile strength so that it doesn't break if it holds a very large fish *(1 mark)*. Wire 5 has the best tensile strength because it can hold the greatest mass before breaking *(1 mark)*.

Pages 109-110

Warm-Up Questions

1) A rock which contains enough metal to make it worthwhile extracting the metal from it.

2) Any one of: e.g. zinc / iron / tin / copper.

3) It uses a lot of energy.

4) Phytomining involves growing plants in soil that contains copper. The plants can't use or get rid of the copper so it builds up in the leaves. The plants can be harvested, dried and burned. The copper is then collected from the ash.

5) Nanotechnology is using and controlling nanoparticles.

Exam Questions

1 (a) It can be extracted by reduction with carbon *(1 mark)*, which is cheaper than electrolysis *(1 mark)*.

(b) The Cu^{2+} ions move towards the negative electrode *(1 mark)*.

2 (a) E.g. the supply of copper-rich ores is limited / demand for copper is growing *(1 mark)*.

(b) (i) bioleaching *(1 mark)*

(ii) Bacteria produce a (leachate) solution that contains copper *(1 mark)*. The copper can be extracted from the leachate *(1 mark)*.

(iii) E.g. this method has a much smaller impact on the environment *(1 mark)*.

(iv) E.g. it's slow *(1 mark)*.

3   How to grade your answer:

0 marks: No positive or negative effects of mining metal ores are given.

1-2 marks: Brief description of one positive and one negative effect of mining metal ores.

3-4 marks: At least two positive and two negative effects of mining metal ores are given. The answer has a logical structure and spelling, grammar and punctuation are mostly correct.

5-6 marks: The answer gives at least three positive and three negative effects of mining metal ores. The answer has a logical structure and uses correct spelling, grammar and punctuation.

Here are some points your answer may include:

<u>Positive effects:</u> Mining metal ores allows useful products to be made from the metal. / The mines provide jobs for workers. / Mining brings money into the local area.
<u>Negative effects:</u> Mining can be very noisy. / Mines damage the landscape. / Mining can lead to a loss of habitats. / Abandoned mine shafts can be dangerous.

4 (a) Any one of: e.g. potassium / sodium / calcium / magnesium / aluminium (any metal above carbon in the reactivity series) *(1 mark)*.

(b) (i) removal of oxygen (or gain of electrons) *(1 mark)*

(ii) zinc oxide + carbon → zinc + carbon dioxide *(1 mark)*

(c) (i) more reactive *(1 mark)*, less reactive *(1 mark)*

(ii) B *(1 mark)*

Page 111

Revision Summary for Section 4

3) Calcium

5) a)

b)

7) $CH_4 + 2O_2 \rightarrow CO_2 + 2H_2O$

Pages 120-121

Warm-Up Questions

1) E.g. volcanic eruptions / earthquakes.

2) A (theoretical) supercontinent/huge piece of land, made from all the present continents joined together.

3) Magma pushes up into the surface of the Earth or right through it. It then cools and turns into a solid.

4) Any two of: e.g. chemicals from limestone are used to make dyes, paints and medicines. / Limestone products are used to neutralise acidic soil/reduce acidity in lakes and rivers. / Limestone is used in power station chimneys to neutralise sulfur dioxide.

5) Any two of: e.g. limestone is widely available. / Limestone is cheaper than granite or marble. / Limestone is an easy rock to cut. / Limestone can be more hard-wearing than marble, but it still looks attractive. / Limestone can be used to produce concrete, which can be poured into moulds to make blocks or panels. This is quick and cheap way of constructing buildings. / Limestone, concrete and cement don't rot when they get wet like wood does. / Limestone, concrete and cement can't be gnawed away by insects. / Concrete is fire-resistant. / Concrete doesn't corrode like a lot of metals do.

Exam Questions

1 (a) The diagram should be labelled:
A – crust *(1 mark)*
B – mantle *(1 mark)*
C – core *(1 mark)*

(b) (i) tectonic plates *(1 mark)*

(ii) Radioactive decay takes place in the mantle *(1 mark)*. This produces heat which causes the mantle to flow in convection currents *(1 mark)*. These currents cause the plates to drift *(1 mark)*.

2 (a) pressure *(1 mark)*, long *(1 mark)*

(b) E.g. limestone / chalk *(1 mark)*.

(c) Sedimentary rocks form from layers of sediment *(1 mark)*. Over millions of years the layers get buried under more layers and the weight pressing down squeezes out the water *(1 mark)*. Fluids flowing through the sediment leave behind natural mineral cement between the sediment particles. This holds them together *(1 mark)*.

3 (a) (i) coastlines *(1 mark)*

(ii) fossils of animals *(1 mark)*

(b) B *(1 mark)*

4 (a) (i) calcium carbonate → calcium oxide *(1 mark)* + carbon dioxide *(1 mark)*

(ii) A Bunsen burner can't reach a high enough temperature to thermally decompose all carbonates of Group 1 metals *(1 mark)*.

(b) Any two of: a calcium salt / carbon dioxide / water *(1 mark each, up to 2 marks)*.

5 (a) Limestone is heated *(1 mark)* with clay *(1 mark)*.

(b) Limestone is made into cement and then mixed with sand and aggregate (water and gravel). *(1 mark for making into cement, 1 mark for sand and aggregate)*

(c) How to grade your answer:

0 marks: No negative impacts are given.

1-2 marks: Brief description of one or two of the negative impacts of quarrying limestone and using it to produce building materials.

3-4 marks: Description of at least three negative impacts of quarrying limestone and using it to produce building materials. The answer has a logical structure and spelling, punctuation and grammar are mostly correct.

5-6 marks: A detailed description of at least five of the negative impacts of quarrying limestone and using it to produce building materials is given. The answer has a logical structure and uses correct spelling, grammar and punctuation.

Here are some points your answer may include:

Quarrying makes big, ugly holes in the landscape. / It changes the landscape forever. / Quarrying processes, such as blasting rocks with explosives make lots of noise and dust. / Quarrying destroys the homes of animals and birds. / Limestone is transported away from the quarry, usually in lorries, which causes noise and pollution. / Waste materials from quarries produce unsightly tips. / Quarried limestone can be used to make cement. Cement factories make a lot of dust, which can cause breathing problems for some people. / Energy is needed to produce cement. The energy is likely to come from burning fossil fuels, which causes pollution.

Page 128

Warm-Up Questions

1) E.g. Cheshire

2) Hot water is pumped underground. The salt dissolves in the water and the salt solution is forced to the surface.

3) E.g. to improve flavour / as a preservative

4) Plasticisers can leach out of plastics and into water ways. They are toxic and can build up in animals like fish.

Exam Questions

1 (a) A — 3
B — 2
C — 4
D — 1 *(1 mark for each correct answer)*

(b) (i) E.g. making margarine *(1 mark)*.

(ii) Any one of, e.g. disinfecting water / making plastics / making hydrochloric acid / making solvents *(1 mark)*.

2 (a) Between 0.0 and 0.8 mg/l the number of bacterial cells falls as the concentration increases *(1 mark)*, but at 1.0 mg/l the number of bacterial cells increases *(1 mark)*.

(b) The result at the chlorine concentration of 1.0 mg/l is an anomalous result *(1 mark)*. In all the other results, the number of bacteria decreases as chlorine concentration increases — here it increases *(1 mark)*.

The result at the chlorine concentration of 1.0 mg/l should be around 20 bacteria.

(c) (i) Water contains organic compounds. Chlorine reacts with these compounds to form chemicals that cause cancer. *(1 mark)*

(ii) Any one of, e.g. it stops algae growing / it gets rid of bad tastes/smells *(1 mark)*.

Pages 133-134

Warm-Up Questions

1) Oxidising — provides oxygen which allows other materials to burn more strongly.

2) neutralisation

3) copper sulfate and water.

4) volcanoes

Exam Questions

1 (a) A — red
   B — pH 7
   C — pH 8/9

   (2 marks if all correct, 1 mark for 2 correct)

   (b) A *(1 mark)*

   (c) C *(1 mark)*

   (d) B *(1 mark)*

   With questions like this, always have a guess if you're not sure. Remember, the examiners can't take marks off you (even for a really silly answer) and if you're stuck between two possibilities you're much more likely to get a mark if you go for one of them than if you put nothing at all.

2 (a) alkalis *(1 mark)*

   (b) magnesium oxide + hydrochloric acid →
       magnesium chloride *(1 mark)* + water *(1 mark)*

   (c) hydrochloric acid *(1 mark)* + copper carbonate → copper chloride + water *(1 mark)* + carbon dioxide *(1 mark)*

3 (a) (i)   nitrogen *(1 mark)*

      (ii) oxygen *(1 mark)*

      (iii) carbon dioxide *(1 mark)*

      (iv) water vapour *(1 mark)*

   (b) A — 3 *(1 mark)*
       B — 2 *(1 mark)*
       C — 4 *(1 mark)*
       D — 1 *(1 mark)*

   (c) The extra carbon dioxide is making them too acidic (which is bad for coral and shellfish) *(1 mark)*. In future, the oceans won't be able to absorb any more carbon dioxide *(1 mark)*.

Page 135

Revision Summary for Section 5

2) b) 3.5 years

Page 143

Warm-Up Questions

1) Two (or more) elements or compounds that aren't chemically bonded together.

2) methane, ethane and propane

3) Long-chain hydrocarbons are cracked to make shorter and more useful products.

4) heated

5) They have a double bond between two of the carbon atoms on the chain.

6) ethanol

Exam Questions

1 (a) C_4H_{10} *(1 mark)*

   (b)

       H   H   H   H
       | | | |
   H — C — C — C — C — H
       | | | |
       H   H   H   H   *(1 mark)*

   (c) Any two of: e.g. butane will have a lower boiling point. / Butane will be less viscous/more runny. / Butane will be more flammable/easier to set on fire *(1 mark each, up to 2 marks)*.

2 (a) (i) There should be an M in the bottom box *(1 mark)*.

      (ii) There should be a B in the top box *(1 mark)*.

   Fractions with longer molecules have a higher boiling point, so condense at the higher temperatures at the bottom of the column. Fractions with shorter molecules have a lower boiling point, so don't condense until they reach the top of the column.

   (b) The crude oil is heated and piped in at the bottom *(1 mark)*. The oil evaporates and rises up the column *(1 mark)* and the fractions are collected at the different levels where they condense *(1 mark)*.

Pages 151-152

Warm-Up Questions

1) complete combustion

2) Because solar and wind power only work when the weather conditions are right. Burning crude oil fractions can be done in any weather.

3) They trap heat that would escape into space and send it back to the Earth.

4) Adding iron to the ocean makes more plants called phytoplankton grow there. The phytoplankton absorb carbon dioxide to use for photosynthesis, removing it from the atmosphere.

Exam Questions

1 (a) global warming / climate change *(1 mark)*

   (b) (i) Sulfur dioxide (or nitrogen oxides) produced from burning fossil fuels mixes with clouds *(1 mark)* and forms dilute sulfuric acid (or nitric acid) *(1 mark)*. This then falls as acid rain *(1 mark)*.

      (ii) Any one of: e.g. makes lakes acidic and many plants and animals die / damages limestone buildings and stone statues / kills trees *(1 mark)*.

   (c) Any two of: e.g. engines need to be converted to work with ethanol. / Ethanol is not widely available. / It may increase food prices if farmers switch to growing crops to make ethanol from growing crops to make food *(1 mark each, up to 2 marks)*.

2 (a) It's a clean fuel — it combines with oxygen to form just water *(1 mark)*.

   (b) Any two of: e.g. you would need a special expensive engine. / Hydrogen isn't widely available. / You still need energy from another source to make hydrogen. / It's hard to store *(1 mark each, up to 2 marks)*.

   (c) high *(1 mark)*, fossil fuels *(1 mark)*.

3 (a) (i) C *(1 mark)*

      (ii) B *(1 mark)*

   (b) (i)   0.028% *(1 mark)*

      (ii) 1875 *(1 mark)*

      (iii) It increased rapidly *(1 mark)*.

4 (a) 356.4 + 774.4 = 1130.8 g *(1 mark)*

   (b) In experiment 1 partial combustion is occurring *(1 mark)* because carbon and carbon monoxide are being produced as well as carbon dioxide and water *(1 mark)*. In experiment 2 complete combustion is occurring *(1 mark)* because only carbon dioxide and water are being produced *(1 mark)*.

   (c) octane + oxygen → carbon + carbon monoxide + carbon dioxide + water *(1 mark)*

Page 156

Warm-Up Questions

1) Many ethene molecules are joined together.
2) poly(butene)
3) Most polymers aren't biodegradable, so they won't rot in the ground.
4) The higher the melting point, the stronger the forces holding the polymer chains together.

Exam Questions

1 (a)

$$n \left(\begin{array}{c} H \quad\quad H \\ C=C \\ H \quad\quad CH_3 \end{array} \right) \longrightarrow \left(\begin{array}{c} H \quad H \\ C-C \\ H \quad CH_3 \end{array} \right)_n$$ *(1 mark)*

(b) B *(1 mark)*

(c) Polymers with closely packed polymer chains will have a high density, whereas polymers with polymer chains that are spread out will have a low density *(1 mark)*.

(d) How to grade your answer:

0 marks: None of the ways that polymers can be modified are described.

1-2 marks: Brief description of one or two ways polymers can be modified.

3-4 marks: Description of more than one way of modifying polymers, with some explanation. The answer has a logical structure and spelling, punctuation and grammar are mostly correct.

5-6 marks: A detailed description of several ways that polymers can be modified is given and these are fully explained. The answer has a logical structure and uses correct spelling, grammar and punctuation.

Here are some points your answer may include:

Polymers can be modified to increase their chain length. Polymers with short chains are easy to shape and have lower melting points. Longer chain polymers are stiffer and have higher melting points. / Polymers can be made stronger by adding cross-linking agents. These agents chemically bond the chains together, making the polymer stiffer, stronger and more heat-resistant. / Plasticisers can be added to a polymer to make it softer and easier to shape. Plasticisers work by getting in between the polymer chains and reducing the forces between them.

Page 160

Warm-Up Questions

1) They provide a lot of energy.
2) E.g. biodiesel.
3) They reduce the amount of cholesterol in the blood.
4) An emulsion is droplets of one liquid suspended in another liquid.

Exam Questions

1 (a) The plant material is crushed *(1 mark)*. The crushed plant material is pressed between metal plates to squash the oil out *(1 mark)*. After this, water and other impurities are removed from the oil *(1 mark)*.

(b) E.g. vegetable oils have higher boiling points than water so they can be used to cook foods at higher temperatures and at faster speeds *(1 mark)*. They give food a different flavour *(1 mark)*. They increase the amount of energy we get from food *(1 mark)*.

(c) (i) diagram 2 *(1 mark)*

(ii) diagram 1 *(1 mark)*

(d) E.g. The mayonnaise emulsion won't separate into oil and water. / The mayonnaise will have a longer shelf-life. / Food companies can make mayonnaise that's lower in fat but still has a good texture *(1 mark)*.

Pages 169-170

Warm-Up Questions

1) The particles in a gas have high energies, they have almost no forces of attraction between them and they are free to move in any direction.
2) Particles that vibrate faster than others pass on their extra kinetic energy to their neighbours.
3) convection
4) E.g. make the surface darker in colour, make the surface less shiny/more matt.
5) Condensation is when a gas turns to a liquid.
6) By lowering the temperature of the surface the gas is condensing on and increasing the surface's area.

Exam Questions

1 (a) The temperature of the water would fall more quickly *(1 mark)* — the rate of cooling would be greater because the difference in temperature between the water and its surroundings is greater *(1 mark)*.

(b) The temperature of the water would fall more quickly *(1 mark)* — metal conducts heat away quicker as it's a better conductor than plastic *(1 mark)*.

2 (a) (i) radiation *(1 mark)*

(ii) conduction *(1 mark)*

(ii) convection *(1 mark)*

(b) Because black surfaces are good absorbers of heat radiation *(1 mark)*.

3 (a) C *(1 mark)*

(b) As the air nearest the floor heats up, it rises, replacing the cooler air *(1 mark)*. The cooler air falls and flows to fill the gap left by the warm air *(1 mark)*. This creates a convection current which spreads heat around the roof space *(1 mark)*.

4 (a) (i) condensation *(1 mark)*

(ii) evaporated *(1 mark)*, lost *(1 mark)*

(b) (i) The air around the liquid will change more often *(1 mark)*. So there will be less evaporated liquid in the air, making it easier for evaporation to happen *(1 mark)*.

(ii) The particles with the most energy evaporate, which decreases the average energy of the remaining particles *(1 mark)*, and so decreases the temperature of the remaining liquid *(1 mark)*.

5 (a) E.g. place the thermometers at equal distances away from the cube. / Place the thermometers at the same height as each other. / Make sure no thermometers are in direct sunlight/a draught *(1 mark)*.

(b) (i) C *(1 mark)* because matt, black surfaces are the best emitters of heat *(1 mark)*.

(ii) D *(1 mark)* because shiny, silver surfaces are the poorest emitters of heat *(1 mark)*.

Page 174

Warm-Up Questions

1) The amount of time it takes for the money saved reducing energy bills to equal the initial cost of the insulation.
2) E.g. loft insulation / cavity walls and insulation / double glazing.
3) conduction and radiation
4) Specific heat capacity is the amount of energy needed to raise the temperature of 1 kg of a substance by 1 °C.

Exam Questions

1 (a) Car engines have 'fins' to increase the surface area *(1 mark)*. This means heat is radiated away quicker and the engine cools quicker *(1 mark)*.

(b) The engine in car **B** will cool quicker *(1 mark)*. This is because although they have the same surface area the fins in car **B** have a smaller volume so will cool more quickly *(1 mark)*.

2 (a) θ = 100 °C – 20 °C = 80 °C
   E = m × c × θ = 0.5 × 80 × 900 = 36 000 J
   (3 marks, allow 1 mark for using the correct temperature and 1 mark for correct substitution into the equation)

(b) Concrete has a high specific heat capacity *(1 mark)* and so will be able to store a lot of heat *(1 mark)*.

3 (a) £300 × 0.25 = £75 *(1 mark)*

(b) (i) Insulation B — it has a lower U-value and is therefore a better insulator *(1 mark)*.

   (ii) 300 – 250 = £50 saved per year *(1 mark)*.
   Payback time = cost ÷ saving per year *(1 mark)*
   = 350 ÷ 50 = 7 years *(1 mark)*

Page 179

Warm-Up Questions

1) chemical energy

2) Energy can be transferred usefully from one form to another, stored or dissipated — but it can never be created or destroyed.

3) E.g. light bulbs / TV screen / computer screen.

4) More of the input energy is transformed into useful energy in modern appliances. / Modern appliances waste less of the energy put in.

5) Some energy is always wasted so less than 100% of the input energy is transformed usefully.

Exam Questions

1 (a) 1200 – 120 – 100 = 980 J *(1 mark)*

(b) Efficiency = useful energy out ÷ total energy in
   = (980 + 100) ÷ 1200 = 1080 ÷ 1200 = 0.9 (or 90%)
   (3 marks, allow 1 mark for the correct useful energy and 1 mark for the correct substitution)

(c) sound energy *(1 mark)*
   Only the energy converted to sound is wasted — kinetic and heat energy are what you want from a hairdryer.

2 (a) D *(1 mark)*

(b) Useful energy out = 100 J – 90 J = 10 J *(1 mark)*
   Efficiency = useful energy out ÷ total energy in (× 100 %)
   = 10 J ÷ 100 J × 100 % = 10 % *(1 mark)*

Pages 188-189

Warm-Up Questions

1) Fossil fuels (coal, oil, natural gas) and nuclear fuels (uranium and plutonium).

2) E.g. nuclear power stations produce radioactive waste which is dangerous as it gives out ionising radiation. / The radioactive waste is hard to get rid of as it stays radioactive for a long time and radioactivity is 'invisible'. / Nuclear power stations take a very long time to start up. / The overall cost of nuclear power is high because it costs a lot to build the power stations. / Nuclear fuel will run out (it's non-renewable).

3) Any two from: e.g. initial costs are high. / They use quite a lot of energy to make. / There's some pollution when you make them. / It's not always practical or affordable to connect them to the National Grid. / They depend on the weather, which is bad for cloudy countries like Britain.

4) With wave power, as waves come into shore they provide an up and down motion which directly drives a turbine. With tidal power, when the tide comes in the water is held back and allowed out through turbines at a controlled speed.

5) Biofuels are renewable energy resources that come from plants or rotting waste.

6) Any two from: e.g. it releases greenhouse gases/contributes to global warming / it causes acid rain / coal mining damages the landscape.

7) carbon capture and storage

Exam Questions

1 (a) 2 000 000 ÷ 4000 = 500 *(1 mark)*

(b) If the wind isn't blowing strongly, the turbines will not generate as much as 4000 W each *(1 mark)*.

(c) Any two from: e.g. they might think it would spoil the view (visual pollution) / cause noise pollution / kill or disturb local wildlife *(1 mark each, up to 2 marks)*.

2 burning/combustion, steam, turbine, generator
   (4 marks, 1 mark for each correct answer)

3 (a) Any two from: e.g. wave / tidal / geothermal / biofuels *(1 mark each, up to 2 marks)*.

(b) Any two from: e.g. set-up time / set-up costs / running costs / impact on environment / social impact *(1 mark each, up to 2 marks)*.

(c) How to grade your answer:

   0 marks: No advantages or disadvantages are given.

   1-2 marks: Brief description of one or two advantages and disadvantages of solar and hydroelectric energy.

   3-4 marks: Description of several advantages and disadvantages of solar and hydroelectric energy. The answer has a logical structure and spelling, punctuation and grammar are mostly correct.

   5-6 marks: A detailed and balanced description of the advantages and disadvantages of solar and hydroelectric energy. are given and these are fully discussed. The answer has a logical structure and uses correct spelling, grammar and punctuation.

   Here are some points your answer may include:

   Advantages of solar compared to hydroelectric: there is less environmental damage with solar energy compared to hydroelectric. / Solar energy can be used almost anywhere, but with hydroelectric you need a good water source to create the reservoir. / Solar energy is useful and cost-effective for small scale power production, like the island would need. But hydroelectric would cost a lot to start up in comparison.

   Disadvantages of solar compared to hydroelectric: solar energy is only reliable in the daytime but hydroelectric can be used all the time. / Solar energy isn't always useful in cloudy countries/those that receive little sunlight, but hydroelectric is always available. / It can be hard/expensive to connect solar power to a grid system compared to the amount of electricity you get back, whereas for hydroelectricity it's relatively easy.

4 (a) Heat energy from underground *(1 mark)*.

(b) The source of energy will never run out *(1 mark)*.

(c) E.g. it costs a lot to drill down several km to the hot rocks *(1 mark)*. There aren't many places where you can drill for geothermal energy *(1 mark)*.

(d) C and D *(1 mark each)*.

5 (a) Renewable — Tidal *(1 mark)*,
   Can affect boats and wildlife habitats — Tidal *(1 mark)*
   Fuel is fairly cheap — Nuclear *(1 mark)*
   The waste produced is very dangerous — Nuclear *(1 mark)*

(b) E.g. Clara — disagree, coal is more efficient (36% compared to 35% for wind) *(1 mark)*. Helen — agree, the lifetime of a coal plant is the longest at 50 years *(1 mark)*.

Page 190

Revision Summary for Section 7

8) Payback time = Initial cost ÷ Annual saving.
   Payback time = 4000 ÷ 100 = 40 years.

11) E = m × c × θ = 0.5 × 1000 × (200 – 20)
   E = 0.5 × 1000 × 180 = 90 000 J

15) Efficiency = Useful energy out ÷ Total energy input
   = 70 ÷ 100 = 0.7 (or 70%)

16)a) 80 J
   b) 20 J
   c) Efficiency = 80 ÷ 100 = 0.8 (or 80%)

Page 194

Warm-Up Questions

1) AC

2) A small-scale generator which is often used on bikes to power the lights.

3) The network of cables and pylons that distributes electricity across the country.

4) increasing

Exam Questions

1 (a) high *(1 mark)*, low *(1 mark)*

(b) The National Grid uses step-up transformers to increase the voltage of the electricity supply, so electricity is sent out at high voltages and low currents *(1 mark)*. This reduces the amount of energy lost as heat and so reduces the cost of supplying electricity *(1 mark)*.

(c) How to grade your answer:

0 marks: No advantages or disadvantages are given.

1-2 marks: Brief description of advantages and disadvantages of underground cables and overhead power lines.

3-4 marks: Description of several advantages and disadvantages of underground cables and overhead power lines. The answer has a logical structure and spelling, punctuation and grammar are mostly correct.

5-6 marks: A detailed and balanced description of the advantages and disadvantages of underground cables and overhead power lines are given and these are fully discussed. The answer has a logical structure and uses correct spelling, grammar and punctuation.

Here are some points your answer may include:

Advantages of underground cables: they don't need as much looking after. / They are hidden by the earth so they don't spoil the view. / They aren't affected by the weather so they're more reliable.

Disadvantages of underground cables: they are more expensive to set up. / They are hard to set up. / If there is a problem it's hard to get to them to fix them.

2 (a) Because electrical current is generated *(1 mark)*.

(b) E.g. move the magnet out of the coil / move the coil away from the magnet / insert the south pole of the magnet into the same end of the coil / insert the north pole of the magnet into the other end of the coil *(1 mark)*

(c) E.g. push the magnet into the coil more quickly / use a stronger magnet / add more turns to the coil *(1 mark)*

(d) Zero / no reading *(1 mark)*

Movement is needed to generate a current.

Page 195

Power = voltage × current
Power = 230 × 12 = 2760 W = 2.76 kW

Page 196

Time (in h) = 3 ÷ 60 = 0.05 h
Energy = power × time
= 2.7 × 0.05 = 0.135 kWh

Page 199

Warm-Up Questions

1) watts (W) or kilowatts (kW)

2) 100 kW appliance

Higher powered appliances cost more to use because they use more energy.

3) Cost = Number of kWh × Price per kWh

4) E.g. cost to buy / energy-efficiency / cost to run / size / shape / whether it needs mains electricity.

Exam Questions

1 (a) Energy = final reading − initial reading = 10 612 − 10 582
= 30 kWh *(1 mark)*

(b) (i) The amount of electrical energy used by a 1 kW appliance left on for one hour *(1 mark)*.

(ii) cost = number of kWh × cost per kWh
cost = 30 × 0.14 = £4.20
(2 marks for correct answer, otherwise 1 mark for correct substitution)

(c) A *(1 mark)* (Power = Voltage × Current = 230 × 2.5 = 575 W)

2 Any three from: e.g. without electricity there can be no refrigeration of food / no refrigeration of vaccines / no communication appliances such as television, phones, internet or radio / lack of electrical lighting could be a risk to health and safety / hospital appliances such as X-ray machines would not work *(1 mark each, up to 3 marks)*.

Page 201

Speed = Frequency × Wavelength
= 19 000 × 0.125 = 2375 m/s

Page 208

Warm-Up Questions

1) distance = speed × time

2) transverse

3) It diffracts / the wave spreads out.

4) true

5) an analogue signal

Exam Questions

1 (a) **A** = wavelength *(1 mark)*

B = amplitude *(1 mark)*

(b) (i) The number of complete waves that pass a certain point each second. / The numbers of waves produced by a source each second *(1 mark)*.

(ii) Speed = frequency × wavelength = 0.5 × 5 = 2.5 m/s
(2 marks for correct answer, otherwise 1 mark for correct substitution)

2 (a) reflection *(1 mark)*

(b)

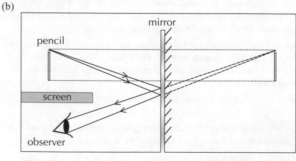

(1 mark for correctly drawn virtual image, 1 mark for rays drawn from virtual image to observer, 1 mark for rays correctly drawn from pencil to mirror)

Page 216

Warm-Up Questions

1) (short-wavelength) radio waves

2) Certain wavelengths of microwave penetrate a few centimetres into the food before being absorbed by water molecules or fat molecules which heats them up. The heat energy is then conducted or convected to other parts of the food.

3) E.g. transferring information short distances / transferring information between mobiles/computers / automatic doors / burglar alarms / security lights / thermal imaging cameras / optical fibres / remote controls.

4) E.g. to carry data over long distances very quickly.

5) Because it damages cells / because it can cause cancer or cell death.

6) Sun Protection Factor

7) ultraviolet

Exam Questions

1 (a)

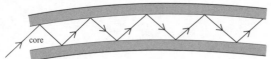

(1 mark)

(b) The light is reflected off the sides of the narrow core from one end of the fibre to the other *(1 mark)*.

(c) infrared *(1 mark)*

2 (a) (i) gamma rays *(1 mark)*

(ii) microwaves *(1 mark)*

(iii) gamma rays *(1 mark)*

(b) (i) Because X-rays mostly pass easily through soft tissue, so the structure of soft tissues doesn't appear on X-ray images *(1 mark)*.

(ii) Any two from: e.g. wear a lead apron / stand behind a concrete screen / leave the room while the X-ray image is being taken. *(1 mark each, up to 2 marks)*

Page 221

Warm-Up Questions

1) E.g. methane / carbon dioxide / water vapour.

2) E.g. volcanoes / wetlands / digestion in animals.

3) E.g. global warming has caused sea water to expand and ice to melt. This has led to a rise in the sea level which could cause the flooding of some low-lying places. / Global warming could lead to more extreme weather like more hurricanes and longer, hotter droughts. / Global warming could cause food crop failure.

4) P-waves and S-waves

5) Because the Earth has a sudden change in properties deep below the surface.

Exam Questions

1 (a) A *(1 mark)* and C *(1 mark)*.

Be careful when describing what data can show. The graph doesn't show a change in CO_2 concentration causes a change in temperature. Only that there's a correlation — as one goes up, so does the other.

(b) The X should be drawn at 25 000 years ago *(1 mark)*.

This is on the lowest dip of the solid black line halfway between 50 (thousand years ago) and 0 (present day).

(c) Man-made — e.g. burning fossil fuels / chopping down and burning trees *(1 mark)*.

Natural — e.g. respiration in plants and animals / volcanic eruptions *(1 mark)*.

2 (a) P-waves *(1 mark)*

(b) S-waves *(1 mark)*

(c) S-waves *(1 mark)*

Page 222

Revision Summary for Section 8

4) Need to change minutes to hours:
$15 \div 60 = 0.25$ h
Energy = Power × Time
Energy = $0.5 \times 0.25 = 0.125$ kWh

7) Speed = Frequency × Wavelength
Speed = $50\ 000 \times 0.03 = 1500$ m/s

Page 226

Warm-Up Questions

1) the Earth

2) Mercury

3) dust and ice

4) E.g. asteroids orbit in the same plane as the planets; comets do not / asteroids were formed at the same time as the planets; comets were not / comets have highly elliptical orbits; asteroids do not / comets have a bright tail; asteroids do not.

Exam Questions

1 (a) A — 3 (Venus)
   B — 4 (Earth)
   C — 2 (Mars)
   D — 1 (comet)   *(1 mark for each correct answer)*

1 must be the comet as it orbits in a different plane from the planets.

(b) A *(1 mark)*

2 (a) telescope *(1 mark)*

(b) How to grade your answer:

0 marks:	No differences or similarities are given.
1-2 marks:	Brief description of at least one similarity or difference between the Ptolemaic, Copernican and current model of the Solar System.
3-4 marks:	Description of more than one similarity or difference between the Ptolemaic, Copernican and current model of the Solar System. The answer has a logical structure and spelling, punctuation and grammar are mostly correct.
5-6 marks:	A detailed description of the similarities and differences between the Ptolemaic, Copernican and current model of the Solar System is given. The answer has a logical structure and uses correct spelling, grammar and punctuation.

Here are some points your answer may include:

The Sun, Moon, stars and other planets were all thought to orbit the Earth in perfect circles in the Ptolemaic model of the Solar System. / The Copernican model differed as it placed the Sun at the centre but everything was still thought to orbit in perfect circles. / The current model has everything orbiting the Sun still but in elliptical orbits not in perfect circles.

3 (a) fastest *(1 mark)*, slowest *(1 mark)*

(b) Heat from the sun melts the comet's ice *(1 mark)*. This leaves a bright tail of debris that we can see from Earth *(1 mark)*.

Page 230

Warm-Up Questions

1) A very large group of stars.

2) parallax

3) Because light pollution makes it hard to pick out dim objects.

4) light years

5) 300 000 km/s / 300 000 000 m/s

Exam Questions

1 (a) the Milky Way *(1 mark)*

(b) thousands of millions *(1 mark)*

(c) thousands of millions *(1 mark)*

(d) The Earth's atmosphere / air pollution will not interfere with the view of a space telescope *(1 mark)*. Light pollution (from e.g. street lamps) will not interfere either *(1 mark)*.

(e) E.g. exploding stars / cosmic microwave background radiation / brown dwarfs *(1 mark)*.

2 (a) Parallax is when something appears to move when you look at it from two different angles *(1 mark)*. Astronomers take pictures of the sky six months apart *(1 mark)*. The apparent movement of a star between the two photos lets you work out how far away it is *(1 mark)*.

(b) Y *(1 mark)*. It appears to move the least *(1 mark)*.

Page 235

Warm-Up Questions

1) A red giant.

2) A white dwarf.

3) All the matter and energy was compressed into a very small space, then there was an explosion/a 'Big Bang'.

4) The low frequency microwave radiation that comes from all parts of the Universe.

5) Any one from, e.g. there are some observations that the theory can't explain. / It's not an explanation for what actually caused the explosion in the first place. / It doesn't explain what conditions were like before the explosion. / It doesn't explain if there was a 'before'. / It doesn't explain why the expansion is speeding up.

Exam Questions

1 (a) Stars form from clouds of dust and gas which spiral in due to gravity *(1 mark)*. Gravitational energy is changed to heat energy, making the temperature rise *(1 mark)*. When the temperature gets hot enough, nuclear fusion happens and huge amounts of heat and light are emitted *(1 mark)*.

(b) The forces acting on a main sequence star are balanced, so it doesn't collapse or explode *(1 mark)*. The heat caused by nuclear fusion provides an outward force to balance the force of gravity pulling everything inwards *(1 mark)*.

(c) planetary nebula *(1 mark)*, white dwarf *(1 mark)*

2 (a) red-shifted *(1 mark)*, Doppler *(1 mark)*

(b) They appear to be moving away from us *(1 mark)*.

(c) Red-shift shows that the Universe is expanding *(1 mark)*. This expansion probably started from a small space or single point which exploded in a big bang *(1 mark)*.

(d) Cosmic microwave background radiation *(1 mark)*.

Index

Index

Index

Make sure you're not missing out on another superb CGP revision book that might just save your life...

...order your **free** catalogue today.

CGP customer service is second to none

We work very hard to despatch all orders the **same day** we receive them, and our success rate is currently 99.9%. We send all orders by **overnight courier** or **First Class** post.
If you ring us today you should get your catalogue or book tomorrow. Irresistible, surely?

- Phone: 0870 750 1252 (Mon-Fri, 8.30am to 5.30pm)
- Fax: 0870 750 1292
- e-mail: orders@cgpbooks.co.uk
- Post: CGP, Kirkby-in-Furness, Cumbria, LA17 7WZ
- Website: www.cgpbooks.co.uk

...or you can ask at any good bookshop.